S0-AEU-743

CHRISTIAN LIGHT PUBLICATIONS INC.
P.O. BOX 1212
Harrisonburg, Virginia 22803-1212
(540) 434-0768

MATH 1000
Teacher's Guide

Author:

Alpha Omega Publications

Editor:

Alan Christopherson, M.S.

Alpha Omega
PUBLICATIONS

804 N. 2nd Ave. E.
Rock Rapids, IA 51246-1759

MATH 1000

LIFEPAC® Overview

MATH SCOPE AND SEQUENCE

KINDERGARTEN

Lessons 1-40	Lessons 41-80	Lessons 81-120	Lessons 121-160
Directions - right, left, high, low, etc.	**Directions** - right, left, high, low, etc.	**Directions** - right, left, high, low, etc.	**Directions** - right, left, high, low, etc.
Comparisons - big, little, alike, different	**Comparisons** - big, little, alike, different	**Comparisons** - big, little, alike, different	**Comparisons** - big, little, alike, different
Matching	**Matching**	**Matching**	**Matching**
Cardinal Numbers - to 9	**Cardinal Numbers** - to 12	**Cardinal Numbers** - to 19	**Cardinal Numbers** - to 100
Colors - red, blue, green, yellow, brown, purple	**Colors** - orange	**Colors** - black, white	**Colors** - pink
Shapes - circle, square, rectangle, triangle	**Shapes** - circle, square, rectangle, triangle	**Shapes** - circle, square, rectangle, triangle	**Shapes** - circle, square, rectangle, triangle
Number Order	**Number Order**	**Number Order**	**Number Order**
Before and After	**Before and After**	**Before and After**	**Before and After**
Ordinal Numbers - to 9th	**Ordinal Numbers** - to 9th	**Ordinal Numbers** - to 9th	**Ordinal Numbers** - to 9th
Problem Solving	**Problem Solving**	**Problem Solving**	**Problem Solving**
	Number Words - to nine	**Number Words** - to nine	**Number Words** - to nine
	Addition - to 9	**Addition** - multiples of 10	**Addition** - to 10 and multiples of 10
		Subtraction - to 9	**Subtraction** - to 10
		Place Value	**Place Value**
		Time/Calendar	**Time/Calendar**
			Money
			Skip Counting - 2's, 5's, 10's
			Greater/Less Than

MATH SCOPE & SEQUENCE

	Grade 1	Grade 2	Grade 3
UNIT 1	**NUMBER ORDER, ADD/SUBTRACT** • Number order, skip-count • Add, subtract to 9 • Story problems • Measurements • Shapes	**NUMBERS AND WORDS TO 100** • Numbers and words to 100 • Operation symbols: +, −, =, >, < • Add and subtract • Place value and fact families • Story problems	**ADD/SUB TO 18 AND PLACE VALUE** • Digits, place value to 999 • Add and subtract • Linear measurements • Operation symbols: +, −, =, ≠, >, < • Time
UNIT 2	**ADD/SUBTRACT TO 10, SHAPES** • Add, subtract to 10 • Number words • Place value • Patterns, sequencing, estimation • Shapes	**ADD/SUBTRACT AND EVEN/ODD** • Numbers and words to 200 • Add, subtract, even and odd • Skip-count 2s, 5s, and 10s • Ordinal numbers, fractions, and money • Shapes	**CARRYING AND BORROWING** • Fact families, patterns, and fractions • Add and subtract with carrying and borrowing • Skip count 2s, 5s, 10s • Money, shapes, lines • Even and odd
UNIT 3	**FRACTIONS, TIME, AND SYMBOLS** • Number sentences • Fractions • Story problems • Time and the = symbol • Oral directions	**ADD WITH CARRYING TO THE 10'S PLACE** • Add with carrying to the 10's place • Subtract • Flat shapes, money, A.M./P.M. • Rounding to the 10's place • Standard measurements	**FACTS OF ADD/SUB AND FRACTIONS** • Add 3 numbers w/ carrying • Coins, weight, volume, A.M./P.M. • Fractions • Skip count 3s, subtract w/ borrowing • Oral instructions
UNIT 4	**ADD TO 18, MONEY, MEASUREMENT** • Add to 18 • Skip-count, even and odd • Money • Shapes and measurement • Place value	**NUMBERS/WORDS TO 999, AND GRAPHS** • Numbers and words to 999 • Addition, subtraction, and place value • Calendar • Measurements and solid shapes • Making change	**ROUND, ESTIMATE, STORY PROBLEMS** • Place value to 9,999 • Rounding to the 10's and estimating • Add and subtract fractions • Roman numerals • 1/4 inch
UNIT 5	**COLUMN ADDITION AND ESTIMATION** • Add three 1-digit numbers • Ordinal numbers • Time and number lines • Estimation and charts • Fractions	**ADD/SUBTRACT TO THE 100'S PLACE** • Data and bar graphs and shapes • Add and subtract to the 100's • Skip-count 3s and place value to the 100's • Add fractions • Temperature	**PLANE SHAPES AND SYMMETRY** • Number sentences • Rounding to the 100's and estimation • Perimeter and square inch • Bar graph, symmetry, and even/odd rules • Temperature
UNIT 6	**NUMBER WORDS TO 99** • Number words to 99 • Add two 2-digit numbers • Symbols: > and < • Fractions • Shapes	**SUBTRACT WITH BORROWING FROM 10'S** • Measurements • Time and money • Subtract w/ borrowing from the 10's place • Add and subtract fractions • Perimeter	**MULTIPLICATION, LINES, AND ANGLES** • Add and subtract to 9,999 • Multiples and multiplication facts for 2 • Area and equivalent fractions • Line graphs, segments, and angles • Money
UNIT 7	**COUNT TO 200, SUBTRACT TO 12** • Number order and place value • Subtract to 12 • Operation signs • Estimation and time • Graphs	**ADD WITH CARRYING TO THE 100'S PLACE** • Add with carrying to the 100's place • Fractions as words • Number order in books • Rounding and estimation	**ADD/SUB MIXED NUMBERS, PROBABILITY** • Multiplication facts for 5 and missing numbers • Add and subtract mixed numbers • Subtract with 0s in the minuend • Circle graphs • Probability
UNIT 8	**ADD/SUBTRACT TO 18** • Addition, subtract to 18 • Group counting • Fractions • Time and measurements • Shapes	**VOLUME AND COIN CONVERSION** • Addition, subtraction, and measurements • Group counting and "thinking" answers • Convert coins • Directions – North, South, East, and West. • Length and width	**MEASUREMENTS AND MULTIPLICATION** • Multiplication facts for 3 & 10, multiples of 4 • Convert units of measurement • Decimals and directions • Picture graphs and missing addends • Length and width
UNIT 9	**SENSIBLE ANSWERS** • Fact families • Sensible answers • Subtract 2-digit numbers • Add three 2-digit numbers	**AREA/SQUARE MEASUREMENT** • Area and square measurement • Add three 2-digit numbers with carrying • Add coins and convert to cents • Fractions and quarter-inches	**MULT, METRICS, AND PERIMETER** • Add and subtract whole numbers, fractions, and mixed numbers • Standard measurements and metrics • Operation symbols • Multiplication facts for 4
UNIT 10	**REVIEW** • Addition, subtraction, and place value • Directions – North, South, East, and West. • Fractions • Patterns	**REVIEW** • Rules for even and odd numbers • Round numbers to the 100's place • Digital clocks and sensible answers • Add three 3-digit numbers	**PROBABILITY, UNITS, AND SHAPES** • Addition and subtraction • Rounding to the 1,000's place and estimating • Probability, equations, and parentheses • Perimeter and area • Multiplication facts for 2, 3, 4, 5, and 10

MATH SCOPE & SEQUENCE

Grade 4	Grade 5	Grade 6	
WHOLE NUMBERS AND FRACTIONS • Naming whole numbers • Naming fractions • Sequencing patterns • Numbers to 1,000	**PLACE VALUE, ADDITION, AND SUBTRACTION** • Place value • Rounding and estimating • Addition • Subtraction	**WHOLE NUMBERS AND ALGEBRA** • Whole numbers and their properties • Operations and number patterns • Algebra	UNIT 1
MULTIPLYING WHOLE NUMBERS • Operation symbols • Multiplication — 1-digit multipliers • Addition and subtraction of fractions • Numbers to 10,000	**MULTIPLYING WHOLE NUMBERS AND DECIMALS** • Multiplying whole numbers • Powers • Multiplying decimals	**DATA ANALYSIS** • Collecting and describing data • Organizing data • Displaying and interpreting data	UNIT 2
SEQUENCING AND ROUNDING • Multiplication with carrying • Rounding and estimation • Sequencing fractions • Numbers to 100,000	**DIVIDING WHOLE NUMBERS AND DECIMALS** • One-digit divisors • Two-digit divisors • Decimal division	**DECIMALS** • Decimal numbers • Multiplying and dividing decimal numbers • The metric system	UNIT 3
LINES AND SHAPES • Plane and solid shapes • Lines and line segments • Addition and subtraction • Multiplication with carrying	**ALGEBRA AND GRAPHING** • Expressions • Functions • Equations • Graphing	**FRACTIONS** • Factors and fractions • The LCM and fractions • Decimals and fractions	UNIT 4
DIVISION AND MEASUREMENTS • Division – 1-digit divisor • Families of facts • Standard measurements • Number grouping	**MEASUREMENT** • The metric system • The customary system • Time • Temperature	**FRACTION OPERATIONS** • Adding and subtracting fractions • Multiplying and dividing fractions • The customary system	UNIT 5
DIVISION, FACTORS, AND FRACTIONS • Division — 1-digit divisors with remainders • Factors and multiples • Improper and mixed fractions • Equivalent fractions	**FACTORS AND FRACTIONS** • Factors • Equivalent fractions • Fractions	**RATIO, PROPORTION, AND PERCENT** • Ratios • Proportions • Percent	UNIT 6
WHOLE NUMBERS AND FRACTIONS • Multiplication — 2-digit multipliers • Simplifying fractions • Averages • Decimals in money problems • Equations	**FRACTION OPERATIONS** • Like denominators • Unlike denominators • Multiplying fractions • Dividing fractions	**PROBABILITY AND GEOMETRY** • Probability • Geometry: Angles • Geometry: Polygons	UNIT 7
WHOLE NUMBERS AND FRACTIONS • Division — 1-digit divisors • Fractions and unlike denominators • Metric units • Whole numbers: +, −, x, ÷	**DATA ANALYSIS AND PROBABILITY** • Collecting data • Analyzing data • Displaying data • Probability	**GEOMETRY AND MEASUREMENT** • Plane figures • Solid figures	UNIT 8
DECIMALS AND FRACTIONS • Reading and writing decimals • Adding and subtracting mixed numbers • Cross multiplication • Estimation	**GEOMETRY** • Geometry • Classifying plane figures • Classifying solid figures • Transformations • Symmetry	**INTEGERS AND TRANSFORMATIONS** • Integers • Integer operations • Transformations	UNIT 9
ESTIMATION, CHARTS, AND GRAPHS • Estimation and data gathering • Charts and graphs • Review numbers to 100,000 • Whole numbers: +, −, x, ÷	**PERIMETER, AREA, AND VOLUME** • Perimeter • Area • Surface area • Volume	**EQUATIONS AND FUNCTIONS** • Equations • More equations and inequalities • Functions	UNIT 10

MATH SCOPE & SEQUENCE

	Grade 7	Grade 8	Grade 9
UNIT 1	**INTEGERS** • Adding and Subtracting Integers • Multiplying and Dividing Integers • The Real Number System	**THE REAL NUMBER SYSTEM** • Relationships • Other Forms • Simplifying	**VARIABLES AND NUMBERS** • Variables • Distributive Property • Definition of signed numbers • Signed number operations
UNIT 2	**FRACTIONS** • Working with Fractions • Adding and Subtracting Fractions • Multiplying and Dividing Fractions	**MODELING PROBLEMS IN INTEGERS** • Equations with Real Numbers • Functions • Integers • Modeling with Integers	**SOLVING EQUATIONS** • Sentences and formulas • Properties • Solving equations • Solving inequalities
UNIT 3	**DECIMALS** • Decimals and Their Operations • Applying Decimals • Scientific Notation • The Metric System	**MODELING PROBLEMS WITH RATIONAL NUMBERS** • Number Theory • Solving Problems with Rational Numbers • Solving Equations and Inequalities	**PROBLEM ANALYSIS AND SOLUTION** • Words and symbols • Simple verbal problems • Medium verbal problems • Challenging verbal problems
UNIT 4	**PATTERNS AND EQUATIONS** • Variable Expressions • Patterns and Functions • Solving Equations • Equations and Inequalities	**PROPORTIONAL REASONING** • Proportions • Percents • Measurement/Similar Figures	**POLYNOMIALS** • Addition of polynomials • Subtraction of polynomials • Multiplication of polynomials • Division of polynomials
UNIT 5	**RATIOS AND PROPORTIONS** • Ratios, Rates, and Proportions • Using Proportions • Fractions, Decimals, and Percents	**MORE WITH FUNCTIONS** • Solving Equations • Families of Functions • Patterns	**ALGEBRAIC FACTORS** • Greatest common factor • Binomial factors • Complete factorization • Word problems
UNIT 6	**PROBABILITY AND GRAPHING** • Probability • Functions • Graphing Linear Equations • Direct Variation	**MEASUREMENT** • Angle Measures and Circles • Polygons • Indirect Measure	**ALGEBRAIC FRACTIONS** • Operations with fractions • Solving equations • Solving inequalities • Solving word problems
UNIT 7	**DATA ANALYSIS** • Describing Data • Organizing Data • Graphing Data and Making Predictions	**PLANE GEOMETRY** • Perimeter and Area • Symmetry and Reflections • Other Transformations	**RADICAL EXPRESSIONS** • Rational and irrational numbers • Operations with radicals • Irrational roots • Radical equations
UNIT 8	**GEOMETRY** • Basic Geometry • Classifying Polygons • Transformations	**MEASURE OF SOLID FIGURES** • Surface Area • Solid Figures • Volume • Volume of Composite Figures	**GRAPHING** • Equations of two variables • Graphing lines • Graphing inequalities • Equations of lines
UNIT 9	**MEASUREMENT AND AREA** • Perimeter • Area • The Pythagorean Theorem	**DATA ANALYSIS** • Collecting and Representing Data • Central Tendency and Dispersion • Frequency and Histograms • Box-and-Whisker Plots • Scatter Plots	**SYSTEMS** • Graphical solution • Algebraic solutions • Determinants • Word problems
UNIT 10	**SURFACE AREA AND VOLUME** • Solids • Prisms • Cylinders	**PROBABILITY** • Outcomes • Permutations and Combinations • Probability and Odds • Independent and Dependent Events	**QUADRATIC EQUATIONS AND REVIEW** • Solving quadratic equations • Equations and inequalities • Polynomials and factors • Radicals and graphing

MATH SCOPE & SEQUENCE

Grade 10

A MATHEMATICAL SYSTEM
- Points, lines, and planes
- Definition of definitions
- Geometric terms
- Postulates and theorems

PROOFS
- Logic
- Reasoning
- Two-column proof
- Paragraph proof

ANGLES AND PARALLELS
- Definitions and measurement
- Relationships and theorems
- Properties of parallels
- Parallels and polygons

CONGRUENCY
- Congruent triangles
- Corresponding parts
- Inequalities
- Quadrilaterals

SIMILAR POLYGONS
- Ratios and proportions
- Definition of similarity
- Similar polygons and triangles
- Right triangle geometry

CIRCLES
- Circles and spheres
- Tangents, arcs, and chords
- Special angles in circles
- Special segments in circles

CONSTRUCTION AND LOCUS
- Basic constructions
- Triangles and circles
- Polygons
- Locus meaning and use

AREA AND VOLUME
- Area of polygons
- Area of circles
- Surface area of solids
- Volume of solids

COORDINATE GEOMETRY
- Ordered pairs
- Distance
- Lines
- Coordinate proofs

REVIEW
- Proof and angles
- Polygons and circles
- Construction and measurement
- Coordinate geometry

Grade 11

SETS, STRUCTURE, AND FUNCTION
- Properties and operations of sets
- Axioms and applications
- Relations and functions
- Algebraic expressions

NUMBERS, SENTENCES, & PROBLEMS
- Order and absolute value
- Sums and products
- Algebraic sentences
- Number and motion problems

LINEAR EQUATIONS & INEQUALITIES
- Graphs
- Equations
- Systems of equations
- Inequalities

POLYNOMIALS
- Multiplying polynomials
- Factoring
- Operations with polynomials
- Variations

RADICAL EXPRESSIONS
- Multiplying and dividing fractions
- Adding and subtracting fractions
- Equations with fractions
- Applications of fractions

REAL NUMBERS
- Rational and irrational numbers
- Laws of Radicals
- Quadratic equations
- Quadratic formula

QUADRATIC RELATIONS & SYSTEMS
- Distance formulas
- Conic sections
- Systems of equations
- Application of conic sections

EXPONENTIAL FUNCTIONS
- Exponents
- Exponential equations
- Logarithmic functions
- Matrices

COUNTING PRINCIPLES
- Progressions
- Permutations
- Combinations
- Probability

REVIEW
- Integers and open sentences
- Graphs and polynomials
- Fractions and quadratics
- Exponential functions

Grade 12

RELATIONS AND FUNCTIONS
- Relations and functions
- Rules of correspondence
- Notation of functions
- Types of functions

SPECIAL FUNCTIONS
- Linear functions
- Second-degree functions
- Polynomial functions
- Other functions

TRIGONOMETRIC FUNCTIONS
- Definition
- Equation of functions
- Trigonometric tables
- Special angles

CIRCULAR FUNCTIONS & GRAPHS
- Circular functions & special angles
- Graphs of sin and cosine
- Amplitude and period
- Phase shifts

IDENTITIES AND FUNCTIONS
- Reciprocal relations
- Pythagorean relations
- Trigonometric identities
- Sum and difference formulas

TRIGONOMETRIC FUNCTIONS
- Trigonometric functions
- Law of cosines
- Law of sines
- Applied problems

INVERSE TRIGONOMETRIC FUNCTIONS
- Inverse functions
- Graphing polar coordinates
- Converting polar coordinates
- Graphing polar equations

QUADRATIC EQUATIONS
- Conic sections
- Circle and ellipse
- Parabola and hyperbola
- Transformations

PROBABILITY
- Random experiments & probability
- Permutations
- Combinations
- Applied problems

CALCULUS
- Mathematical induction
- Functions and limits
- Slopes of functions
- Review

UNIT 1
UNIT 2
UNIT 3
UNIT 4
UNIT 5
UNIT 6
UNIT 7
UNIT 8
UNIT 9
UNIT 10

STRUCTURE OF THE LIFEPAC CURRICULUM

The LIFEPAC curriculum is conveniently structured to provide one Teacher's Guide containing teacher support material with answer keys and ten student worktexts for each subject at grade levels two through twelve. The worktext format of the LIFEPACs allows the student to read the textual information and complete workbook activities all in the same booklet. The easy-to-follow LIFEPAC numbering system lists the grade as the first number(s) and the last two digits as the number of the series. For example, the Language Arts LIFEPAC at the 6th grade level, 5th book in the series would be LAN0605.

Each LIFEPAC is divided into three to five sections and begins with an introduction or overview of the booklet as well as a series of specific learning objectives to give a purpose to the study of the LIFEPAC. The introduction and objectives are followed by a vocabulary section which may be found at the beginning of each section at the lower levels or in the glossary at the high school level. Vocabulary words are used to develop word recognition and should not be confused with the spelling words introduced later in the LIFEPAC. The student should learn all vocabulary words before working the LIFEPAC sections to improve comprehension, retention, and reading skills.

Each activity or written assignment in grades 2 through 12 has a number for easy identification, such as 1.1. The first number corresponds to the LIFEPAC section and the number to the right of the decimal is the number of the activity.

Teacher checkpoints, which are essential to maintain quality learning, are found at various locations throughout the LIFEPAC. The teacher should check 1) neatness of work and penmanship, 2) quality of understanding (tested with a short oral quiz), 3) thoroughness of answers (complete sentences and paragraphs, correct spelling, etc.), 4) completion of activities (no blank spaces), and 5) accuracy of answers as compared to the answer key (all answers correct).

The self test questions in grades 2 through 12 are also number coded for easy reference. For example, 2.015 means that this is the 15th question in the self test of Section 2. The first number corresponds to the LIFEPAC section, the zero indicates that it is a self test question, and the number to the right of the zero the question number.

The LIFEPAC test is packaged at the center of each LIFEPAC. It should be removed and put aside before giving the booklet to the student for study.

Answer and test keys in grades 2 through 12 have the same numbering system as the LIFEPACs. The student may be given access to the answer keys (not the test keys) under teacher supervision so that he can score his own work.

A thorough study of the Scope & Sequence by the teacher before instruction begins is essential to the success of the student. The teacher should become familiar with expected skill mastery and understand how these grade-level skills fit into the overall skill development of the curriculum. The teacher should also preview the objectives that appear at the beginning of each LIFEPAC for additional preparation and planning.

TEST SCORING AND GRADING

Answer keys and test keys give examples of correct answers. They convey the idea, but the student may use many ways to express a correct answer. The teacher should check for the essence of the answer, not for the exact wording. Many questions are high level and require thinking and creativity on the part of the student. Each answer should be scored based on whether or not the main idea written by the student matches the model example. "Any Order" or "Either Order" in a key indicates that no particular order is necessary to be correct.

Most self tests and LIFEPAC tests at the lower elementary levels are scored at 1 point per answer; however, the upper levels may have a point system awarding 2 to 5 points for various answers or questions. Further, the total test points will vary; they may not always equal 100 points. They may be 78, 85, 100, 105, etc.

Example 1

Example 2

A score box similar to ex. 1 above is located at the end of each self test and on the front of the LIFEPAC test. The bottom score, 72, represents the total number of points possible on the test. The upper score, 58, represents the number of points your student will need to receive an 80% or passing grade. If you wish to establish the exact percentage that your student has achieved, find the total points of his correct answers and divide it by the bottom number (in this case 72.) For example, if your student has a point total of 65, divide 65 by 72 for a grade of 90%. Referring to ex. 2, on a test with a total of 105 possible points, the student would have to receive a minimum of 84 correct points for an 80% or passing grade. If your student has received 93 points, simply divide the 93 by 105 for a percentage grade of 89%. Students who receive a score below 80% should review the LIFEPAC and retest using the appropriate Alternate Test found in the Teacher's Guide.

The following is a guideline to assign letter grades for completed LIFEPACs based on a maximum total score of 100 points.

Example:

LIFEPAC Test	=	60% of the Total Score (or percent grade)
Self Test	=	25% of the Total Score (average percent of self tests)
Reports	=	10% or 10* points per LIFEPAC
Oral Work	=	5% or 5* points per LIFEPAC

*Determined by the teacher's subjective evaluation of the student's daily work.

Example:

LIFEPAC Test Score	=	92%	92 x .60 = 55 points
Self Test Average	=	90%	90 x .25 = 23 points
Reports			= 8 points
Oral Work			= 4 points

TOTAL POINTS	= 90 points

Grade Scale based on point system:

100 – 94	=	A
93 – 86	=	B
85 – 77	=	C
76 – 70	=	D
Below 70	=	F

TEACHER HINTS AND STUDYING TECHNIQUES

LIFEPAC Activities are written to check the level of understanding of the preceding text. The student may look back to the text as necessary to complete these activities; however, a student should never attempt to do the activities without reading (studying) the text first. Self tests and LIFEPAC tests are never open book tests.

Language arts activities (skill integration) often appear within other subject curriculum. The purpose is to give the student an opportunity to test his skill mastery outside of the context in which it was presented.

Writing complete answers (paragraphs) to some questions is an integral part of the LIFEPAC Curriculum in all subjects. This builds communication and organization skills, increases understanding and retention of ideas, and helps enforce good penmanship. Complete sentences should be encouraged for this type of activity. Obviously, single words or phrases do not meet the intent of the activity, since multiple lines are given for the response.

Review is essential to student success. Time invested in review where review is suggested will be time saved in correcting errors later. Self tests, unlike the section activities, are closed book. This procedure helps to identify weaknesses before they become too great to overcome. Certain objectives from self tests are cumulative and test previous sections; therefore, good preparation for a self test must include all material studied up to that testing point.

The following procedure checklist has been found to be successful in developing good study habits in the LIFEPAC curriculum.

1. Read the introduction and Table of Contents.
2. Read the objectives.
3. Recite and study the entire vocabulary (glossary) list.
4. Study each section as follows:
   a. Read the introduction and study the section objectives.
   b. Read all the text for the entire section, but answer none of the activities.
   c. Return to the beginning of the section and memorize each vocabulary word and definition.
   d. Reread the section, complete the activities, check the answers with the answer key, correct all errors, and have the teacher check.
   e. Read the self test but do not answer the questions.
   f. Go to the beginning of the first section and reread the text and answers to the activities up to the self test you have not yet done.
   g. Answer the questions to the self test without looking back.
   h. Have the self test checked by the teacher.
   i. Correct the self test and have the teacher check the corrections.
   j. Repeat steps a–i for each section.
5. Use the SQ3R method to prepare for the LIFEPAC test.

   Scan the whole LIFEPAC.
   Question yourself on the objectives.
   Read the whole LIFEPAC again.
   Recite through an oral examination.
   Review weak areas.

6. Take the LIFEPAC test as a closed book test.
7. LIFEPAC tests are administered and scored under direct teacher supervision. Students who receive scores below 80% should review the LIFEPAC using the SQ3R study method and take the Alternate Test located in the Teacher's Guide. The final test grade may be the grade on the Alternate Test or an average of the grades from the original LIFEPAC test and the Alternate Test.

GOAL SETTING AND SCHEDULES

Each school must develop its own schedule, because no single set of procedures will fit every situation. The following is an example of a daily schedule that includes the five LIFEPAC subjects as well as time slotted for special activities.

Possible Daily Schedule

8:15 – 8:25	Pledges, prayer, songs, devotions, etc.
8:25 – 9:10	Bible
9:10 – 9:55	Language Arts
9:55 – 10:15	Recess (juice break)
10:15 – 11:00	Math
11:00 – 11:45	History & Geography
11:45 – 12:30	Lunch, recess, quiet time
12:30 – 1:15	Science
1:15 –	Drill, remedial work, enrichment*

*__Enrichment:__ *Computer time, physical education, field trips, fun reading, games and puzzles, family business, hobbies, resource persons, guests, crafts, creative work, electives, music appreciation, projects.*

Basically, two factors need to be considered when assigning work to a student in the LIFEPAC curriculum.

The first is time. An average of 45 minutes should be devoted to each subject, each day. Remember, this is only an average. Because of extenuating circumstances a student may spend only 15 minutes on a subject one day and the next day spend 90 minutes on the same subject.

The second factor is the number of pages to be worked in each subject. A single LIFEPAC is designed to take three to four weeks to complete. Allowing about three to four days for LIFEPAC introduction, review, and tests, the student has approximately 15 days to complete the LIFEPAC pages. Simply take the number of pages in the LIFEPAC, divide it by 15 and you will have the number of pages that must be completed on a daily basis to keep the student on schedule. For example, a LIFEPAC containing 45 pages will require three completed pages per day. Again, this is only an average. While working a 45-page LIFEPAC, the student may complete only one page the first day if the text has a lot of activities or reports, but go on to complete five pages the next day.

Long-range planning requires some organization. Because the traditional school year originates in the early fall of one year and continues to late spring of the following year, a calendar should be devised that covers this period of time. Approximate beginning and completion dates can be noted on the calendar as well as special occasions such as holidays, vacations and birthdays. Since each LIFEPAC takes three to four weeks or 18 days to complete, it should take about 180 school days to finish a set of ten LIFEPACs. Starting at the beginning school date, mark off 18 school days on the calendar and that will become the targeted completion date for the first LIFEPAC. Continue marking the calendar until you have established dates for the remaining nine LIFEPACs making adjustments for previously noted holidays and vacations. If all five subjects are being used, the ten established target dates should be the same for the LIFEPACs in each subject.

TEACHING SUPPLEMENTS

The sample weekly lesson plan and student grading sheet forms are included in this section as teacher support materials and may be duplicated at the convenience of the teacher.

The student grading sheet is provided for those who desire to follow the suggested guidelines for assignment of letter grades as previously discussed. The student's self test scores should be posted as percentage grades. When the LIFEPAC is completed the teacher should average the self test grades, multiply the average by .25 and post the points in the box marked self test points. The LIFEPAC percentage grade should be multiplied by .60 and posted. Next, the teacher should award and post points for written reports and oral work. A report may be any type of written work assigned to the student whether it is a LIFEPAC or additional learning activity. Oral work includes the student's ability to respond orally to questions which may or may not be related to LIFEPAC activities or any type of oral report assigned by the teacher. The points may then be totaled and a final grade entered along with the date that the LIFEPAC was completed.

The Student Record Book, which was specifically designed for use with the Alpha Omega curriculum, provides space to record weekly progress for one student over a nine week period as well as a place to post self test and LIFEPAC scores. The Student Record Books are available through the current Alpha Omega catalog; however, unlike the enclosed forms, these books are not for duplication and should be purchased in sets of four to cover a full academic year.

WEEKLY LESSON PLANNER

Week of:

	Subject	Subject	Subject	Subject
Monday				
Tuesday	Subject /	Subject /	Subject /	Subject /
Wednesday	Subject /	Subject /	Subject /	Subject /
Thursday	Subject /	Subject /	Subject /	Subject /
Friday	Subject /	Subject /	Subject /	Subject /

WEEKLY LESSON PLANNER

Week of:

	Subject	Subject	Subject	Subject
Monday				

	Subject	Subject	Subject	Subject
Tuesday				

	Subject	Subject	Subject	Subject
Wednesday				

	Subject	Subject	Subject	Subject
Thursday				

	Subject	Subject	Subject	Subject
Friday				

Student Name _____   Year _____

Bible

LP	Self Test Scores by Sections 1	2	3	4	5	Self Test Points	LIFEPAC Test	Oral Points	Report Points	Final Grade	Date
01											
02											
03											
04											
05											
06											
07											
08											
09											
10											

History & Geography

LP	Self Test Scores by Sections 1	2	3	4	5	Self Test Points	LIFEPAC Test	Oral Points	Report Points	Final Grade	Date
01											
02											
03											
04											
05											
06											
07											
08											
09											
10											

Language Arts

LP	Self Test Scores by Sections 1	2	3	4	5	Self Test Points	LIFEPAC Test	Oral Points	Report Points	Final Grade	Date
01											
02											
03											
04											
05											
06											
07											
08											
09											
10											

Student Name _____   Year _____

Math

LP	Self Test Scores by Sections 1	2	3	4	5	Self Test Points	LIFEPAC Test	Oral Points	Report Points	Final Grade	Date
01											
02											
03											
04											
05											
06											
07											
08											
09											
10											

Science

LP	Self Test Scores by Sections 1	2	3	4	5	Self Test Points	LIFEPAC Test	Oral Points	Report Points	Final Grade	Date
01											
02											
03											
04											
05											
06											
07											
08											
09											
10											

Spelling/Electives

LP	Self Test Scores by Sections 1	2	3	4	5	Self Test Points	LIFEPAC Test	Oral Points	Report Points	Final Grade	Date
01											
02											
03											
04											
05											
06											
07											
08											
09											
10											

INSTRUCTIONS FOR TENTH GRADE MATH

The LIFEPAC curriculum from grades 2 through 12 is structured so that the daily instructional material is written directly into the LIFEPACs. The student is encouraged to read and follow this instructional material in order to develop independent study habits. The teacher should introduce the LIFEPAC to the student, set a required completion schedule, complete teacher checks, be available for questions regarding both content and procedures, administer and grade tests, and develop additional learning activities as desired. Teachers working with several students may schedule their time so that students are assigned to a quiet work activity when it is necessary to spend instructional time with one particular student.

Math is a subject that requires skill mastery. But skill mastery needs to be applied toward active student involvement. Measurements require measuring cups, rulers, empty containers. Boxes and other similar items help the study of solid shapes. Construction paper, beads, buttons, beans are readily available and can be used for counting, base ten, fractions, sets, grouping, and sequencing. Students should be presented with problem situations and be given the opportunity to find their solutions.

Any workbook assignment that can be supported by a real world experience will enhance the student's ability for problem solving. There is an infinite challenge for the teacher to provide a meaningful environment for the study of math. It is a subject that requires constant assessment of student progress. Do not leave the study of math in the classroom.

The Teacher Notes section of the Teacher's Guide lists the required or suggested materials for the LIFEPACs and provides additional learning activities for the students. Additional learning activities provide opportunities for problem solving, encourage the student's interest in learning and may be used as a reward for good study habits.

MATH 1001

Unit 1: A Mathematical System

TEACHER NOTES

MATERIALS NEEDED FOR LIFEPAC	
Required	Suggested
(None)	• an instrument to make straight lines such as a ruler or straightedge

ADDITIONAL LEARNING ACTIVITIES

Section 1: Undefined Terms

1. On graph paper, have students make each of the following diagrams that represent tables. Dimensions should be written along the sides.

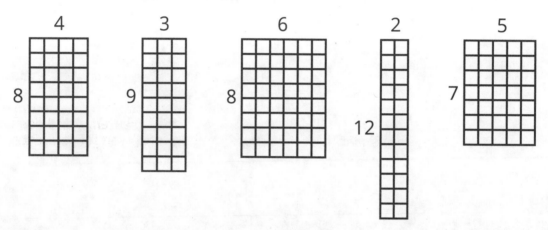

Have students draw the path a small ball would take for each table, starting at the lower left-hand corner, and moving the ball at a 45° angle with each side of the table. The ball always moves one unit up or down for one unit left or right. If the ball stops in a corner, mark the corner with a large dot. At that point the path of the ball terminates; otherwise, it continues rebounding at a 45° angle as it hits each side or end.

Do you think the ball will always end up in a corner?

If the ball starts from the lower left-hand corner, do you think it can stop in any of the four corners?

Section 2: Basic Definitions

1. Discuss these questions with your class.

   a. Can a ray have more than one name?

   b. Can a ray have two end points?

   c. How many line segments are in a line?

2. Have students draw the following figure. Ask them to determine the number of triangles of any size in the figure.

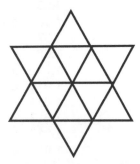

3. During their study of geometry, the students will be learning the definition of many terms. Encourage them to learn each new term as it is presented because later terms will be defined by using earlier terms. New terms will be defined as they need them in their study of geometry. Many of the definitions, theorems, and postulates in this unit will be needed in later units. Lists of these kept and maintained will be very helpful for future reference. The student should start a notebook now! Then as definitions, theorems, and postulates are given in the LIFEPAC they should be added to the notebook and used for reference.

Section 3: Geometric Statements

1. Discuss these questions with your class.

   a. Are any two points always collinear?

   b. Will any two noncollinear lines intersect?

   c. Do any postulates and theorems exist other than the ones used in the LIFEPAC?

2. Research Euclid, a Greek mathematician of 300 B.C., for whom Euclidean geometry is named.

3. Write several general statements such as "all rectangles have four sides." Then write several specific statements such as "a square has four equal sides." Devise a postulate or a theorem of your own. Remember that a postulate is a statement accepted without proof and that a theorem is a general statement that can be proved. Prove your theorem(s).

Administer the LIFEPAC Test.

The test is to be administered in one session. Give no help except with directions.
Evaluate the tests and review areas where the students have done poorly.
Review the pages and activities that stress the concepts tested.
If necessary, administer the Alternate LIFEPAC Test

ANSWER KEYS

SECTION 1

1.1 location or position

1.2 a dot

1.3 Example:

1.4 infinite number

1.5 none

1.6 no

1.7 points

1.8 straight

1.9 a. $\overleftrightarrow{AB}$
      b. $\overleftrightarrow{CD}$
      c. $\overleftrightarrow{EF}$

1.10 infinite number

1.11 A line exceeds indefinitely in both directions.

1.12 a. flat
      b. points

1.13 a. plane R
      b. plane S
      c. plane T

1.14 infinitely long

1.15 no thickness

1.16 no

SELF TEST 1

1.01 plane (table top)

1.02 line (arrow)

1.03 planes (cover and pages of book)

1.04 points (marbles)

1.05 lines (parallel railroad tracks)

1.06 points (freckles)

1.07 e

1.08 c

1.09 a

1.010 b

1.011 f

1.012 d

1.013 $\overleftrightarrow{AC}$

1.014 a. intersects
       b. E

1.015 point T

1.016 B or R (same plane)

1.017 a. $\overleftrightarrow{AC}$
       b. line x
       c. line w

1.018 S

1.019 S, E, A, C, T

1.020 C, R, A, B

SECTION 2

2.1   unacceptable (not restrictive enough)
2.2   unacceptable (not restrictive enough)
2.3   unacceptable (too restrictive)
2.4   acceptable
2.5   space
2.6   no (some are coplanar)
2.7   yes
2.8   a. S
          Either order:
          b. R
          c. T
2.9 $UV + VW = UW$
2.10 false (they are coplanar)
2.11 true
2.12 true
2.13 false (they are coplanar)
2.14 true
2.15 true
2.16 true
2.17 false (the three points are not collinear)
2.18 true (definition of a plane)
2.19 true
2.20 no (do not have the same end point)
2.21 yes
2.22 Either order:
          a. $\overrightarrow{AC}$
          b. $\overrightarrow{AB}$
2.23 Any order:
          a. $\overline{CA}$
          b. $\overline{CB}$
          c. $\overline{AB}$
          d. $\overline{AD}$
2.24 yes
2.25 point B
2.26 opposite rays
2.27 midpoint of $\overline{CB}$
2.28 no (the figure formed is not a straight line)
2.29 no (the three points are not collinear)

SELF TEST 2

2.01 The points must be collinear.
2.02 Either order:
          a. $\overline{SA} = \overline{AM}$
          b. $\overline{SA} + \overline{AM} = \overline{SM}$
2.03 $GO + OD = GD$

2.04 no (point O is not necessarily in a position such that $GO = OD$)
2.05 $\overrightarrow{SA}$

2.06 midpoint

2.07 U is between N and S.

2.08 U is between N and S.

2.09 one

2.010 Any order:
           $\overline{NU}$, $\overline{UT}$, and $\overline{NT}$

2.011 space
2.012 line
2.013 line
2.014 c
2.015 c
2.016 c
2.017 b
2.018 b
2.019 b
2.020 b
2.021 b
2.022 b
2.023 d
2.024 d

SECTION 3

3.1 Postulate 5: If two planes intersect, then their intersection is a line.

3.2 one

3.3 Postulate 2: Through any two different points, exactly one line exists.

3.4 a. no
b. Postulate 2: Through any two different points, exactly one line exists.

3.5 a. no
b. The three points cannot be on one line.

3.6 Postulate 1: Space contains at least four points not all in one plane.

3.7 Postulate 2: Through any two different points, exactly one line exists.

3.8 Postulate 3: Through any three points that are not on one line, exactly one plane exists.

3.9 Postulate 4: If two points lie in a plane, the line containing them lies in that plane.

3.10 Postulate 1: A plane contains at least three points not all on one line.

3.11 false (undefined terms are used to state some postulates)

3.12 false (a postulate does not require proof)

3.13 false (two planes intersect in exactly one line)

3.14 true

3.15 false (a plane must have at least 3 points)

3.16 false (the intersection of two planes is exactly one line)

3.17 the multiplication by one postulate

3.18 the commutative postulate for addition

3.19 the distributive postulate

3.20 the addition of zero postulate

3.21 the additive inverse postulate

3.22 the multiplication by one postulate

3.23 the addition of zero postulate

3.24 the commutative postulate of multiplication

3.25 the distributive postulate

3.26 the multiplicative inverse postulate

3.27 the addition postulate of inequality

3.28 the multiplication postulate of inequality

3.29 the multiplication postulate of inequality

3.30 the transitive postulate of equality

3.31 the symmetric postulate of equality

3.32 the comparison postulate

3.33 the multiplication postulate of inequality

3.34 the transitive postulate of inequality

3.35 the multiplication postulate of inequality

3.36 the reflexive postulate of equality

3.37 three collinear points
Example:

3.38 three noncollinear points
Example:

3.39 two intersecting lines
Example:

3.40 two nonintersecting lines
Example:

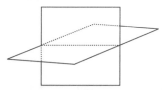

3.41 two intersecting planes
Example:

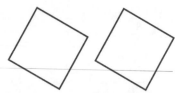

3.42 two nonintersecting planes
Example:

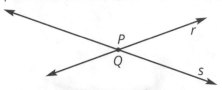

3.43 false (skew lines do not lie in one plane)

3.44 true

3.45 false (two intersecting lines lie in one plane)

3.46 false (three noncollinear points determine a plane)

3.47 true

3.48 They are the same point. Or, they are the point of intersection.

3.49 Theorem 1-1: If two lines intersect, then their intersection is exactly one point.

3.50   They lie in plane *N*.

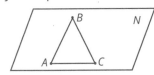

3.51   Postulate 4: If two points lie in a plane, the line containing them lies in that plane.
3.52   an infinite number
3.53   an infinite number
3.54   exactly one
3.55   exactly one
3.56   planes: *BCE*, *BEA*, *CED*, *AED*, *ABCD*, *ACE*, and *BDE*
3.57   the division property of equality
3.58   the multiplication property of equality
3.59   the subtraction property of equality
3.60   the addition property of equality
3.61   the multiplication property of equality
3.62   the addition property of equality
3.63   the multiplication property of equality
3.64   true
3.65   false (If $a + 2 < b + 3$, then $a < b + 1$.)
3.66   true
3.67   false (If $2 > -a$, then $a > -2$.)
3.68   the subtraction property of equality
3.69   the division property of equality
3.70   the addition property of equality
3.71   the subtraction property of equality
3.72   the division property of equality
3.73   the distributive postulate
3.74   the subtraction property of equality
3.75   the division property of equality
3.76   the distributive postulate
3.77   the subtraction property of equality
3.78   the subtraction property of equality
3.79   the division property of equality
3.80   the distributive postulate
3.81   the distributive postulate
3.82   the zero product property
3.83   the subtraction property of equality

SELF TEST 3

3.01   Example: line *l* intersects *m* at *P*.

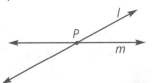

3.02   Example: Plane *A* contains line *l* and point *P*.

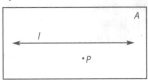

3.03   Example: Line *l* intersects line *m*; plane *A* contains both lines.

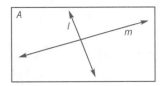

3.04   Example: $\overleftrightarrow{PQ}$, $\overleftrightarrow{PR}$, $\overleftrightarrow{PS}$, $\overleftrightarrow{QR}$, $\overleftrightarrow{QS}$, and $\overleftrightarrow{RS}$ are six different lines.

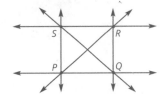

3.05   Example: *A*, *B*, *C*, and *D* are not all in one plane.

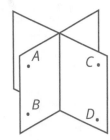

3.06   false (an undefined term can be used in a theorem)
3.07   true
3.08   false (two intersecting lines lie in one plane)
3.09   true
3.010 false (a segment has exactly two endpoints)
3.011 theorem
3.012 defined
3.013 postulate
3.014 line *AB*

3.015 line

3.016 b

3.017 d

3.018 c

3.019 a

3.020 Theorem 1-1: If two lines intersect, then their intersection is exactly one point.

3.021 Postulate 2: Through any two different points, exactly one line exists.

3.022 Postulate 4: If two points lie in a plane, the line containing them lies in that plane.

3.023 Postulate 5: If two planes intersect, then their intersection is a line.

3.024 the subtraction property of equality

3.025 the reflexive postulate of equality

LIFEPAC TEST

1. c
2. d
3. a
4. e
5. b
6. space
7. *A*

8. *BC*

9. midpoint

10. proof
11. prove
12. two
13. four
14. three

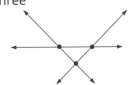

15. -*a*
16. lines *AB* and *CD* intersecting at point *P*

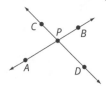

17. line *l* and point *Q* not on *l*, both in plane *T*

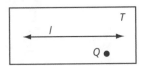

18. segment *UV* with midpoint *M*

19. collinear and coplanar points *A*, *B*, *C*, and *D*

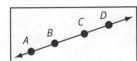

20. opposite rays $\vec{AC}$ and $\vec{AB}$

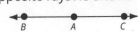

ALTERNATE LIFEPAC TEST

1. e
2. d
3. b
4. a
5. c
6. collinear
7. Either order:
   a. *P*
   b. *Q*
8. *RS*
9. midpoint
10. postulate
11. theorem
12. line
13. four
14. four
15. c
16.

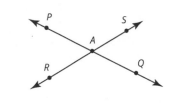

17.

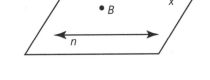

18.

19.

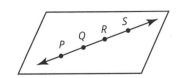

20.

MATH 1001

ALTERNATE LIFEPAC TEST

NAME _____

DATE _____

SCORE _____

After each model in Column I, write the matching term from Column II (each answer, 2 points).

Column I

1. A •——• B ——▶ _____

2. ◀——• A •—• B ——▶ _____

3. • Q _____

4. A •————————• B _____

5. A •——• B —• C _____

Column II

a. $\overline{AB}$

b. Point Q

c. $AB + BC = AC$

d. $\overleftrightarrow{AB}$

e. $\overrightarrow{AB}$

Complete the following statements (each answer, 3 points).

6. Two or more points all on the same line are called _____ points.

7. The two end points of $\overline{PQ}$ are a. _____ and b. _____ .

8. If point P is between R and S, then $RP + PS =$ _____ .

9. If $AB = BC$ on AC, point B is called the _____ of $\overline{AC}$.

10. A _____ is a statement we accept without proof.

11. A _____ is a statement we must prove.

12. A _____ contains at least two points.

13. Space contains at least _____ points.

14. How many planes are determined by four noncoplanar points? _____

15. _____ $+ (-c) = 0.$

Sketch and label the following conditions (each answer, 5 points).

16. Two lines, $\overleftrightarrow{PQ}$ and $\overleftrightarrow{RS}$, intersecting in a point A.

17. A line n and a point B not on n that are both in plane X.

18. A segment with midpoint A and end points C and D.

19. Collinear and coplanar points P, Q, R, and S.

20. Opposite rays $\overrightarrow{XY}$ and $\overrightarrow{XZ}$.

MATH 1002

Unit 2: Proofs

TEACHER NOTES

MATERIALS NEEDED FOR LIFEPAC	
Required	Suggested
• a ruler or a straightedge	(None)

ADDITIONAL LEARNING ACTIVITIES

Section 1: Logic

1. Let one student think of a statement (it may be true or false) and tell the group. Then let students, in turn, respond with the negation, conditional, contrapositive, converse, and inverse of the original statement. Students may alternate thinking of statements and responding with the other statements. Students may also tell whether their statement is true or false. The Compiled Truth Table from the LIFEPAC may be used if necessary.

Section 2: Reasoning

1. Discuss these questions with your class.

    a. Why is deductive reasoning more reliable than inductive reasoning?

    b. Can all definitions, postulates, and theorems be proved by deductive reasoning?

2. Have the class draw the following figure. Ask them to determine the number of squares of any size.

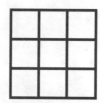

Next have the class draw the following figure. Ask them to determine the number of squares of any size.

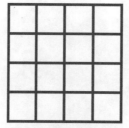

On the basis of the relationship between the size of the squares and their corresponding numbers of total squares, can the class state a hypothesis and a conclusion? Is this type of reasoning an example of inductive or deductive reasoning?

3. Have the students solve the following logic problem. A ship tied up in a harbor has a rope ladder hanging over its side. Each rung of the ladder is one inch in diameter and the rungs are eight inches apart, center to center. The ladder hangs down into the water, the water just covering the fifth rung from the bottom. If the tide rises at a uniform rate of twelve inches per hour, how many rungs will be submerged after two hours?

Section 3: Proof Formats

1. Discuss these questions with your class.

   a. In a two-column proof (direct proof), what happens when one of the statements is incorrect? when one of the reasons is incorrect?

   b. A postulate is a statement accepted without proof, and a theorem is a statement that can be proved. What are the reasons for accepting postulates to be true without proving them?

2. Prove the following statement in a direct proof (two-column proof) and then in an indirect proof (paragraph proof); then compare the two proofs. For the indirect proof, remember to write the *To Prove* and the *Given*.

$$3(x + 5) - 6 = 21$$

Administer the LIFEPAC Test.

The test is to be administered in one session. Give no help except with directions.
Evaluate the tests and review areas where the students have done poorly.
Review the pages and activities that stress the concepts tested.
If necessary, administer the Alternate LIFEPAC Test

ANSWER KEYS

SECTION 1

1.1 statement
1.2 statement
1.3 statement
1.4 statement
1.5 statement
1.6 not a statement (not a true or false statement)
1.7 not a statement (do not know what x represents)
1.8 no statement (Who is *he*?)
1.9 statement
1.10 statement
1.11 false (If p is true and q is false, then p and q is false.)
1.12 false (If p is true and q is false, then p and q is false.)
1.13 true (If p is true and q is true, then p and q is true.)
1.14 false (If p is false and q is false, then p and q is false.)
1.15 false (If p is false and q is false, then p and q is false.)
1.16 true (If p is true and q is true, then p and q is true.)
1.17 true (If p is true and q is true, then p and q is true.)
1.18 false (If p is false and q is true, then p and q is false.)
1.19 false (If p is false and q is true, then p and q is false.)
1.20 true (If p is true and q is true, then p and q is true.)
1.21 true (If p is true or q is true, then p or q is true.)
1.22 true (If p is true or q is false, then p or q is true.)
1.23 true (If p is false or q is true, then p or q is true.)
1.24 false (If p is false or q is false, then p or q is false.)
1.25 true (If p is true or q is true, then p or q is true.)
1.26 true (If p is true or q is true, then p or q is true.)
1.27 true (If p is true or q is false, then p or q is true.)
1.28 true (If p is true or q is true, then p or q is true.)

1.29 false (If p is false or q is false, then p or q is false.)
1.30 true (If p is false or q is true, then p or q is true.)
1.31 The grass is not green.
1.32 This rose is not white.
1.33 $5 + 4 \neq 90$
1.34 $5 \not> -5$
1.35 Geometry is not interesting.
1.36 A line has length.
1.37 All pigs are not fat. Or, not all pigs are fat.
1.38 My dog does not have fleas.
1.39 Two points do not determine a line.
1.40 A line does have a midpoint.
1.41 true (If p is true and q is true, then $p \to q$ is true.)
1.42 false (If p is true and q is false, then $p \to q$ is false.)
1.43 true (If p is false and q is true, then $p \to q$ is true.)
1.44 true (If p is false and q is false, then $p \to q$ is true.)
1.45 true (If p is false and q is false, then $p \to q$ is true.)
1.46 true (If p is false and q is true, then $p \to q$ is true.)
1.47 false (If p is true and q is false, then $p \to q$ is false.)
1.48 false (If p is true and q is false, then $p \to q$ is false.)
1.49 false (If p is true and q is false, then $p \to q$ is false.)
1.50 true (If p is true and q is true, then $p \to q$ is true.)
1.51 a. If $x > 7$, then $x > 5$.
b. true (If p is true and q is true, then $p \to q$ is true.)
1.52 a. If $x > 7$, then $x \not> 5$.
b. false (If p is true and q is false, then $p \to q$ is false.)
1.53 a. If $x \not> 7$, then $x > 5$.
b. true (If p is false and q is true, then $p \to q$ is true.)
1.54 a. If $x \not> 7$, then $x \not> 5$.
b. true (If p is false and q is false, then $p \to q$ is true.)
1.55 a. If $x > 5$, then $x > 7$.
b. true (If p is true and q is true, then $q \to p$ is true.)

1.56 a. If $x > 5$, then $x \not> 7$.
b. false (If p is false and q is true, then $q \to p$ is false.)

1.57 a. If $x \not> 5$, then $x > 7$.
b. true (If p is true and q is false, then $q \to p$ is true.)

1.58 a. If $x \not> 5$, then $x \not> 7$.
b. true (If p is false and q is false, then $q \to p$ is true.)

1.59 Converse: If two angles have the same vertex, then they are adjacent.

Inverse: If two angles are not adjacent, then the angles do not have the same vertex.

Contrapositive: If two angles do not have the same vertex, then the two angles are not adjacent.

1.60 Converse: If tomorrow is Wednesday, then today is Thursday.

Inverse: If today is not Thursday, then tomorrow is not Wednesday.

Contrapositive: If tomorrow is not Wednesday, then today is not Thursday.

1.61 Converse: If a polygon is a rectangle, then it is a square.

Inverse: If a polygon is not a square, then it is not a rectangle.

Contrapositive: If a polygon is not a rectangle, then it is not a square.

1.62 Converse: If the intersection of two lines is a point, then they intersect.

Inverse: If two lines do not intersect, then their intersection is not one point.

Contrapositive: If the intersection of two lines is not one point, then the two lines do not intersect.

1.63 Example:

Conditional: If Jack is the student's name, then the student is a male.

Converse: If the student is a male, then Jack is the student's name.

1.64 Example:
Conditional: If you work diligently, you will enjoy your job.

Converse: If you enjoy your job, you will work diligently.

1.65 This cannot be done because the conditional and the contrapositive have the same truth value.

SELF TEST 1

1.01 conjunction
1.02 disjunction
1.03 Either order:
a. conditional
b. implication
1.04 false (only two possibilities exist)
1.05 $q \to p$
1.06 $\sim r \to \sim s$
1.07 $\sim t \to \sim s$
1.08 true (If p is true and q is true, then $p \to q$ is true.)
1.09 true (If p is true or q is false, then p or q is true.)
1.010 false (If p is true and q is false, then p and q is false.)
1.011 false (If p is true and q is false, then $p \to q$ is false.)
1.012 true (If p is false and q is true, then $p \to q$ is true.)
1.013 true (If p is false and q is true, then $p \to q$ is true.)
1.014 false (If p is true and q is false, then $p \to q$ is false.)
1.015 false ($\sim(\sim p)$)
1.016 Conditional and contrapositive (b) are equivalent.
1.017 Either order:
a. Converse (c) and
b. inverse (a) are equivalent.
1.018 a. If $-6 < 5$, then $3 < 2$.
b. false (If p is false and q is true, then $q \to p$ is false.)
1.019 a. If $3 \not< 2$, then $-6 \not< 5$.
b. false (If p is true and q is false, then $p \to q$ is false.)
1.020 a. If $-6 \not< 5$, then $3 \not< 2$.
b. true (If p is true and q is false, then $q \to p$ is true.)

SECTION 2

2.1	neither (both are the same length)
2.2	$\overline{BD}$
2.3	neither (both are the same length)
2.4	"Stop, look and listen."
2.5	yes
2.6	Examples: A box in a corner, a box in front of a box, a box with the corner removed.
2.7	A woman is elected president.
2.8	A certain map uses four colors and has two regions colored alike that touch in more than one point.
2.9	Some numbers are less than 0, such as -2.
2.10	Allen gets a score below 90% on a test.
2.11	You are allergic to that fruit.
2.12	The rest will be snakes.
2.13	You will have a true-false test today.
2.14	Any number added to 0 equals that number.
2.15	Donald is the oldest.
2.16	No one is working.
2.17	Cathy's dad is fishing.
2.18	The figure is a square or a rhombus.
2.19	$x = 0$
2.20	Planes R and S intersect in a line.
2.21	Zelda lives in Zee.
2.22	My pet likes lettuce.
2.23	$SR + RT = ST$
2.24	The triangle does not have a right angle. (The conditional and the contrapositive are equivalent.)
2.25	No conclusion can be drawn. (Not enough information is given.)
2.26	Theorem 1-1: If two lines intersect, then their intersection is exactly one point.
2.27	Definition of bisector: A line that intersects the segment at its midpoint.
2.28	Definition of midpoint: The point on a segment that divides the segment into two equal segments.
2.29	Definition of betweenness: Three points are collinear and $AB + BC = AC$.
2.30	Postulate: If a plane contains a line, it contains the points of the line.

SELF TEST 2

2.01	deductive (general to specific)
2.02	inductive (specific to general)
2.03	deductive (general to specific)
2.04	deductive (general to specific)
2.05	neither (no reasoning)
2.06	$x = 2$ (the division property of equality)
2.07	$g = h$ (the division property of equality)
2.08	$t = 23$

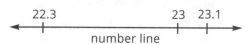

2.09	q is false (If p is true and q is false, then $p \rightarrow q$ is false.)
2.010	q is true (If p is true and q is true, then p and q is true.)
2.011	cannot
2.012	conjunction
2.013	disjunction
2.014	inductive (specific to general)
2.015	deductive (general to specific)
2.016	q (If p is true and q is true, then $p \rightarrow q$ is true.)
2.017	$2x + 2 = 11 - x$ $3x + 2 = 11$ Addition property of equality
2.018	$3x = 9$ Subtraction property of equality
2.019	$x = 3$ Division property of equality
2.020	If dogs do not scratch all night, then they do not have fleas.

SECTION 3

3.1 If two rays are opposite, then they form a straight line.

3.2 If Sam plays the piano, then Joe will sing.

3.3 If a man lives in Chicago, then he lives in Illinois.

3.4 If an angle exists, then it has exactly one bisector.

3.5 If you have a triangle, then the sum of the angles is 180°.

3.6 Example: *l* is parallel to *m* drawn through point *P*.

3.7 Example: Plane *R* is parallel to Plane *S*. Planes *R* and *S* are cut by Plane *T*. Line *l* is parallel to line *m*.

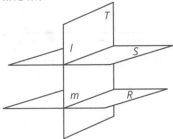

3.8 Example: In triangle *ABC*, ∠1 is equal to ∠2. Side *AB* is equal to side *CB*.

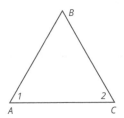

3.9 Example: In triangle *ABC*, segment *MN* joins midpoints *M* and *N* and is one-half the length of segment *AB*.

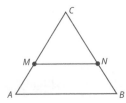

3.10 Example: Point *B* is between *A* and *C*. $AB + BC = AC$.

3.11 Given: Line *l*; point *P* not on *l*.

3.12 Given: Plane *R* is parallel to plane *S*; plane *T* cuts planes *R* and *S*.

3.13 Given: △*ABC* with ∠1 = ∠2.

3.14 Given: △*ABC* with midpoints *M* and *N*.

3.15 Given: Point *B* is between points *A* and *C*.

3.16 To Prove: *m* is parallel to *l*.

3.17 To Prove: *l* is parallel to *m*.

3.18 To Prove: $AB = BC$

3.19 To Prove: $MN = \frac{1}{2} AB$

3.20 To Prove: $AB + BC = AC$

1. **STATEMENT**
   $12 - x = 20 - 5x$
   REASON
   Given

3.21 2. **STATEMENT**
   $12 + 4x = 20$
   REASON
   Addition property of equality

3.22 3. **STATEMENT**
   $4x = 8$
   REASON
   Subtraction property of equality

3.23 4. **STATEMENT**
   $x = 2$
   REASON
   Division property of equality

1. **STATEMENT**
   $2(x + 3) = 8$
   REASON
   Given

3.24 2. **STATEMENT**
   $2x + 6 = 8$
   REASON
   Distributive postulate

3.25 3. **STATEMENT**
   $2x = 2$
   REASON
   Subtraction property of equality

3.26 4. **STATEMENT**
   $x = 1$
   REASON
   Division property of equality

1. **STATEMENT**
   $x(x + 4) = x(x + 2) + 1$
   REASON
   Given

3.27 2. **STATEMENT**
   $x^2 + 4x = x^2 + 2x + 1$
   REASON
   Distributive postulate

43

3.28 3. **STATEMENT**
$2x = 1$
REASON
Subtraction property of equality

3.29 4. **STATEMENT**
$x = \dfrac{1}{2}$
REASON
Division property of equality

3.30 1. **STATEMENT**
$x^2 + 6x + 2x + 12 = 0$
REASON
Given

3.31 2. **STATEMENT**
$x^2 + 8x + 12 = 0$
REASON
Substitution

3.32 3. **STATEMENT**
$(x + 6)(x + 2) = 0$
REASON
Distributive postulate

3.33 4. **STATEMENT**
$x + 6 = 0$ or $x + 2 = 0$
REASON
Zero product postulate

3.34 5. **STATEMENT**
$x = -6$ or $x = -2$
REASON
Subtraction property of equality

3.35 Apples do not make good pies.
3.36 The sun is not hot today.
3.37 $3 + 2 \neq 7$
3.38 A right angle does not measure less than 90°.
3.39 Seven is not a prime number.
3.40 A line does not contain at least 2 points.
3.41 Its square is not odd.
3.42 They intersect in more than one point.
3.43 Its leaves are not in groups of three.
3.44 $x = 4$
3.45 The sides opposite are equal.
3.46 Suppose $x \not< 25$, say $x = 26$. Then $2(26) < 50$ or $52 < 50$. This is a contradiction, so $x \not< 25$ is false and $x < 25$ is true.
3.47 A triangle cannot have two right angles. Suppose a triangle had two right angles. Then the sum of the angles would be more than 180°, but this fact contradicts the fact that the sum is 180°. Therefore, that a triangle cannot have two right angles is true.

SELF TEST 3

3.01 six
3.02 if-then
3.03 if
3.04 then
3.05 plan or analysis
3.06 always
3.07 always
3.08 always
3.09 never (both columns should have the same number of steps)
3.010 sometimes (only if the plan applies)
3.011 On $\overrightarrow{AB}$, AB is a given distance from end point A.

3.012 Point m is the only midpoint of AB.

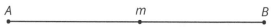

3.013 One plane through points A, B, and C.

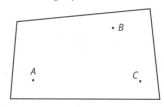

3.014 Jersey has a tail.
3.015 $\angle 1 = \angle 2$
3.016 S, O, N form a plane.
3.017 Bruce has no beans for supper tonight.

    1. **STATEMENT**
$2x + x + 4 = -17$
REASON
Given

3.018 2. **STATEMENT**
$3x + 4 = -17$
REASON
Substitution

3.019 3. **STATEMENT**
$3x = -21$
REASON
Subtraction property of equality

3.020 4. **STATEMENT**
$x = -7$
REASON
Division property of equality

LIFEPAC TEST

1. b. disjunction
2. d. conditional
3. a. conjunction
4. d. conditional
5. b. disjunction
6. Converse: If two angles are complementary, then they add to 90°.
7. Inverse: If two angles do not add to 90°, then they are not complementary.
8. Contrapositive: If two angles are not complementary, then they do not add to 90°.
9. Converse: If the flowers bloom, then it rained.
10. Inverse: If it does not rain, then the flowers will not bloom.
11. Contrapositive: If the flowers do not bloom, then it did not rain.
12. inductive (specific to general)
13. deductive (general to specific)
14. deductive (general to specific)
15. inductive (specific to general)
16. never (If p is true and q is false, then $p \rightarrow q$ is false.)
17. always (If p is false or q is true, then p or q is true.)
18. always (If p is true and $\sim q$ is false, then $p \rightarrow \sim q$ is false.)
19. always (If p is false and q is false, then $p \rightarrow q$ is true.)
20. sometimes (p is sometimes true and sometimes false.)
21. Given: Triangle ABC with angle B = 90°
22. To Prove: $\angle A + \angle C$ = 90°
23. Given: Paul is older than Bill; Fred is younger than Bill.
24. To Prove: Bill's age is between Paul's and Fred's.
25. Suppose x = 2; then $(2)^2 + 2 = 4$, which means $4 + 2 = 4$ or $6 = 4$. This is a contradiction because $4 = 4$. Therefore, x = 2 is false and $x \neq 2$ is true.

ALTERNATE LIFEPAC TEST

1. b. disjunction
2. a. conjunction
3. d. conditional
4. b. disjunction
5. c. negation
6. If tomorrow is Tuesday, then today is Monday.
7. If today is not Monday, then tomorrow is not Tuesday.
8. If tomorrow is not Tuesday, then today is not Monday.
9. If a polygon is a parallelogram, then it is a rectangle.
10. If a polygon is not a rectangle, then it is not a parallelogram.
11. If a polygon is not a parallelogram, then it is not a rectangle.
12. inductive (general to specific)
13. deductive (specific to general)
14. deductive (specific to general)
15. inductive (general to specific)
16. never
17. never
18. always
19. always
20. always
21. $\triangle ABC$ with $\angle A = \angle B$ (two angles of a triangle are equal)
22. $BC = AC$ (the sides opposite those angles are equal)
23. Sue is younger than Joan; Joan is younger than Jill.
24. Jill is the oldest of the three girls.
25. Suppose x = 4; then $3(4) - 2 = 7$, which means $12 - 2 = 7$ or $10 = 7$. This statement is a contradiction because $7 = 7$. Therefore, x = 4 is false and $x \neq 4$ is true.

MATH 1002

ALTERNATE LIFEPAC TEST

NAME _____

DATE _____

SCORE _____

71 / 88

Write the letter and the term that describes each statement (each answer, 2 points).

    a. conjunction   b. disjunction   c. negation   d. conditional

1. _____ All sides are equal or a square has three angles.

2. _____ The grass is green and the sky is blue.

3. _____ If a figure has three sides, then it is a triangle.

4. _____ Geometry is hard or rabbits are white.

5. _____ A triangle does not have six sides.

Write the converse, inverse, and contrapositive of these statements (each answer, 4 points).

    If today is Monday, then tomorrow is Tuesday.

6. Converse: _____

    _____

7. Inverse: _____

    _____

8. Contrapositive: _____

    _____

    If a polygon is a rectangle, then it is a parallelogram.

9. Converse: _____

    _____

10. Inverse: _____

    _____

11. Contrapositive: _____

    _____

Write *inductive* **or** *deductive* **to state which type of reasoning is used** (each answer, 2 points).

12. _____ Sarah observes several robins' nests and comes to the conclusion that all robins' eggs are blue.

13. _____ If a girl is a cheerleader at West High, then she must be a junior. Susan is a cheerleader at West High, so she is a junior.

14. _____ All geometry students have studied algebra. Bob is a geometry student, so he has studied algebra.

15. _____ Stanley looks at ten pennies and notices Lincoln's head on them. He decides that all pennies are Lincoln-head pennies.

Answer with *always, sometimes,* **or** *never* (each answer, 4 points).

16. When p is true and q is false, then p and q is _____ true.

17. If p is true and q is false, then $p \to q$ is _____ true.

18. If $p \to q$ is true and p is true, then q is _____ true.

19. If p is true and q is true, then $\sim q \to \sim p$ is _____ true.

20. If q is true and $\sim q$ is false, then $q \to \sim q$ is _____ false.

Write the *Given* **and** *To Prove* **in the following proofs** (each answer, 4 points).

If two angles of a triangle are equal, the sides opposite those angles are equal.

21. Given: _____

22. To Prove: _____

If Sue is younger than Joan and Joan is younger than Jill, then Jill is the oldest of the three girls.

23. Given: _____

24. To Prove: _____

Give an indirect proof of the following statement (10 points).

25.   If $3x - 2 = 7$, then $x \neq 4$.

_____

_____

_____

_____

_____

MATH 1003

Unit 3: Angles and Parallels

TEACHER NOTES

MATERIALS NEEDED FOR LIFEPAC	
Required	Suggested
• straightedges and protractors	(None)

ADDITIONAL LEARNING ACTIVITIES

Section 1: Angle Definitions and Measurement

1. Discuss these questions with your class.

    a. How many acute angles can be in a 90° angle? an obtuse angle?

    b. When do two acute angles equal a right angle? an obtuse angle?

Section 2: Angle Relationships and Theorems

1. Discuss these questions with your class.

    a. When are complementary angles equal? supplementary angles?

    b. When are vertical angles complementary? supplementary?

2. Review the essential differences between two-column proofs and paragraph proofs.

3. Have students draw the three squares in one continuous line without crossing any lines or taking the pencil off the paper.

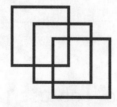

4. Given triangle *ABC*, have the students find the measure of ∠*DEB*.

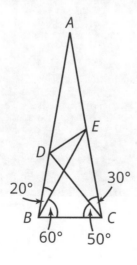

5. Have the student draw a set of angles such that *AO* and *DO* ⊥ *CF*, ∠*AOB* and ∠*BOC* are complementary and adjacent, ∠*ACF* and ∠*COD* are vertical angles, and $\overrightarrow{OE}$ and $\overrightarrow{OB}$ are opposite rays. Then have the student name all of the obtuse ∠'s, acute ∠'s, rt. ∠'s, complementary ∠'s, supplementary ∠'s, vertical ∠'s, and ⊥ lines.

Section 3: Parallels

1. Have the students find as many parallel lines, parallel planes, and transversals as possible in the classroom. Use the theorems in the LIFEPAC to prove that the lines and planes are parallel.

2. From the figure indicated, have the students remove exactly two matches so that exactly two squares remain.

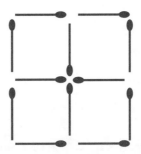

Section 4: Applying Parallels to Polygons

1. Have the class discuss which provides more information about triangles: classification by sides or classification by angles.

2. Have the students draw any triangle, quadrilateral, pentagon, hexagon, and octagon. Then have them measure the exterior angles of each figure and add the measures to see that the sum of the exterior angles is always 360°.

3. Let the student complete the following table. The left side of the table lists the classifications of triangles according to the number of equal sides they have. The top of the table lists the classifications of triangles according to the size of their angles.

	acute	obtuse	right	equiangular
scalene				
isosceles				
equilateral				

Then have the student draw and label an example of each possible combination. Not all combinations are possible.

Administer the LIFEPAC Test.

ANSWER KEYS

SECTION 1

1.1 ∠1, ∠S, ∠RST, ∠TSR
1.2 S
1.3 $\overrightarrow{SR}$, $\overrightarrow{ST}$
1.4 $\overrightarrow{BA}$, $\overrightarrow{BC}$
1.5 B
1.6 ∠CFD, ∠DFE, ∠CFE
1.7 ∠CFE
1.8 $\overrightarrow{FD}$
1.9 $\overrightarrow{FD}$
1.10 ∠AOD, ∠BOC
1.11 ∠AOB, ∠DOC
1.12 a. and b.

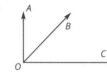

c. Acute and equal angles are formed.

1.13 a.

b. These lines are parallel to each other.

1.14 a. Example:

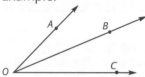

b. The sum of the measures of ∠AOB and ∠BOC equals the measure of ∠AOC.

1.15 a.

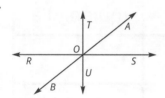

b. The measures of ∠AOS and ∠BOR are equal.

c. ∠AOT and ∠BOU are equal.

1.16 a. Examples:

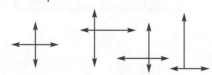

b. Right angles are formed.

1.17 a. Examples:

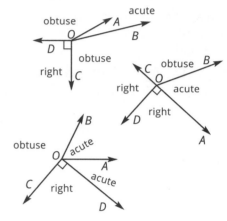

b. ∠AOD can be obtuse, acute, or right.

1.18 90°
1.19 greater than 90° and less than 180°
1.20 less than 90°
1.21 a. ∠AOX = 40°
b. ∠BOX = 60°
c. ∠BOA = |60 − 40| = 20°
d. ∠COB = |80 − 60| = 20°
e. ∠DOX = 120°
f. ∠BOE = |140 − 60| = 80°
g. ∠EOD = |140 − 120| = 20°
h. ∠AOD = |120 − 40| = 80°
i. ∠AOC = |80 − 40| = 40°

1.22 ∠BOA, ∠COB, ∠EOD
1.23 ∠AOX, ∠COA, ∠DOC, or ∠ZOE
1.24 ∠EOZ = |180 − 140| = 40°
∠AOX = |40 − 0| = 40°
yes
1.25 $\overrightarrow{OB}$
1.26 a. $\overrightarrow{OB}$
b. ∠COB = |80 − 60| = 20°
∠BOA = |60 − 40| = 20°
yes
1.27 ∠AOX, ∠AOB, ∠AOC, ∠AOD, ∠AOE, ∠AOZ
1.28 m ∠COX = m ∠AOX + m ∠COA
|80 − 0| = |40 − 0| + |80 − 40|
80 = 40 + 40
80° = 80°
yes
1.29 m ∠COB = |80 − 60| = 20°
m ∠BOA = |60 − 40| = 20°
Yes, they are equal.
1.30 $\overrightarrow{OB}$ is the ∠ bisector of ∠COA.

1.31   Examples:

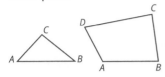

$\angle A =$ 55°
$\angle B =$ 47°
$\angle C = \underline{\;78°\;}$
           180°

The angles of any triangle add to 180°.

$\angle A =$ 115°
$\angle B =$ 75°
$\angle C =$ 90°
$\angle D = \underline{\;80°\;}$
           360°

The angles of any quadrilateral add to 360°.

1.32 $\dfrac{2}{3} \times \dfrac{60}{1} = \dfrac{120}{3} = 40'$

1.33 $\dfrac{45}{60} = \dfrac{5 \cdot 3 \cdot 3}{5 \cdot 3 \cdot 4} = \dfrac{3}{4}°$

1.34 $\dfrac{3}{4} \times \dfrac{60}{1} = \dfrac{180}{4} = 45''$

1.35   yes; 60″ = 1′ and 60′ = 1°

1.36   m $\angle ROT$ = m $\angle ROS$ + m $\angle SOT$
m $\angle ROS$ = 20° 15′ 40″
m $\angle SOT = \underline{10°\ \ 12'\ \ 30''}$
            30° 27′ ~~70″~~
                $\underline{+\ 1'}$ 60″ = 1′
m $\angle ROT$ = 30° 28′ 10″

1.37   m $\angle SOT$ = m $\angle ROT$ – m $\angle ROS$
                      61   68
m $\angle ROT$ = ~~62°~~ ~~8′~~ 12″
m $\angle ROS = \underline{41°\ \ 12'}$
m $\angle SOT$ = 20° 56′ 12″

1.38   m $\angle ROS$ = m $\angle ROT$ – m $\angle SOT$
m $\angle ROT$ = 48° 12′ 16″
m $\angle SOT = \underline{\ 7°\ \ \ 5'\ \ \ \ 8''}$
m $\angle ROS$ = 41°   7′   8″

1.39   m $\angle ROT$ = m $\angle ROS$ + m $\angle SOT$
m $\angle ROS$ = 28°   4′ 16″
m $\angle SOT = \underline{31°\ \ 48'\ \ 50''}$
            59° 52′ ~~66″~~
                $\underline{+\ 1'}$ 60″ = 1′
m $\angle ROT$ = 59° 53′   6″

1.40   m $\angle SOT$ = m $\angle ROT$ – m $\angle ROS$
m $\angle ROT$ = 52° 52′ 52″
m $\angle ROS = \underline{15°\ \ 22'\ \ 40''}$
m $\angle SOT$ = 37° 30′ 12″

SELF TEST 1

1.01   Example:

1.02 O
1.03 $\overrightarrow{OW}$, $\overrightarrow{ON}$
1.04

1.05

1.06   greater than 90° but less than 180°
1.07   less than 90°

1.08   m $\angle CXA$ = m $\angle BXA$ + m $\angle CXB$

m $\angle BXA$ = 30° 20′
m $\angle CXB = \underline{40°\ \ 35'}$
m $\angle CXA$ = 70° 55′

1.09   m $\angle CXB$ = m $\angle DXB$ – m $\angle DXC$
                  69   74   72
m $\angle DXB = \underline{~~70°~~\ \ ~~15'~~\ \ ~~12''~~}$
m $\angle DXC = \underline{30°\ \ 30'\ \ 20''}$
m $\angle CXB$ = 39° 44′ 52″

1.010 $\angle DXA$
1.011 m $\angle DXA$
1.012 no
1.013 no

1.014 20° 15′ 18″
        30° 41′ 32″
        $\underline{\ 2°\ \ 30'\ \ 15''}$
        52° 86′ ~~65″~~
            $\underline{+\ 1}$
        52° ~~87′~~   5″
        $\underline{+\ 1}$
        53° 27′   5″

1.015   49   100
        60° ~~50′~~ ~~40″~~
        $\underline{30°\ \ 40'\ \ 50''}$
        30°   9′ 50″

1.016 Given
1.017 Addition property of equality
1.018 Angle addition theorem
1.019 Angle addition theorem
1.020 Substitution

SECTION 2

2.1 b

2.2 e

2.3 a

2.4 c

2.5 1. **STATEMENT**
   ∠2, ∠3 are complementary ∠'s;
   ∠1, ∠3 are complementary ∠'s.
   REASON
   Given

2. **STATEMENT**
   m ∠2 + m ∠3 = 90°
   m ∠1 + m ∠3 = 90°
   REASON
   Definition of complementary ∠'s

3. **STATEMENT**
   m ∠1 + m ∠3 = m ∠2 + m ∠3
   REASON
   Substitution

4. **STATEMENT**
   m ∠1 = m ∠2
   REASON
   Subtraction property of equality

2.6 ∠APZ, ∠ZPB

2.7 ∠WPB

2.8 ∠APW, ∠WPZ

2.9 $\vec{PA}, \vec{PB}$

2.10 ∠APW, ∠BPZ

2.11 ∠APW, ∠WPB

2.12 ∠APW, ∠ZPB
   ∠APW, ∠APZ
   ∠WPZ, ∠WPB

2.13 ∠APZ, ∠ZPB

2.14 m ∠WPZ = m ∠APZ – m ∠APW
   = 90 – 20
   = 70°

2.15 ∠BCD, ∠CDA

2.16 ∠ABC

2.17 ∠BCA, ∠ACD

2.18 ∠ABC

2.19 $\overline{BC}, \overline{AD}$

2.20 ∠CAD, ∠ACD

2.21 ∠BCA

2.22 m ∠ABC = 110°
   180° – 110° = 70°
   m ∠BAD = 40° + 30° = 70°
   ∠BAD is the supplement.

2.23 m ∠CAB = 40°
   90 – 40 = 50
   No angle has a measure of 50°.

2.24 no

2.25 m ∠x + m ∠x = 90
   2m ∠x = 90
   m ∠x = 45°

2.26 m ∠x + m ∠x = 180
   2m ∠x = 180
   m ∠x = 90°

2.27 Let x = first ∠ measure.
   3x = second ∠ measure.
   x + 3x = 90°
   4x = 90°
   $x = 22\frac{1}{2}°$
   $3x = 67\frac{1}{2}°$

2.28 90° – 3x

2.29 (3x – 10) + (2x + 20) = 90
   5x + 10 = 90
   5x = 80
   x = 16
   3x – 10 = 38°
   2x + 20 = 52°

2.30 2x + 20 = 5x – 34
   -3x = -54
   x = 18
   2x + 20 = 56°
   5x – 34 = 56°

2.31 Given

2.32 Exterior sides in opposite rays

2.33 Definition of supplementary ∠'s

2.34 Substitution

2.35 Vertical ∠'s are =

2.36 Substitution

2.37 Definition of supplementary ∠'s

2.38 1. **STATEMENT**
   ∠1, ∠2 are rt. ∠'s.
   REASON
   Given

2. **STATEMENT**
   m∠1 = 90°
   m∠2 = 90°
   REASON
   Definition of rt. ∠'s

3. **STATEMENT**
   m∠1 = m∠2
   REASON
   Substitution

2.39 90°
2.40 30°
2.41 40°
2.42 no
2.43 yes
2.44 30°
2.45 90°
2.46 90°
2.47 180°
2.48 a. ∠1 and ∠2
     b. ∠3 and ∠4
2.49 m ∠3 = 90° – m ∠4

$$\overset{89}{\cancel{90°}}\ 60'$$

m ∠4 = 20° 15'
m ∠3 = 69° 45'

2.50 Theorem 3-1, angle addition theorem
2.51 Theorem 3-3, ⊥'s form rt. ∠'s
2.52 Theorem 3-4, exterior sides in perpendicular lines
2.53 Theorem 3-2, exterior sides are opposite rays
2.54 Given
2.55 Exterior sides in ⊥ lines
2.56 Definition of rt. ∠
2.57 Angle addition theorem
2.58 Substitution
2.59 Subtraction property of equality

SELF TEST 2

2.01 Example:

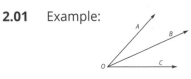

2.02

2.03 The angles are supplementary.
2.04 The angles are complementary.
2.05 They are equal to one another.
2.06 rt. ∠'s
2.07 equal
2.08 equal
2.09 The lines are perpendicular.
2.010 90°
2.011 180°
2.012 m ∠B = 180° – m ∠A

$$\overset{179}{\cancel{180°}}\ 60'$$

m ∠A = 37° 15'
        142° 45'

2.013 Vertical angles are equal; therefore, m ∠D = m ∠C = 63° 15' 47".

2.014

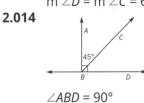

∠ABD = 90°
∠CBD = ∠ABD – ∠ABC
∠CBD = 90° – 45°
∠CBD = 45°

2.015

m ∠CBD = 180°– m ∠ABC
m ∠CBD = 180°– 45°
m ∠CBD = 135°

2.016 Vertical angles are equal; therefore, $\overline{BD}$ and $\overline{CA}$ are straight segments
m ∠BOC = 180° – ∠ BOA
m ∠BOC = 180° – 30°
m ∠BOC = 150°

2.017 Given
2.018 Theorem 3-2, exterior sides in opposite rays
2.019 Definition of supplementary ∠'s
2.020 Substitution

SECTION 3

3.1 never
3.2 sometimes
3.3 sometimes
3.4 always
3.5 always
3.6 sometimes
3.7 sometimes
3.8 sometimes
3.9 sometimes
3.10 always

3.11 1. **STATEMENT**
$l \parallel m$
REASON
Given

2. **STATEMENT**
m $\angle 1$ = m $\angle 3$
REASON
If lines $\parallel$, corresponding $\angle$'s =.

3. **STATEMENT**
m $\angle 2$ = m $\angle 3$
REASON
Vertical $\angle$'s =.

4. **STATEMENT**
m $\angle 1$ = m $\angle 2$
REASON
Substitution

3.12 60°
3.13 60°
3.14 60°
3.15 120°
3.16 120°
3.17 120°
3.18 120°
3.19 Either order:
a. $\angle 2$ and $\angle 3$
b. $\angle 6$ and $\angle 7$
3.20 Either order:
a. $\angle 1$ and $\angle 4$
b. $\angle 5$ and $\angle 8$
3.21 1. **STATEMENT**
$a \parallel b$, m $\angle 2$ = m $\angle 3$
REASON
Given

2. **STATEMENT**
m $\angle 1$ = m $\angle 2$
REASON
P8: If lines $\parallel$, corresponding $\angle$'s =.

3. **STATEMENT**
m $\angle 1$ = m $\angle 3$
REASON
Substitution

3.22 1. **STATEMENT**
$c \parallel d$, m $\angle 4$ = m $\angle 5$
REASON
Given

2. **STATEMENT**
m $\angle 4$ = m $\angle 7$
REASON
If lines $\parallel$, alternate interior $\angle$'s =.

3. **STATEMENT**
m $\angle 5$ = m $\angle 8$
REASON
Vertical $\angle$'s =.

4. **STATEMENT**
m $\angle 7$ = m $\angle 8$
REASON
Substitution

3.23 1. **STATEMENT**
$a \parallel b$, $c \parallel d$
REASON
Given

2. **STATEMENT**
m $\angle 1$ = m $\angle 6$
REASON
Vertical $\angle$'s =.

3. **STATEMENT**
m $\angle 6$ = m $\angle 8$
REASON
Corresponding $\angle$'s =.

4. **STATEMENT**
m $\angle 8$ = m $\angle 16$
REASON
Corresponding $\angle$'s =.

5. **STATEMENT**
m $\angle 1$ = m $\angle 16$
REASON
Substitution

3.24 1. **STATEMENT**
$s \parallel t$
REASON
Given

2. **STATEMENT**
∠5, ∠7 are supplementary
REASON
Exterior sides in opposite rays

3. **STATEMENT**
m ∠5 + m ∠7 = 180°
REASON
Definition of supplementary ∠'s

4. **STATEMENT**
m ∠1 = m ∠5
REASON
Corresponding ∠'s =.

5. **STATEMENT**
m ∠1 + m ∠7 = 180°
REASON
Substitution

6. **STATEMENT**
∠1, ∠7 are supplementary
REASON
Definition of supplementary ∠'s

3.25 1. **STATEMENT**
s || t
REASON
Given

2. **STATEMENT**
∠1, ∠3 are supplementary
REASON
Exterior sides in opposite rays

3. **STATEMENT**
m ∠1 + m ∠3 = 180°
REASON
Definition of supplementary ∠'s

4. **STATEMENT**
m ∠1 = m ∠5
REASON
Corresponding ∠'s =.

5. **STATEMENT**
m ∠5 + m ∠3 = 180°
REASON
Substitution

6. **STATEMENT**
∠3, ∠5 are supplementary
REASON
Definition of supplementary ∠'s

3.26 1. **STATEMENT**
m ∠1 = m ∠2
REASON
Given

2. **STATEMENT**
m ∠1 = m ∠3
REASON
Vertical ∠'s =.

3. **STATEMENT**
m ∠2 = m ∠3
REASON
Substitution

4. **STATEMENT**
l || m
REASON
If corresponding ∠'s =, then lines are ||.

3.27 true
If 2 ∠'s have equal measure, then each has a measure of 28°; false.

3.28 false
If 2 ∠'s are equal, then they are both obtuse; false.

3.29 true
If $x = -5$, then $3 - 2x =$
$3 - 2(-5) =$
$3 + 10 = 13$; true

3.30 false
If $x = 5$, then $x^2 = 25$; true

3.31 false
If 2 ∠'s are not equal, then they are supplementary; false.

3.32 $\overline{AD} || \overline{BC}$
3.33 $\overline{AD} || \overline{BC}$
3.34 $\overline{AB} || \overline{DC}$
3.35 none
3.36 $\overline{DC} || \overline{AB}$
3.37 none
3.38 $\overline{AD} || \overline{BC}$
3.39 $\overline{AD} || \overline{BC}$
3.40 none
3.41 none
3.42 none
3.43 $\overline{DC} || \overline{AB}$
3.44 none

3.45 1. **STATEMENT**
m ∠2 = 122°
m ∠3 = 58°
REASON
Given

2. **STATEMENT**
∠3, ∠5 are supplementary
REASON
Exterior sides in opposite rays

3. **STATEMENT**
m ∠3 + m ∠5 = 180°
REASON
Definition of supplementary ∠'s

4. **STATEMENT**
58° + m ∠5 = 180°
REASON
Substitution

5. **STATEMENT**
m ∠5 = 122°
REASON
Subtraction property of equality

6. **STATEMENT**
m ∠2 = m ∠5
REASON
Substitution

7. **STATEMENT**
l || m
REASON
If corresponding ∠'s =, then lines are ||.

3.46 1. **STATEMENT**
m ∠6 = m ∠8, b || c
REASON
Given

2. **STATEMENT**
m ∠7 = m ∠8
REASON
If lines ||, corresponding ∠'s =.

3. **STATEMENT**
m ∠6 = m ∠7
REASON
Substitution

4. **STATEMENT**
a || b
REASON
If alternate interior ∠'s =, then lines ||.

3.47 1. **STATEMENT**
j || k, m ∠1 = m ∠3
REASON
Given

2. **STATEMENT**
m ∠1 = m ∠2
REASON
If lines ||, corresponding ∠'s =.

3. **STATEMENT**
m ∠2 = m ∠3
REASON
Substitution

4. **STATEMENT**
l || m
REASON
If alternate interior ∠'s =, then lines ||.

3.48 1. **STATEMENT**
∠A, ∠B, ∠C, ∠D are rt. ∠'s
REASON
Given

2. **STATEMENT**
$\overline{DA} \perp \overline{AB}$, $\overline{DA} \perp \overline{DC}$, $\overline{CD} \perp \overline{AD}$, $\overline{AB} \perp \overline{AD}$
REASON
If rt. ∠'s formed, lines are ⊥.

3. **STATEMENT**
$\overline{AD}$ || $\overline{BC}$, $\overline{AB}$ || $\overline{DC}$
REASON
If two lines are ⊥ to another line, they are ||.

3.49 1. **STATEMENT**
m ∠1 + m ∠5 = 180°
m ∠1 + m ∠4 = 180°
REASON
Given

2. **STATEMENT**
m ∠1 + m ∠5 = m ∠1 + m ∠4
REASON
Substitution

3. **STATEMENT**
m ∠5 = m ∠4
REASON
Subtraction property of equality

4. **STATEMENT**
$\overrightarrow{YZ}$ || $\overrightarrow{UV}$
REASON
If alternate interior ∠'s =, then lines ||.

3.50 1. **STATEMENT**
∠1, ∠2 are supplementary ∠'s
REASON
Given

2. **STATEMENT**
m ∠1 + m ∠2 = 180°
REASON
Definition of supplementary ∠'s

3. **STATEMENT**
∠1, ∠3 are supplementary ∠'s
REASON
Exterior sides in opposite rays

4. **STATEMENT**
   m ∠1 + m ∠3 = 180°
   REASON
   Definition of supplementary ∠'s

5. **STATEMENT**
   m ∠1 + m ∠2 = m ∠1 + m ∠3
   REASON
   Substitution

6. **STATEMENT**
   m ∠2 = m ∠3
   REASON
   Subtraction property of equality

7. **STATEMENT**
   l || *m*
   REASON
   If alternate interior ∠'s =, then lines ||.

SELF TEST 3

3.01 no point in common
3.02 plane
3.03 parallel
3.04 equal
3.05 line
3.06 parallel
3.07 parallel
3.08 complementary
3.09 supplementary
3.010

$$\begin{array}{r} \overset{89}{\cancel{90°}}\ \overset{59}{\cancel{60'}}\ 60'' \\ -\ 45°\ 12'\ 10'' \\ \hline 44°\ 47'\ 50'' \end{array}$$

3.011 yes
3.012 no
3.013 yes
3.014 yes
3.015 yes
3.016 *l* || *m*
3.017 Theorem 3-12, alternate interior ∠'s =
3.018 ∠2 , ∠3 are supplementary
3.019 Definition of supplementary ∠'s
3.020 m ∠2 + m ∠1 = 180°
3.021 Definition of supplementary ∠'s
3.022 Given
3.023 Substitution
3.024 Definition of alternate interior ∠'s
3.025 *l* || *m*

SECTION 4

4.1 isosceles and equilateral

4.2 scalene

4.3 isosceles

4.4 isosceles

4.5 scalene

4.6 acute

4.7 right

4.8 obtuse

4.9 right

4.10 acute and equiangular

4.11 $m \angle 4 = m \angle 2 + m \angle 3$
$= 50 + 100$
$= 150°$

4.12 $m \angle 1 + m \angle 2 + m \angle 3 = 180°$
$30 + 45 + m \angle 3 = 180°$
$75 + m \angle 3 = 180°$
$m \angle 3 = 105°$

4.13 $m \angle 4 = m \angle 2 + m \angle 3$
$= a° + b°$

4.14 $m \angle 3 = m \angle 4 - m \angle 2$
$= 150 - 40$
$= 110°$

4.15 $m \angle 1 = 180° - (m \angle 2 + m \angle 3)$
$= 180° - (2x° + 5x°)$
$= 180° - 7°x$

4.16 $m \angle 1 + m \angle 2 + m \angle 3 = 180°$
$3x + 4x + 2x = 180°$
$9x = 180°$
$x = 20°$

4.17 $m \angle 2 + m \angle 3 = m \angle 4$
$\dfrac{4}{3} x + 20 = 2x$
$4x + 60 = 6x$
$60 = 2x$
$30° = x$

4.18 $m \angle 1 = 180° - m \angle 2$
$= 180° - 50°$
$= 130°$

4.19 $m \angle M + m \angle P + m \angle 2 = 180°$
$m \angle P = 180° - (m \angle M + m \angle 2)$
$= 180° - (90° + 30°)$
$= 180° - 120°$
$= 60°$

4.20 $m \angle M + m \angle P + m \angle 2 = 180°$
$90° + 2m \angle P = 180°$
$2m \angle P = 90°$
$m \angle P = 45°$

4.21 $m \angle M + m \angle P = m \angle 1$
$90° + 40° = m \angle 1$
$130° = m \angle 1$

4.22 a. $m \angle 1 = 180° - (m \angle P + m \angle O)$
$= 180° - (38° + 70°)$
$= 180° - 108°$
$m \angle 1 = 72°$

b. $m \angle 2 = m \angle P + m \angle O$
$= 38° + 70°$
$m \angle 2 = 108°$

4.23 a. $m \angle 2 = 180° - m \angle 1$
$= 180° - 46°$
$m \angle 2 = 134°$

b. $m \angle O = 180° - (m \angle 1 + m \angle P)$
$= 180° - (46° + 38°)$
$= 180° - 84°$
$m \angle O = 96°$

4.24 a. $m \angle P = 180° - (m \angle O + m \angle 1)$
$= 180° - (90° + 35°)$
$= 180° - 125°$
$m \angle P = 55°$
$m \angle 2 = m \angle O + m \angle P$
$= 90° + 55°$
$m \angle 2 = 145°$

b. $m \angle P = 55°$

4.25 a. $m \angle P = 180° - (m \angle O + m \angle 1)$
$= 180° - (90° + 63°)$
$= 180° - 153°$
$m \angle P = 27°$
$m \angle 2 = m \angle O + m \angle P$
$= 90° + 27°$
$m \angle 2 = 117°$

b. $m \angle P = 27°$

4.26 $m \angle O + m \angle P + m \angle 1 = 180°$
$m \angle O = m \angle P$; let $m \angle O + m \angle P = 2m \angle O$
$2m \angle O = 180° - m \angle 1$
$2m \angle O = 180° - 36°$
$2m \angle O = 144°$
$m \angle O = 72°$
$m \angle 2 = m \angle O + m \angle P = 2m \angle O$
$m \angle 2 = 144°$

4.27 through 4.31

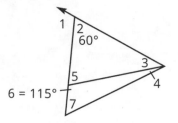

4.27   ∠1 and ∠2 are supplementary
    ∠1 = 180° − m ∠2
       = 180° − 60°
   m ∠1 = 120°

4.28   120° = m ∠3 + m ∠5
    120° = m ∠3 + (180° − m ∠6)
    120° = m ∠3 + (180° − 115°)
    120° = m ∠3 + 65°
    120° − 65°= m ∠3
       55° = m ∠3

4.29   m ∠4 = 180 − (m ∠6 + m ∠7)
       = 180° − (m ∠6 + m ∠3)
       = 180° − (115° + 55°)
       = 180° − 170°
   m ∠4 = 10°

4.30   ∠5 and ∠6 are supplementary
   m ∠5 = 180° − m ∠6
       = 180° − 115°
   m ∠5 = 65°

4.31   m ∠7 = m ∠3 = 55°

4.32 through 4.36

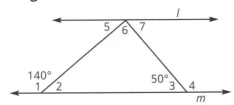

4.32   ∠1 and ∠2 are supplementary
   m ∠2 = 180° − m ∠1
       = 180° − 140°
   m ∠2 = 40°

4.33   ∠3 and ∠4 are supplementary
   m ∠4 = 180° − m ∠3
       = 180° − 50°
   m ∠4 = 130°

4.34   m ∠5 = 180° − (m ∠6 + m ∠7)
       = 180° − (90° + 50°)
       = 180° − 140°
   m ∠5 = 40°

4.35   m ∠6 = 180° − (m ∠2 + m ∠3)
       = 180° − (40° + 50°)
       = 180° − 90°
   m ∠6 = 90°

4.36   ∠3 and ∠7 are alternate interior ∠'s;
   m ∠3 = m ∠7
   m ∠7 = 50°

4.37   1.   **STATEMENT**
        $\overline{JK} \perp \overline{MN}$
        REASON
        Given

   2.   **STATEMENT**
        ∠MKJ is rt. ∠
        REASON
        ⊥'s form rt. ∠'s

   3.   **STATEMENT**
        △MKJ is rt. △
        REASON
        Definition of rt. △

   4.   **STATEMENT**
        ∠1, ∠2 are complementary
        REASON
        Acute ∠'s of rt. △ are complementary.

4.38   1.   **STATEMENT**
        m ∠5 = m ∠6
        REASON
        Given

   2.   **STATEMENT**
        m ∠1 = m ∠2
        REASON
        Vertical ∠'s are =

   3.   **STATEMENT**
        m ∠3 = m ∠4
        REASON
        If 2 ∠'s of one △ = 2 ∠'s of another △,
        then third ∠'s are =.

4.39   1.   **STATEMENT**
        $\overline{AC} \perp \overline{CD}$, $\overline{DB} \perp \overline{AB}$
        REASON
        Given

   2.   **STATEMENT**
        ∠C is rt. ∠, ∠B is rt. ∠
        REASON
        ⊥'s form rt. ∠'s

   3.   **STATEMENT**
        m ∠C = m ∠B
        REASON
        All rt. ∠'s are =

   4.   **STATEMENT**
        m ∠1 = m ∠2
        REASON
        Vertical ∠'s are =

5. **STATEMENT**
   m ∠A = m ∠D
   REASON
   If 2 ∠'s of one △ = 2 ∠'s of another △, then third ∠'s are =.

4.40 3 triangles

4.41 4 triangles

4.42 6 triangles

4.43 2 triangles

4.44 (n – 2) triangles

4.45 11 + 2 = 13 sides
4.46 (7 – 2)180 = 5(180) = 900°
4.47 (12 – 2)180 = 10(180) = 1,800°
4.48 (20 – 2)180 = 18(180) = 3,240°
4.49 (100 – 2)180 = 98(180)
                          = 17,640°
4.50 360 – (80 + 90 + 103) =
      360 – 273 = 87°
4.51 360 ÷ 6 = 60°
4.52 360 ÷ 5 = 72°
4.53 $360 ÷ 16 = 22\frac{1}{2}°$
4.54 360 ÷ 90 = 4 sides
4.55 360 ÷ 72 = 5 sides
4.56 360 ÷ 1 = 360 sides
4.57 $\frac{(8 – 2)180}{8} = \frac{(6)180}{8} = 135°$
4.58 $\frac{(10 – 2)180}{10} = \frac{8(180)}{8} = 144°$
4.59 $\frac{(n – 2)180°}{n}$
4.60 $\frac{(n – 2)180}{n} = 60$
      180n – 360 = 60n
           120n = 360
               n = 3 sides

SELF TEST 4

4.01 isosceles
4.02 scalene
4.03 180°
4.04 remote interior
4.05 pentagon
4.06 regular
4.07 parallel
4.08 180°
4.09 less than
4.010 complementary
4.011 acute, scalene
4.012 right, isosceles
4.013 acute, equilateral
4.014 obtuse, scalene
4.015 right, scalene
4.016 right, adjacent, supplementary
4.017 acute, adjacent, complementary
4.018 acute, vertical
4.019 right, vertical, supplementary
4.020 obtuse, adjacent

LIFEPAC TEST

1. Note: There may be more than one correct solution for the proof.

1. **STATEMENT**
$\overleftrightarrow{AB} \perp \overleftrightarrow{CD}$
REASON
Given

2. **STATEMENT**
m $\angle 1$ = m $\angle COB$
REASON
Definition of $\perp$ lines

3. **STATEMENT**
m $\angle COB$ = m $\angle 2$ + m $\angle 3$ + m $\angle 4$
REASON
Angle addition theorem

4. **STATEMENT**
m $\angle 1$ = m $\angle 2$ + m $\angle 3$ + m $\angle 4$
REASON
Substitution

5. **STATEMENT**
m $\angle 3$ = m $\angle 7$
REASON
Vertical $\angle$'s are =.

6. **STATEMENT**
m $\angle 1$ = m $\angle 2$ + m $\angle 4$ + m $\angle 7$
REASON
Substitution

2. Note: There may be more than one correct solution for the proof.

1. **STATEMENT**
$\overline{AB}$ || $\overline{CD}$
REASON
Given

2. **STATEMENT**
m $\angle 1$ = m $\angle 2$ + m $\angle 4$
REASON
Exterior $\angle$ of $\triangle$ = sum of remote interior $\angle$'s.

3. **STATEMENT**
m $\angle 3$ = m $\angle 4$
REASON
If lines ||, alternate interior $\angle$'s =.

4. **STATEMENT**
m $\angle 1$ = m $\angle 2$ + m $\angle 3$
REASON
Substitution

3. true
4. true
5. false
6. true
7. false
8. false
9. d
10. c
11. b
12. a
13. e
14. f
15. at least 2
16. 2
17. regular
18. 3
19. An interior $\angle$ is supplementary to an exterior $\angle$.
An exterior $\angle$ = 180° – interior $\angle$
= 180° – 120°
= 60°

20. 90°
21. $\angle 1$ = 90° – 50° = 40°

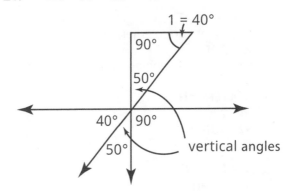

22. $\angle 1$ = 60° (vertical $\angle$'s)

ALTERNATE LIFEPAC TEST

1. 1. **STATEMENT**
    l || *m*
    REASON
    Given

    2. **STATEMENT**
    ∠1 = ∠3; ∠2 = ∠4
    REASON
    If lines are ||, corresponding ∠'s =.

    3. **STATEMENT**
    ∠1, ∠2 are supplementary
    ∠3, ∠4 are supplementary
    REASON
    Exterior sides in opposite rays

    4. **STATEMENT**
    ∠3 + ∠4 = 180°
    REASON
    Definition of supplementary ∠'s

    5. **STATEMENT**
    ∠1 + ∠4 = 180°
    REASON
    Substitution

    6. **STATEMENT**
    ∠1, ∠4 are supplementary
    REASON
    Definition of supplementary ∠'s

2. 1. **STATEMENT**
    m ∠2 = m ∠3
    REASON
    Given

    2. **STATEMENT**
    ∠1, ∠2 are supplementary
    ∠3, ∠4 are supplementary
    REASON
    Exterior sides in opposite rays

    3. **STATEMENT**
    m ∠1 = m ∠4
    REASON
    Two ∠'s supplementary to = ∠'s are =.

    4. **STATEMENT**
    ∠1, ∠5 are supplementary
    REASON
    Exterior sides in opposite rays

    5. **STATEMENT**
    ∠5, ∠4 are supplementary
    REASON
    Substitution

3. e or f
4. g
5. h
6. c
7. a
8. e
9. b
10. d
11. i
12. f
13. 360°
14. 360°
15. 180°
16. Either order:
    a. ∠D
    b. ∠DCB
17. ∠B
18. Either order:
    a. ∠BAC
    b. ∠CAD
19. ∠BCA
20. ∠B

MATH 1003

ALTERNATE LIFEPAC TEST

NAME _____

DATE _____

SCORE _____

105
131

Complete the following proofs (each answer, 4 points).

1. Given: *l* || *m*
    To Prove: ∠1 and ∠4 are supplementary.

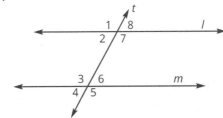

STATEMENT	REASON
1. _____	1. _____
2. _____	2. _____
3. _____	3. _____
4. _____	4. _____
5. _____	5. _____
6. _____	6. _____

2. Given: m ∠2 = m ∠3
    To Prove: ∠5 and ∠4 are supplementary.

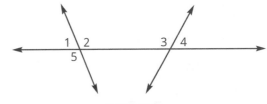

STATEMENT	REASON
1. _____	1. _____
2. _____	2. _____
3. _____	3. _____
4. _____	4. _____
5. _____	5. _____

Write the letter for the correct answer on the blank (each answer, 2 points).

3. _____ scalene △

4. _____ obtuse ∠

5. _____ acute △

6. _____ pentagon

7. _____ quadrilateral

8. _____ right △

9. _____ hexagon

10. _____ acute ∠

11. _____ octagon

12. _____ obtuse △

a.

b.

c.

d.

e.

f.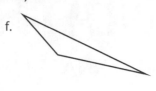

g.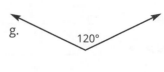

h.

i.

j.

Complete the following statements (each answer, 3 points).

13. The sum of the angles of a quadrilateral is _____ .

14. The sum of the exterior angles, one at each vertex, of a pentagon is _____ .

15. The sum of the angles of a triangle is _____ .

Name the following angles. Use the figure given (each answer, 2 points).

16. Two right angles:

    a. _____ and b. _____

17. An obtuse angle: _____

18. Two equal adjacent angles:

    a. _____ and b. _____

19. A complement to angle *DAB*: _____

20. A supplement to angle *DCA*: _____

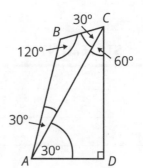

MATH 1004

Unit 4: Congruency

TEACHER NOTES

MATERIALS NEEDED FOR LIFEPAC	
Required	Suggested
• straightedges and protractors	(None)

ADDITIONAL LEARNING ACTIVITIES

Section 1: Triangles

1. Let one student read the "If" part of Postulate 11, 12, 13, or 14, or of Theorem 4-1, 4-2, 4-3, or 4-4. Then let a second student draw and label an appropriate figure to illustrate the postulate or theorem. Then let a third student say the "then" part of the postulate or theorem (without using the LIFEPAC). Repeat the procedure with each of the other postulates or theorems.

2. Draw any angle. Use only a compass and a straightedge to construct the bisector of the angle.

Section 2: Corresponding Parts

1. Discuss these questions with your class.

   a. If four lines in the same plane intersect at the same point, how many different pairs of vertical angles are formed?

   b. According to Theorem 4-5 in the LIFEPAC, the altitude to the base of an isosceles triangle bisects the base. When are all of the altitudes equal to all of the medians?

2. Let one student read Theorem 4-6 or 4-7 from the LIFEPAC. Then let another student draw and label an appropriate figure to illustrate the theorem. Repeat the procedure for the other theorem.

3. Let one student read the "If" part of Theorem 4-8 from the LIFEPAC. Then let a second student draw and label an appropriate figure to illustrate the theorem (representative figures are included in the LIFEPAC). Then let a third student say the "then" part of the theorem (without using the LIFEPAC).

4. Use a ruler and a protractor to construct a right triangle with a 45° angle and a right triangle with a 30° angle. What relationships can you discover about the various angles and sides of these right triangles?

Section 3: Inequalities

1. With your class, discuss what geometric figure is formed by any two coplanar, nonparallel lines cut by a transversal.

2. Let one student read the "If" part of Theorem 4-9, 4-10, 4-12, or 4-13 from the LIFEPAC. Then let a second student draw and label an appropriate figure (representative figures are included in the LIFEPAC with each theorem). Then let a third student say the "then" part of the theorem (without using the LIFEPAC). Repeat the procedure for each of the other theorems.

3. Let one student read Theorem 4-11 (triangle inequality theorem) from the LIFEPAC. Let another student draw an appropriate figure to illustrate the theorem. Then let a third student write three lengths for the sides of the triangle and check to be sure by adding all possible combinations of two sides that a triangle can be constructed with those measurements.

Section 4: Quadrilaterals

1. Discuss these questions with your class. How many diagonals can be drawn in a square? a regular pentagon? a regular hexagon? a regular *n*-gon?

2. Let one student read from the LIFEPAC Theorem 4-15, 4-20, 4-21, 4-22, 4-23, 4-24, or 4-25. Then let another student draw and label an appropriate figure to illustrate the theorem (representative figures are included in the LIFEPAC with each theorem). Repeat the procedure with each of the other theorems.

3. Let one student read the "If" part of Theorem 4-14, 4-16, 4-17, 4-18, or 4-19 from the LIFEPAC. Then let a second student draw and label an appropriate figure to illustrate the theorem (representative figures are included in the LIFEPAC with each theorem). Then let a third student say the "then" part of the theorem (without using the LIFEPAC). Repeat the procedure with each of the other theorems.

4. Draw all the diagonals of a pentagon. Find the number of triangles, quadrilaterals, pentagons, and trapezoids of any size that are formed.

5. Draw all the diagonals of a hexagon. Find the number of triangles, quadrilaterals, pentagons, and trapezoids of any size that are formed.

Administer the LIFEPAC Test.

The test is to be administered in one session. Give no help except with directions.
Evaluate the tests and review areas where the students have done poorly.
Review the pages and activities that stress the concepts tested.
If necessary, administer the Alternate LIFEPAC Test

ANSWER KEYS

SECTION 1

1.1 *S*
1.2 *R*
1.3 *T*
1.4 *R*
1.5 *K*
1.6 *O*
1.7 true
1.8 false
1.9 false
1.10 false
1.11 false
1.12 true
1.13 true
1.14 false
1.15 false
1.16 $\overline{AC}$
1.17 $\overline{BD}$
1.18 $\overline{AD}$
1.19 ∠2
1.20 ∠4
1.21 ∠*C*
1.22 $\overline{TU}$
1.23 $\overline{RU}$
1.24 $\overline{TR}$
1.25 ∠6
1.26 ∠8
1.27 ∠*S*
1.28 ∠*A*
1.29 ∠*W*
1.30 $\overline{SA}$
1.31 $\overline{SW}$
1.32 ∠*S*
1.33 $\overline{WA}$
1.34 SAS
1.35 SSS
1.36 AAS
1.37 SAS
1.38 SAS
1.39 ASA
1.40 AAS

1.41 1. **STATEMENT**
   AM = MB
   DM = MC
   REASON
   Given

2. **STATEMENT**
   ∠1 = ∠2
   REASON
   Vertical ∠'s are =.

3. **STATEMENT**
   △*AMD* ≅ △*BMC*
   REASON
   SAS

1.42 1. **STATEMENT**
   $\overline{AD}$ || $\overline{BC}$
   AD = BC
   REASON
   Given

2. **STATEMENT**
   ∠1 = ∠3
   ∠2 = ∠4
   REASON
   If lines || , alternate interior ∠'s =.

3. **STATEMENT**
   △*ADM* ≅ △*BCM*
   REASON
   ASA

1.43 1. **STATEMENT**
   RT = RU
   TS = US
   REASON
   Given

2. **STATEMENT**
   RS = RS
   REASON
   Reflexive

3. **STATEMENT**
   △*RST* ≅ △*RSU*
   REASON
   SSS

1.44 1. **STATEMENT**
   CM ⊥ *AB*
   ∠3 = ∠4
   REASON
   Given

2. **STATEMENT**
   ∠1 = ∠2
   REASON
   Definition of ⊥ lines

3. **STATEMENT**
   CM = CM
   REASON
   Reflexive

4. **STATEMENT**
   △AMC ≅ △BMC
   REASON
   ASA

1.45 1. **STATEMENT**
   DC || AB
   AD || BC
   REASON
   Given

2. **STATEMENT**
   ∠2 = ∠3
   ∠1 = ∠4
   REASON
   If lines || , then alternate interior ∠'s =.

3. **STATEMENT**
   AC = AC
   REASON
   Reflexive

4. **STATEMENT**
   △ACD ≅ △CAB
   REASON
   ASA

1.46 BC = ST = 8
1.47 RT = AC = 12
1.48 ∠C = ∠T = 20°
1.49 ∠B = 180° − (∠A + ∠C)
         = 180° − (40° + 20°)
         = 180° − 60°
         = 120°
1.50 ∠S = ∠B = 120°
1.51 ∠R = ∠A = 40°
1.52 RS = AB = 6
1.53 HA
1.54 LA
1.55 LA
1.56 LL
1.57 HL
1.58 1. **STATEMENT**
         ∠3, ∠4 are rt. ∠'s
         RS = RT
         REASON
         Given

2. **STATEMENT**
   RZ = RZ
   REASON
   Reflexive

3. **STATEMENT**
   △RZS ≅ △RZT
   REASON
   HL

1.59 1. **STATEMENT**
   ∠3, ∠4 are rt. ∠'s
   AX = BX
   REASON
   Given

2. **STATEMENT**
   CX = CX
   REASON
   Reflexive

3. **STATEMENT**
   △AXC ≅ △BXC
   REASON
   LL

1.60 1. **STATEMENT**
   AB ⊥ BD
   AB ⊥ BC
   AC = AD
   REASON
   Given

2. **STATEMENT**
   ∠ABC, ∠ABD are rt. ∠'s
   REASON
   ⊥'s form rt. ∠'s

3. **STATEMENT**
   AB = AB
   REASON
   Reflexive

4. **STATEMENT**
   △ABC ≅ △ABD
   REASON
   HL

1.61 1. **STATEMENT**
   ∠D, ∠B are rt. ∠'s
   DC || AB
   REASON
   Given

2. **STATEMENT**
   ∠1 = ∠2
   REASON
   If lines || , then alternate interior ∠'s =.

3. **STATEMENT**
   AC = AC
   REASON
   Reflexive

4. **STATEMENT**
   △*ADC* ≅ △*CBA*
   REASON
   HA

1.62 1. **STATEMENT**
   RS ⊥ *ST*
   RS ⊥ *SQ*
   ∠*STR* = ∠*SQR*
   REASON
   Given

2. **STATEMENT**
   RS = RS
   REASON
   Reflexive

3. **STATEMENT**
   ∠*RST*, ∠*RSQ* are rt. ∠'s
   REASON
   ⊥'s form rt. ∠'s

4. **STATEMENT**
   △*RST* ≅ △*RSQ*
   REASON
   LA

SELF TEST 1

1.01 ∠*W*
1.02 ∠*X*
1.03 ∠*Y*
1.04 *WX*
1.05 *XY*
1.06 *WY*
1.07 Either order:
   a. *JL*
   b. *JK*
1.08 Either order:
   a. ∠*J*
   b. ∠*K*
1.09 $\overline{JK}$
1.010 Either order (two possible sets of answers):
   JL and *JK*, or, *KL* and *KJ*
1.011 If two angles and the included side of one triangle are equal to two angles and the included side of another triangle, then the triangles are congruent.
1.012 If the hypotenuse and a leg of one right triangle are equal to the hypotenuse and leg of another right triangle, then the triangles are congruent.
1.013 If three sides of one triangle are equal to three sides of another triangle, then the triangles are congruent.
1.014 If a leg and an acute angle of one right triangle are equal to the corresponding parts of another right triangle, then the triangles are congruent.
1.015 If two sides and the included angle of one triangle are equal to two sides and the included angle of another triangle, then the triangles are congruent.

1.016 **STATEMENT**
   CA||*DB*; *E* is midpoint of $\overline{AD}$.
   REASON
   Given

1.017 **STATEMENT**
   ∠*A* = ∠*D*
   ∠*C* = ∠*B*
   REASON
   If lines ||, then alternate interior angles =.

1.018 **STATEMENT**
   EA = ED
   REASON
   Definition of midpoint

1.019 **STATEMENT**
$\triangle AEC \cong \triangle BED$
REASON
AAS

1.020 SAS
1.021 HL
1.022 SSS
1.023 ASA
1.024 HA
1.025 ASA

SECTION 2

2.1 1. **STATEMENT**
$AB = CD$
$BC = DA$
REASON
Given

2. **STATEMENT**
$AC = AC$
REASON
Reflexive

3. **STATEMENT**
$\triangle ABC \cong \triangle CDA$
REASON
SSS

4. **STATEMENT**
$\angle B = \angle D$
REASON
CPCTE

2.2 1. **STATEMENT**
$AB = CD$
$\angle 1 = \angle 4$
REASON
Given

2. **STATEMENT**
$AC = AC$
REASON
Reflexive

3. **STATEMENT**
$\triangle ABC \cong \triangle CDA$
REASON
SAS

4. **STATEMENT**
$AD = CB$
REASON
CPCTE

2.3 1. **STATEMENT**
$\angle 1 = \angle 4$
$\angle 2 = \angle 3$
REASON
Given

2. **STATEMENT**
$AC = AC$
REASON
Reflexive

3. **STATEMENT**
$\triangle ABC \cong \triangle CDA$
REASON
ASA

4. **STATEMENT**
$AB = CD$
REASON
CPCTE

2.4 1. **STATEMENT**
$\angle 1 = \angle 4$
$\angle B = \angle D$
REASON
Given

2. **STATEMENT**
$AC = AC$
REASON
Reflexive

3. **STATEMENT**
$\triangle ABC \cong \triangle CDA$
REASON
AAS

4. **STATEMENT**
$AD = CB$
REASON
CPCTE

2.5 1. **STATEMENT**
$AB \parallel CD$
$AD \parallel CB$
REASON
Given

2. **STATEMENT**
$\angle 1 = \angle 4$
$\angle 2 = \angle 3$
REASON
If lines ||, then alternate interior ∠'s =.

3. **STATEMENT**
$AC = AC$
REASON
Reflexive

4. **STATEMENT**
$\triangle ABC \cong \triangle CDA$
REASON
ASA

5. **STATEMENT**
$AD = CB$
REASON
CPCTE

2.6 1. **STATEMENT**
$AB \parallel DC$
$AB = CD$
REASON
Given

2. **STATEMENT**
$\angle 1 = \angle 4$
REASON
If lines ||, then alternate interior ∠'s =.

3. **STATEMENT**
$AC = AC$
REASON
Reflexive

4. **STATEMENT**
$\triangle ABC \cong \triangle CDA$
REASON
SAS

5. **STATEMENT**
$\angle 2 = \angle 3$
REASON
CPCTE

2.7 1. **STATEMENT**
$AB = CD$
$AD = CB$
REASON
Given

2. **STATEMENT**
$AC = AC$
REASON
Reflexive

3. **STATEMENT**
$\triangle ABC \cong \triangle CDA$
REASON
SSS

4. **STATEMENT**
$\angle 1 = \angle 4$
REASON
CPCTE

5. **STATEMENT**
$\overline{DC} \parallel \overline{AB}$
REASON
If alternate interior ∠'s =, then lines ||.

2.8 1. **STATEMENT**
$\overline{TQ}$ bisects $\angle RTS$
$\angle R = \angle S$
REASON
Given

2. **STATEMENT**
$\angle 1 = \angle 2$
REASON
Definition of ∠ bisector

3. **STATEMENT**
$TQ = TQ$
REASON
Reflexive

4. **STATEMENT**
$\triangle RTQ \cong \triangle STQ$
REASON
AAS

5. **STATEMENT**
$\angle 3 = \angle 4$
REASON
CPCTE

6. **STATEMENT**
$\overline{TQ} \perp \overline{RS}$
REASON
Definition of $\perp$

2.9 1. **STATEMENT**
$\overline{TQ}$ bisects $\overline{RS}$
$RT = ST$
REASON
Given

2. **STATEMENT**
$RQ = SQ$
REASON
Definition of bisector of segment

3. **STATEMENT**
$TQ = TQ$
REASON
Reflexive

4. **STATEMENT**
$\triangle RTQ \cong \triangle STQ$
REASON
SSS

5. **STATEMENT**
$\angle 3 = \angle 4$
REASON
CPCTE

6. **STATEMENT**
$\overline{TQ} \perp \overline{RS}$
REASON
Definition of $\perp$ bisector

2.10 1. **STATEMENT**
$\overline{TQ}$ is $\perp$ bisector of RS
REASON
Given

2. **STATEMENT**
$\angle 3 = \angle 4$
$RQ = QS$
REASON
Definition of $\perp$ bisector

3. **STATEMENT**
$TQ = TQ$
REASON
Reflexive

4. **STATEMENT**
$\triangle RTQ \cong \triangle STQ$
REASON
SAS

5. **STATEMENT**
$\angle R = \angle S$
REASON
CPCTE

2.11 1. **STATEMENT**
$\angle 2 = \angle 3$
$\angle 4 = \angle 5$
REASON
Given

2. **STATEMENT**
$\angle 1 = \angle 3$
REASON
Vertical $\angle$'s are =

3. **STATEMENT**
$\angle 1 = \angle 2$
REASON
Substitution

4. **STATEMENT**
$VR = VR$
REASON
Reflexive

5. **STATEMENT**
$\triangle VSR \cong \triangle VTR$
REASON
ASA

6. **STATEMENT**
$RS = RT$
REASON
CPCTE

2.12 1. **STATEMENT**
$\triangle ABC, \triangle DEF$ are rt. $\triangle$'s
$AB = DE$
$\angle A = \angle D$
REASON
Given

2. **STATEMENT**
$\triangle ABC \cong \triangle DEF$
REASON
LA

3. **STATEMENT**
$BC = EF$
REASON
CPCTE

2.13 1. **STATEMENT**
$\angle A$, $\angle B$ are rt. $\angle$'s
$AC = BD$
REASON
Given

2. **STATEMENT**
$\angle AMC = \angle BMD$
REASON
Vertical $\angle$'s are =

3. **STATEMENT**
$\triangle AMC \cong \triangle BMD$
REASON
LA

4. **STATEMENT**
$MC = MD$
REASON
CPCTE

2.14 1. **STATEMENT**
$\angle 1 = \angle 2$
$\angle 3 = \angle 4$
D midpoint of $\overline{BE}$
$BC = DE$
REASON
Given

2. **STATEMENT**
$BD = DE$
REASON
Definition of midpoint

3. **STATEMENT**
$BC = BD$
REASON
Substitution

4. **STATEMENT**
$\triangle ABD \cong \triangle EBC$
REASON
ASA

5. **STATEMENT**
$\angle A = \angle E$
REASON
CPCTE

2.15 1. **STATEMENT**
$\angle S = \angle T$
$RV = UV$
REASON
Given

2. **STATEMENT**
$\angle 1 = \angle 2$
REASON
Vertical $\angle$'s are =

3. **STATEMENT**
$\triangle RSV \cong \triangle UTV$
REASON
AAS

4. **STATEMENT**
$SR = TU$
REASON
CPCTE

2.16 BCA
2.17 AED
2.18 BDA
2.19 BDC
2.20 BOC
2.21 AEC
2.22 AFC
2.23 AFB
2.24 EDF
2.25 EGD
2.26 EGC
2.27 EBC
2.28 DGC
2.29 DAC
2.30 EAD
2.31 CGB

2.32 1. **STATEMENT**
$RM = SN$
$\angle MRS = \angle NSR$
REASON
Given

2. **STATEMENT**
$RS = RS$
REASON
Reflexive

3. **STATEMENT**
$\triangle MRS \cong \triangle NSR$
REASON
SAS

4. **STATEMENT**
$\angle RMS = \angle SNR$, $SM = RN$
REASON
CPCTE

2.33

1. **STATEMENT**
   $RM = SN$
   $SM = RN$
   REASON
   Given

2. **STATEMENT**
   $RS = RS$
   REASON
   Reflexive

3. **STATEMENT**
   $\triangle MRS \cong \triangle NSR$
   REASON
   SSS

4. **STATEMENT**
   $\angle RMS = \angle SNR$
   REASON
   CPCTE

2.34

1. **STATEMENT**
   $RT = ST$
   $MT = NT$
   REASON
   Given

2. **STATEMENT**
   $\angle T = \angle T$
   REASON
   Reflexive

3. **STATEMENT**
   $\triangle RTN \cong \triangle STM$
   REASON
   SAS

4. **STATEMENT**
   $\angle RNT = \angle SMT$
   REASON
   CPCTE

2.35

1. **STATEMENT**
   $RM = SN$
   $TM = TN$
   REASON
   Given

2. **STATEMENT**
   $\angle T = \angle T$
   REASON
   Reflexive

3. **STATEMENT**
   $RM + TM = SN + TN$
   REASON
   Addition property of equality

4. **STATEMENT**
   $RM + TM = RT$
   $SN + TN = ST$
   REASON
   Betweenness

5. **STATEMENT**
   $RT = ST$
   REASON
   Substitution

6. **STATEMENT**
   $\triangle RTN \cong \triangle STM$
   REASON
   SAS

7. **STATEMENT**
   $RN = SM$
   REASON
   CPCTE

2.36

1. **STATEMENT**
   $AD = BC$
   $BC \perp AE$
   $AD \perp BE$
   REASON
   Given

2. **STATEMENT**
   $\angle D, \angle C$ are rt. $\angle$'s
   REASON
   $\perp$'s form rt. $\angle$'s

3. **STATEMENT**
   $\angle E = \angle E$
   REASON
   Reflexive

4. **STATEMENT**
   $\triangle ADE \cong \triangle BCE$
   REASON
   LA

5. **STATEMENT**
   $\angle A = \angle B$
   REASON
   CPCTE

2.37

1. **STATEMENT**
   $CF = DF$
   $FC \perp AE$
   $FD \perp BE$
   REASON
   Given

2. **STATEMENT**
   $\angle C, \angle D$ are rt. $\angle$'s
   REASON
   $\perp$'s form rt. $\angle$'s

3. **STATEMENT**
   $FE = FE$
   REASON
   Reflexive

4. **STATEMENT**
   $\triangle FCE \cong \triangle FDE$
   REASON
   HL

5. **STATEMENT**
   $\angle 1 = \angle 2$
   REASON
   CPCTE

2.38 1. **STATEMENT**
   $AD \perp BE$
   $BC \perp AE$
   $AF = BF$
   REASON
   Given

2. **STATEMENT**
   $\angle C, \angle D$ are rt. $\angle$'s
   REASON
   $\perp$'s form rt. $\angle$'s

3. **STATEMENT**
   $\angle AFC = \angle BFD$
   REASON
   Vertical $\angle$'s are =.

4. **STATEMENT**
   $\triangle AFC \cong \triangle BFD$
   REASON
   HA

5. **STATEMENT**
   $AC = BD$
   REASON
   CPCTE

2.39 $\overline{CR}$
2.40 $\overline{AM}$
2.41 $\overline{BL}$
2.42 $\overline{BT}$
2.43 $\overline{AS}$
2.44 $\overline{CN}$
2.45 Q
2.46 P

2.47 1. **STATEMENT**
   $AC = BC$
   REASON
   Given

2. **STATEMENT**
   $\angle 1 = \angle 2$
   REASON
   Base $\angle$'s of isosceles $\triangle$ are =

3. **STATEMENT**
   $\angle 2 = \angle 3$
   REASON
   Vertical $\angle$'s are =

4. **STATEMENT**
   $\angle 1 = \angle 3$
   REASON
   Substitution

2.48 1. **STATEMENT**
   $\angle 3 = \angle 1$
   REASON
   Given

2. **STATEMENT**
   $\angle 3 = \angle 2$
   REASON
   Vertical $\angle$'s are =

3. **STATEMENT**
   $\angle 1 = \angle 2$
   REASON
   Substitution

4. **STATEMENT**
   $AC = BC$
   REASON
   If two $\angle$'s of $\triangle$ are =, sides opposite are =.

2.49 1. **STATEMENT**
   $RA = RB$
   $\overrightarrow{RS} \parallel \overline{AB}$
   REASON
   Given

2. **STATEMENT**
   $\angle A = \angle B$
   REASON
   Base $\angle$'s of isosceles $\triangle$ are =

3. **STATEMENT**
   $\angle A = \angle 2$
   REASON
   If lines $\parallel$, alternate interior $\angle$'s =.

4. **STATEMENT**
   $\angle B = \angle 1$
   REASON
   If lines $\parallel$, corresponding $\angle$'s =.

5. **STATEMENT**
   $\angle 1 = \angle 2$
   REASON
   Substitution

2.50

1. **STATEMENT**
$\overrightarrow{RS} \parallel \overline{AB}$
$\angle 1 = \angle 2$
REASON
Given

2. **STATEMENT**
$\angle B = \angle 1$
REASON
If lines ||, corresponding ∠'s =.

3. **STATEMENT**
$\angle A = \angle 2$
REASON
If lines ||, alternate interior ∠'s =.

4. **STATEMENT**
$\angle A = \angle B$
REASON
Substitution

5. **STATEMENT**
$RA = RB$
REASON
If two ∠'s of △ are =, sides opposite are =.

2.51

1. **STATEMENT**
$DF = EF$
REASON
Given

2. **STATEMENT**
$\angle 1 = \angle 2$
REASON
Base ∠'s of isosceles △ are =

3. **STATEMENT**
$\angle 1, \angle 3$ are supplementary
$\angle 2, \angle 4$ are supplementary
REASON
Exterior sides in opposite rays

4. **STATEMENT**
$\angle 3 = \angle 4$
REASON
Two ∠'s supplementary to equal ∠'s are equal.

2.52

1. **STATEMENT**
$\angle 3 = \angle 4$
REASON
Given

2. **STATEMENT**
$\angle 1, \angle 3$ are supplementary
$\angle 2, \angle 4$ are supplementary
REASON
Exterior sides in opposite rays

3. **STATEMENT**
$\angle 1 = \angle 2$
REASON
Two ∠'s supplementary to equal ∠'s are equal.

4. **STATEMENT**
$DF = EF$
REASON
If 2 ∠'s of △ are =, the sides opposite the ∠'s are =.

2.53

1. **STATEMENT**
$AR = AQ$
$RT = QS$
REASON
Given

2. **STATEMENT**
$\angle R = \angle Q$
REASON
Base ∠'s of isosceles △ are =

3. **STATEMENT**
$\triangle RAT \cong \triangle QAS$
REASON
SAS

4. **STATEMENT**
$\angle RAT = \angle QAS$
REASON
CPCTE

2.54

1. **STATEMENT**
$AR = AQ$
$\angle 1 = \angle 3$
REASON
Given

2. **STATEMENT**
$\angle R = \angle Q$
REASON
Base ∠'s of isosceles △ are =

3. **STATEMENT**
$\triangle ARS \cong \triangle AQT$
REASON
ASA

4. **STATEMENT**
$AS = AT$
REASON
CPCTE

2.55

1. **STATEMENT**
$\angle R = \angle Q$
$AS = AT$
REASON
Given

2. **STATEMENT**
∠5 = ∠6
REASON
Base ∠'s of isosceles △ are =

3. **STATEMENT**
∠4, ∠5 are supplementary
∠6, ∠7 are supplementary
REASON
Exterior sides in opposite rays

4. **STATEMENT**
∠4 = ∠7
REASON
Two ∠'s supplementary to equal angles
are =.

5. **STATEMENT**
△RAS ≅ △QAT
REASON
AAS

6. **STATEMENT**
RS = QT
REASON
CPCTE

SELF TEST 2

2.01 ∠XTY
2.02 ∠X
2.03 ∠XYT
2.04 TX
2.05 XY
2.06 TY
2.07 ∠E
2.08 ∠F
2.09 ∠FCE
2.010 EF
2.011 FC
2.012 EC
2.013 △AFG
2.014 △FCG
2.015 △AFC
2.016 △DCE

2.017 **STATEMENT**
$\overline{AP}$ || $\overline{BC}$
AD = CB
REASON
Given

2.018 **STATEMENT**
AC = AC
REASON
Reflexive

2.019 **STATEMENT**
∠2 = ∠3
REASON
If lines ||, alternate interior ∠'s =.

2.020 **STATEMENT**
△ACD ≅ △CAB
REASON
SAS

2.021 **STATEMENT**
∠1 = ∠4
REASON
CPCTE

2.022 **STATEMENT**
$\overline{AB}$ || $\overline{DC}$
REASON
If alternate interior ∠'s =, then lines ||.

2.023 **Given:**
△RAS is isosceles △; AM is median

2.024 **To Prove:**
△RAM ≅ SAM

2.025 STATEMENT
△*RAS* is isosceles △; *AM* is median
REASON
Given

2.026 STATEMENT
AR = AS
REASON
Definition of isosceles △

2.027 STATEMENT
AM = AM
REASON
Reflexive

2.028 STATEMENT
RM = MS
REASON
Definition of median

2.029 STATEMENT
△*RAM* ≅ *SAM*
REASON
SSS

SECTION 3

3.1   1. **STATEMENT**
$\overline{PT} \perp \overleftrightarrow{RT}$
REASON
Given

2. **STATEMENT**
T is rt. ∠
REASON
⊥ forms rt. ∠

3. **STATEMENT**
∠*T* > ∠*R*
REASON
Rt. ∠ is greater than acute ∠.

4. **STATEMENT**
PR > *PT* or *PT* < *PR*
REASON
If two ∠'s of △ ≠, then side opposite larger ∠ is longer.

3.2   a. ∠*B*
b. ∠*A*
c. ∠*C*

3.3   a. ∠*T*
b. ∠*R*
c. ∠*S*

3.4   a. ∠*T*
b. ∠*M*
c. ∠*S*

3.5   a. ∠*B*
b. ∠*A*
c. ∠*C*

3.6   a. $\overline{MO}$
b. $\overline{MP}$
c. $\overline{PO}$

3.7   a. $\overline{DE}$
b. $\overline{OE}$
c. $\overline{OD}$

3.8   a. $\overline{NA}$
b. $\overline{MA}$
c. $\overline{MN}$

3.9   yes
3.10   yes
3.11   no; 2 yds. + 5 yds. ≯ 10 yds.
3.12   yes
3.13   no; 1mm + 2mm ≯ 3mm
3.14   yes
3.15   <
3.16   <
3.17   >
3.18   <
3.19   >
3.20   >

3.21 >

3.22 >

3.23 <

3.24 1. **STATEMENT**
$BC = EF$
REASON
Given

2. **STATEMENT**
$AC = AB + BC$
REASON
Betweenness

3. **STATEMENT**
$AC > BC$
REASON
If $a = b + c$ and $c > 0$, then $a > b$.

4. **STATEMENT**
$AC > EF$
REASON
Substitution

3.25 1. **STATEMENT**
$\angle DBC = \angle RST$
REASON
Given

2. **STATEMENT**
$\angle ABC = \angle DBC + \angle ABD$
REASON
Angle addition theorem

3. **STATEMENT**
$\angle ABC > \angle DBC$
REASON
If $a = b + c$ and $c > 0$, then $a > b$.

4. **STATEMENT**
$\angle ABC > \angle RST$
REASON
Substitution

3.26 1. **STATEMENT**
$\triangle WXY$, $\angle 1$ an exterior $\angle$
REASON
Given

2. **STATEMENT**
$\angle 1 = \angle 2 + \angle 3$
REASON
Exterior $\angle$ = sum of remote interior $\angle$'s

3. **STATEMENT**
$\angle 1 > \angle 2$
REASON
If $a = b + c$ and $c > 0$, then $a > b$.

3.27 1. **STATEMENT**
$WX > XY$
REASON
Given

2. **STATEMENT**
$\angle 3 > \angle 4$
REASON
Angle opposite longer side is larger $\angle$.

3. **STATEMENT**
$\angle 1 = \angle 3 + \angle 2$
REASON
Exterior $\angle$ = sum of remote interior $\angle$'s

4. **STATEMENT**
$\angle 1 > \angle 3$
REASON
If $a = b + c$ and $c > 0$, then $a > b$.

5. **STATEMENT**
$\angle 1 > \angle 4$
REASON
Transitive

3.28 **Given:** $\triangle ABC$ is rt. $\triangle$
To Prove: $AC > AB$
$AC > BC$

1. **STATEMENT**
$\triangle ABC$ is rt. $\triangle$
REASON
Given

2. **STATEMENT**
$\angle B$ is rt. $\angle$
REASON
Definition of rt. $\triangle$

3. **STATEMENT**
$\angle B = 90°$
REASON
Definition of rt. $\angle$

4. **STATEMENT**
$90° = \angle A + \angle C$
REASON
Acute $\angle$'s of rt. $\triangle$ are complementary.

5. **STATEMENT**
$90° > \angle A$
REASON
If $a = b + c$ and $c > 0$, then $a > b$.

6. **STATEMENT**
$\angle B > \angle A$
REASON
Substitution

7. **STATEMENT**
   AC > BC
   REASON
   Side opposite larger ∠ is longer.

8. **STATEMENT**
   90° = ∠*C* + ∠*A*
   REASON
   Commutative for addition

9. **STATEMENT**
   90° > ∠*C*
   REASON
   If *a* = *b* + *c* and *c* > 0, then *a* > *b*.

10. **STATEMENT**
    ∠*B* > ∠*C*
    REASON
    Substitution

11. **STATEMENT**
    AC > AB
    REASON
    Side opposite larger angle is longer.

3.29 5 and 25
3.30 0 and 24
3.31 a. |*a – b*|
          b. *a + b*
3.32 >
3.33 >
3.34 <
3.35 >
3.36 >
3.37 <
3.38 >
3.39 <
3.40 =
3.41 =
3.42 <
3.43 <
3.44 >
3.45 >
3.46 =
3.47 =
3.48 <
3.49 >
3.50 >
3.51 =
3.52 <
3.53 <
3.54 >
3.55 <
3.56 =

SELF TEST 3

3.01 > 0
3.02 longer
3.03 a. sides
          b. sides
3.04 <
3.05 a. 5
          b. 11
3.06 >
3.07 >
3.08 <
3.09 <
3.010 >
3.011 =
3.012 =
3.013 ≅

3.014 **STATEMENT**
           ∠*A* = ∠*B*
           M is midpoint of *AB*
           REASON
           Given

3.015 **STATEMENT**
           AM = MB
           REASON
           Definition of midpoint

3.016 **STATEMENT**
           AC = BC
           REASON
           Sides opposite = ∠'s are =.

3.017 **STATEMENT**
           △*AMC* ≅ △*BMC*
           REASON
           SAS

SECTION 4

4.1 Opposite sides of ▱ are ||.

4.2 Opposite sides of ▱ are =.

4.3 Opposite ∠'s of ▱ are =.

4.4 They are supplementary ∠'s.

4.5 ∠1 = ∠5, ∠2 = ∠6, ∠3 = ∠7, ∠4 = ∠8, ∠9 = ∠10

4.6 RS = UT, RU = ST, RW = WT, UW = WS

4.7 △RSW ≅ △TUW, △RWU ≅ △TWS, △RST ≅ △TUR, △STU ≅ △URS

4.8 180°

4.9 SSS

4.10 1. **STATEMENT**
ABCD is ▱
REASON
Given

2. **STATEMENT**
Draw diagonal DB
REASON
Auxiliary line

3. **STATEMENT**
△ABD ≅ △CDB
REASON
Two ≅ △'s formed by diagonal

4. **STATEMENT**
∠A = ∠C
REASON
CPCTE

4.11 1. **STATEMENT**
ABCD is ▱
REASON
Given

2. **STATEMENT**
Draw diagonal DB
REASON
Auxiliary line

3. **STATEMENT**
△DAB ≅ △BCD
REASON
Two ≅ △'s formed by diagonal

4. **STATEMENT**
AB = DC, AD = BC
REASON
CPCTE

4.12 1. **STATEMENT**
▱ABCD
REASON
Given

2. **STATEMENT**
BT = TD
REASON
Diagonals of ▱ bisect each other.

3. **STATEMENT**
∠1 = ∠2
REASON
Vertical ∠'s are =.

4. **STATEMENT**
BC || AD
REASON
Definition of ▱

5. **STATEMENT**
∠3 = ∠4
REASON
If lines ||, then alternate interior ∠'s =.

6. **STATEMENT**
△BET ≅ △DFT
REASON
ASA

7. **STATEMENT**
ET = FT
REASON
CPCTE

4.13 1. **STATEMENT**
∠A, ∠B, and ∠C are rt. ∠'s
REASON
Given

2. **STATEMENT**
DA ⊥ AB, CB ⊥ AB
REASON
If rt. ∠'s are formed, then lines are ⊥.

3. **STATEMENT**
DA || CB
REASON
Two lines ⊥ to same line are ||.

4. **STATEMENT**
DC ⊥ BC, AB ⊥ BC
REASON
If rt. ∠'s are formed, then lines are ⊥.

5. **STATEMENT**
AB || DC
REASON
Two lines ⊥ to same line are ||.

6. **STATEMENT**
ABCD is ▱
REASON
Definition of ▱

4.14 1. **STATEMENT**
$RSTU$ is $\square$
$RSQP$ is $\square$
REASON
Given

  2. **STATEMENT**
$UT = RS$, $RS = PQ$
REASON
Opposite sides of $\square$ are =.

  3. **STATEMENT**
$PQ = UT$
REASON
Substitution

4.15 1. **STATEMENT**
$DO = OB$
$AO = OC$
REASON
Given

  2. **STATEMENT**
$\angle DOC = \angle AOB$
REASON
Vertical $\angle$'s are =.

  3. **STATEMENT**
$\triangle AOB \cong \triangle COD$
REASON
SAS

  4. **STATEMENT**
$\angle 1 = \angle 2$
$AB = DC$
REASON
CPCTE

  5. **STATEMENT**
$AB \parallel DC$
REASON
If alternate interior $\angle$'s are =, then $\parallel$.

  6. **STATEMENT**
$ABCD$ is $\square$
REASON
If two sides = and $\parallel$, then $\square$.

4.16 $\overline{UT}$
4.17 $VS \parallel UT$

$VS = \dfrac{1}{2}UT$

$= \dfrac{1}{2}(20)$

$= 10$

4.18 24
4.19 60°
4.20 180°

4.21 $\angle 3 = 180° - \angle 2$
$= 180° - 120°$
$= 60°$
4.22 $\overline{SM}$
4.23 $\overline{VM}$
4.24 $\overline{RT}$
4.25 $\overline{AB}$
4.26 $\overline{ST}$
4.27 $\overline{CB}$
4.28 $\overline{AB}$
4.29 $\overline{RT}$
4.30 paralellogram

4.31 through 4.34

$$2(2x + 60) + 2(x + 30) = 360$$
$$4x + 120 + 2x + 60 = 360$$
$$6x + 180 = 360$$
$$6x = 180$$
$$x = 30°$$

4.31 $\angle H = 2x + 60 = 120°$
4.32 $\angle A = x + 30 = 60°$
4.33 $\angle L = \angle H = 120°$
4.34 $\angle T = \angle A = 60°$
4.35 Either order:
 a. $\overline{FL}$
 b. $\overline{GA}$
4.36 Either order:
 a. $\overline{GF}$
 b. $\overline{AL}$
4.37 Either order:
 a. $\angle G$
 b. $\angle L$
4.38 Any order:
 a. $\angle A$
 b. $\angle X$
 c. $\angle Z$
4.39 1. **STATEMENT**
$ABEF$ is $\square$
$EB \parallel DC$
REASON
Given

  2. **STATEMENT**
$\overline{AF} \parallel \overline{BE}$
$\overline{FE} \parallel \overline{AB}$
REASON
Opposite sides of $\square$ are =.

  3. **STATEMENT**
$\overline{AF} \parallel \overline{CD}$
REASON
Transitive

4. **STATEMENT**
$\overline{FD} \parallel \overline{AC}$
REASON
Part of $\overleftrightarrow{FE}$ and $\overleftrightarrow{AB}$

5. **STATEMENT**
$ACDF$ is $\square$
REASON
Definition of $\square$

4.40 **Given:** $RSTU$ is rectangle
To Prove: $RT = US$

1. **STATEMENT**
$RSTU$ is rectangle
REASON
Given

2. **STATEMENT**
$RU = TS$
REASON
Opposite sides of $\square$ = (definition of rectangle).

3. **STATEMENT**
$RS = RS$
REASON
Reflexive

4. **STATEMENT**
$\angle S$, $\angle R$ are rt. $\angle$'s
REASON
Definition of rectangle

5. **STATEMENT**
$\triangle RST \cong \triangle SRU$
REASON
LL

6. **STATEMENT**
$RT = US$
REASON
CPCTE

4.41 **Given:** $ABCD$ is rhombus
To Prove: $AC \perp DB$

1. **STATEMENT**
$ABCD$ is rhombus
REASON
Given

2. **STATEMENT**
$AD = AB$
REASON
All sides of rhombus = (definition of rhombus).

3. **STATEMENT**
$DO = OB$
REASON
Diagonals of $\square$ bisect each other.

4. **STATEMENT**
$AO = AO$
REASON
Reflexive

5. **STATEMENT**
$\triangle DOA \cong \triangle BOA$
REASON
SSS

6. **STATEMENT**
$\angle 1 = \angle 2$
REASON
CPCTE

7. **STATEMENT**
$AC \perp DB$
REASON
Definition of $\perp$ lines

4.42 **Given:** $ABCD$ is rhombus
To Prove: DB bisects $\angle B$ and $\angle D$

1. **STATEMENT**
$ABCD$ is rhombus
REASON
Given

2. **STATEMENT**
$\triangle ADB \cong \triangle CDB$
REASON
Diagonals of $\square$ make $\cong$ $\triangle$'s.

3. **STATEMENT**
$\angle 1 = \angle 2$, $\angle 3 = \angle 4$
REASON
CPCTE

4. **STATEMENT**
DB bisects $\angle B$ and $\angle D$
REASON
Definition of $\angle$ bisector

4.43 **Given:** $ABCD$ is $\square$, $AC = BD$
To Prove: $ABCD$ is rectangle

1. **STATEMENT**
$ABCD$ is $\square$
$AC = BD$
REASON
Given

2. **STATEMENT**
$\angle A = \angle C$
$\angle B = \angle D$
REASON
Opposite $\angle$'s of $\square$ are =.

3. **STATEMENT**
$DA = CB$
REASON
Opposite sides of $\square$ are =.

4. **STATEMENT**
$AB = AB$
REASON
Reflexive

5. **STATEMENT**
$\triangle DAB \cong \triangle CBA$
REASON
SSS

6. **STATEMENT**
$\angle A = \angle B$
REASON
CPCTE

7. **STATEMENT**
$\angle A + \angle B = 180°$
REASON
Interior $\angle$'s on same side of transversal are supplementary.

8. **STATEMENT**
$2\angle A = 180°$
REASON
Substitution

9. **STATEMENT**
$\angle A = 90°$
REASON
Division property of equality

10. **STATEMENT**
$ABCD$ is rectangle
REASON
Definition of rectangle

4.44 **Given:** $AB = BC = CD = DA$
To Prove: $ABCD$ is rhombus

1. **STATEMENT**
$AB = BC = CD = DA$
REASON
Given

2. **STATEMENT**
$ABCD$ is $\square$
REASON
Both pairs of opposite sides are =.

3. **STATEMENT**
$ABCD$ is rhombus
REASON
Definition of rhombus

4.45 **Given:** $ABCD$ is rectangle
K, L, M, N are midpoints
To Prove: $KLMN$ is a parallelogram

1. **STATEMENT**
$ABCD$ is rectangle
K, L, M, N are midpoints
REASON
Given

2. **STATEMENT**
Draw diagonal $\overline{AC}$
REASON
Auxiliary line

3. **STATEMENT**
$\overline{NM} \parallel \overline{AC}$
$NM = \frac{1}{2}AC$
$\overline{KL} \parallel \overline{AC}$
$KL = \frac{1}{2}AC$
REASON
Midpoint segment of $\triangle$ is $\parallel$ to third side and $= \frac{1}{2}$ third side.

4. **STATEMENT**
$NM = KL$
REASON
Substitution

5. **STATEMENT**
$\overline{NM} \parallel \overline{KL}$
REASON
Transitive

6. **STATEMENT**
$KLMN$ is $\square$
REASON
If two sides = and $\parallel$, then $\square$.

4.46 false
4.47 true
4.48 false
4.49 true
4.50 false
4.51 true
4.52 false
4.53 true
4.54 true
4.55 HJ
4.56 $\angle GJI = \angle GHI = 120°$
4.57 $AB = DC = 12$

4.58 $\angle A$ or $\angle B$ or $\angle D$ or $90°$

4.59 $ON = PO = 8$

4.60 $GH = HI = 16$

4.61   Either order:

a. H

b. J

4.62 $BD = AC = 20$

4.63 $PN = MO = 10$

4.64 $<$

4.65 $MN = \frac{1}{2}(RO + ES)$

$= \frac{1}{2}(10 + 6)$

$= \frac{1}{2}(16)$

$= 8$

4.66 $\frac{1}{2}(x + y)$

4.67 $MN = \frac{1}{2}(RO + ES)$

$24 = \frac{1}{2}(30 + ES)$

$48 = 30 + ES$

$ES = 18$

4.68 $MN = \frac{1}{2}(RO + ES)$

$24 = \frac{1}{2}(RO + 10)$

$48 = RO + 10$

$RO = 38$

4.69   a. $\angle Q = \angle P = 50°$

b. $\angle R = \frac{1}{2}[360° - (\angle P + \angle Q)]$

$= \frac{1}{2}[360° - (50 + 50)]$

$= \frac{1}{2}(260)$

$\angle R = 130°$

c. $\angle S = \angle R = 130°$

4.70   a. $\angle Q = \angle P = 60°$

b. $\angle R = \frac{1}{2}[360° - (\angle P + \angle Q)]$

$= \frac{1}{2}[360° - (60 + 60)]$

$= \frac{1}{2}(240)$

$\angle R = 120°$

c. $\angle S = \angle R = 120°$

4.71   a. $\angle S = \angle R = 100°$

b. $\angle P = \frac{1}{2}[360° - (\angle R + \angle S)]$

$= \frac{1}{2}[360° - (100 + 100)]$

$= \frac{1}{2}(160)$

$\angle P = 80°$

c. $\angle Q = \angle P = 80°$

4.72   a. $\angle Q = 180° - \angle S$

$= 180° - 120°$

$\angle Q = 60°$

b. $\angle R = \angle S = 120°$

c. $\angle P = \angle Q = 60°$

4.73 $QS = RP = 12$

4.74   1. **STATEMENT**

$AE = HD$

$AB = DC$

$\angle B = \angle C$

REASON

Definition of square

2. **STATEMENT**

$BC = BC$

REASON

Reflexive

3. **STATEMENT**

$\triangle ABC \cong \triangle DCB$

REASON

SAS

4. **STATEMENT**

$BD = AC$

REASON

CPCTE

5. **STATEMENT**

$\angle EAC = \angle HDB$

REASON

All rt. $\angle$'s =.

6. **STATEMENT**

$\triangle EAC \cong \triangle HDB$

REASON

SAS$\triangle$

7. **STATEMENT**

$HB = EC$

REASON

CPCTE

SELF TEST 4

4.01 median $= \frac{1}{2}(BO + TA)$

$\qquad = \frac{1}{2}(12 + 6)$

median $= 9$

4.02 Since *BOAT* is an isosceles trapezoid,
$\angle B = \angle O$ and $\angle A = \angle T$.
$\angle B + \angle O + \angle A + \angle T = 360°$
$\qquad 2\angle O + 2(130) = 360°$
$\qquad\qquad\qquad 2\angle O = 100°$
$\qquad\qquad\qquad \angle O = 50°$

4.03 Any order:
a. *ATSR*
b. *RTSB*
c. *RTCS*

4.04 *R* is midpoint of *AB*; *S* is midpoint of *BC*

$RS = \frac{1}{2}AC$

$5 = \frac{1}{2}AC$

$AC = 10$

4.05 $P \triangle RST = RS + ST + TR$
$P \triangle ABC = AB + BC + CA$

$RS = \frac{1}{2}AC$

$ST = \frac{1}{2}BA$

$RT = \frac{1}{2}BC$

$P \triangle RST = \frac{1}{2}P \triangle ABC$

$\qquad\qquad = \frac{1}{2}(20)$

$P \triangle RST = 10$

4.06 *AC* and *BD* are the diagonals of $\square ABCD$.
$AC = BD$
$10 = BD$

4.07 $BD = AC$
$BD = DE + BE$

$BE = \frac{1}{2}AC$

$\qquad = \frac{1}{2}(12)$

$BE = 6$

4.08 All sides of a rhombus are equal. The diagonals of a rhombus bisect two angles of the rhombus.
$\therefore \angle 1 = \angle 2 = 25°$.

4.09 $\angle 1 = 35°, \therefore \angle 2 = 35°$
The diagonals of a rhombus are perpendicular.
$\therefore \angle 3 = 90°$.
$\angle 4 = 180° - (\angle 2 + \angle 3)$
$\qquad = 180° - (35° + 90°)$
$\qquad = 180° - 125°$
$\angle 4 = 55°$

4.010 $\angle 5 = \angle 1 = 20°$

4.011 All sides of a rhombus are equal.
$\therefore P = 4(5) = 20$

4.012 *UT*

4.013 *UX*

4.014 $\triangle TUR$

4.015 $\triangle UXR$

4.016 $\angle RTU$

4.017 $\angle R$

4.018 *QS*

4.019 $\triangle SRM$

4.020 $>$

4.021 $<$

4.022 $=$

4.023 HL

4.024 SAS

4.025 CPCTE

LIFEPAC TEST

1. HL
2. none
3. ASA
4. AAS
5. HA or AAS
6. SAS or LL
7. AAS
8. ASA
9. LA or AAS
10. SSS
11. Exterior sides in opposite rays
12. Given
13. Supplementary to equal $\angle$'s
14. Given
15. Reflexive
16. ASA
17. CPCTE
18. $\overline{DC}$

19. $\angle CBD = 180° - (\angle DCB + \angle CDB)$
    $= 180° - (37\frac{1}{2} + 37\frac{1}{2})°$
    $= 180° - 75°$
    $= 105°$

20. $\angle ADB = 180° - (\angle A + \angle ABD)$
    $= 180° - (60 + 60)°$
    $= 180° - 120°$
    $= 60°$

21. always
22. always
23. always
24. sometimes

ALTERNATE LIFEPAC TEST

1. SSS
2. none
3. HL
4. SAS
5. ASA
6. AAS
7. none
8. AAS
9. none
10. SAS
11. Given
12. If lines ||, alternate interior $\angle$'s are =.
13. Vertical $\angle$'s are =.
14. AAS
15. CPCTE
16. always
17. sometimes
18. always
19. never
20. always
21. >
22. >
23. >
24. <
25. $2" < x < 8"$

MATH 1004

ALTERNATE LIFEPAC TEST

NAME _____

DATE _____

SCORE _____

$\dfrac{56}{70}$

Write *SSS, SAS, ASA, AAS, HL, LA, LL,* **or** *HA* **to indicate the method you would use to prove the two triangles congruent. If no method applies, write** *none* (each answer, 3 points).

1. _____

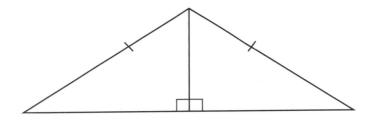

2. _____

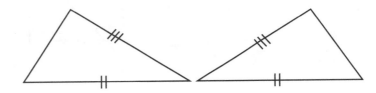

3. _____

4. _____

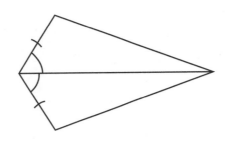

5. _____

6. _____

7. _____

8. _____

9. _____

10. _____

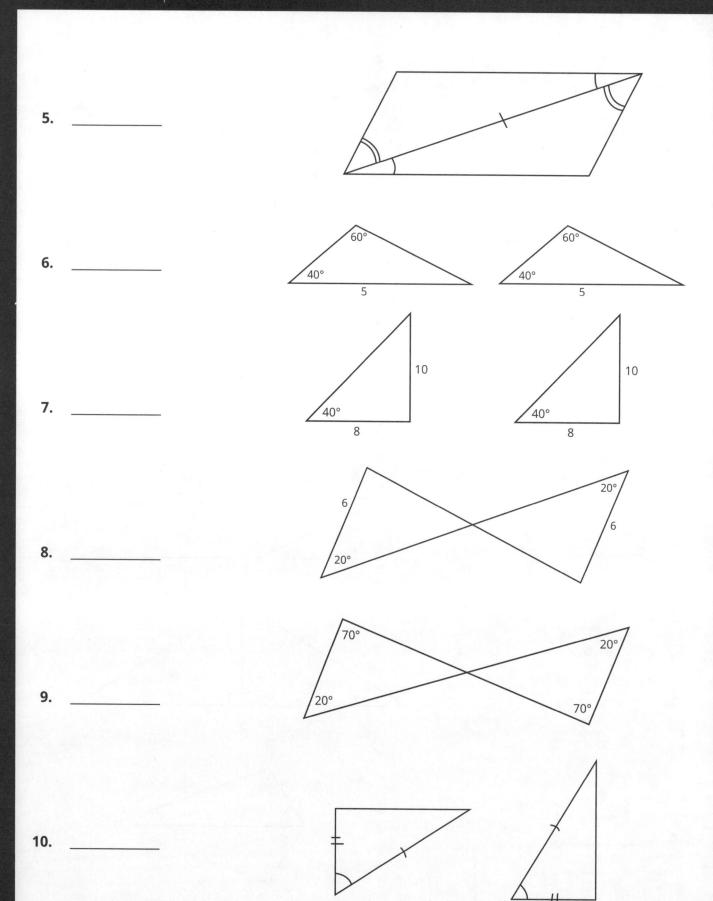

Write the reasons for this proof (each answer, 4 points).

Given: $\overline{AB} \parallel \overline{DE}$
$BC = CE$

To Prove: $AC = CD$

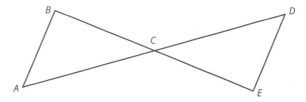

STATEMENT	REASON
11. $\overline{AB} \parallel \overline{DE}$, $BC = CE$	**11.** _____
12. $\angle A = \angle D$	**12.** _____
13. $\angle ACB = \angle DCE$	**13.** _____
14. $\triangle ABC \cong \triangle DEC$	**14.** _____
15. $AC = CD$	**15.** _____

Write *always, sometimes* **or** *never* (each answer, 2 points).

16. If the diagonals are perpendicular and equal, then the quadrilateral is _____ a rhombus.

17. If the opposite sides of a quadrilateral are equal, then the figure is _____ a square.

18. If the opposite sides of a quadrilateral are parallel, then the figure is _____ a parallelogram.

19. A trapezoid _____ has both pairs of sides parallel.

20. If two sides of one triangle are equal to two sides of another and the included angles are equal, then the triangles are _____ congruent.

Complete the following problems with <, >, **or** = (each answer, 4 points).

21. $AB < BC$

    A _____ C

22. $\angle B > \angle C$

    AC _____ AB

23. If $AB = DE$, $AC = DF$, and $\angle A > \angle D$,

    then BC _____ EF.

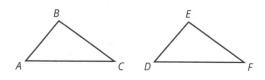

24. If $TR = YX$, $RS = XW$ and $TS > YW$,

    then $\angle X$ _____ $\angle R$.

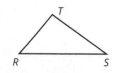
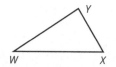

Answer the following question (4 points).

25. If two sides of a triangle have measures of 3" and 5", what range of size can the third side

    have? _____

MATH 1005

Unit 5: Similar Polygons

TEACHER NOTES

MATERIALS NEEDED FOR LIFEPAC	
Required	Suggested

• straightedges, rulers, and protractors
• trigonometric table for angles between 0°
  and 90° giving sine, cosine, and tangent
  ratios
	(None)

ADDITIONAL LEARNING ACTIVITIES

Section 1: Principles of Algebra

1. The size of a motion picture on a screen is the square of the distance from the projector to the screen. Have the class determine the size of a picture at 4 ft.; 7 ft. The answer will be in square feet.

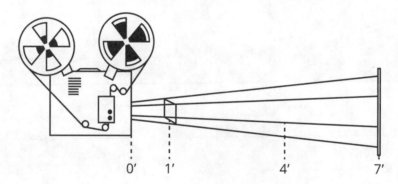

2. Two players may play the following proportion game. The first player names a proportion, but with one term missing. The second player must solve the proportion. If his answer is correct, he receives one point. Pencils and paper may be used. If a student is not sure of the correct answer of a problem, he should write out the problem and ask the teacher after the game. No points should be given for that round. A game consists of 35 points.

Example: First player: $\dfrac{8}{x} = \dfrac{3}{24}$

Second player: $24x = 24$, so $x = 1$

3. Locate a photograph of several people you know. The photograph should be a full-length shot of its subjects and should have relatively few people in it. Locate two or more persons in the photograph who are standing at the same distance from the camera. Find out and record the height of each of these persons. Then, from the photograph, measure the heights of these persons. Write the ratio of the scaled-down height of each person in the photograph to their respective actual height. Write the ratios as a proportion and check to see that they are equal.

If one subject is farther away in the photograph than another subject, how does this distance affect the proportion? If you took a picture of two people of any height but at different distances from the camera and noted the distance from the camera to each person, would the ratios of each person's height in the photograph to their respective actual height make a true proportion (would the ratios be equal)?

Section 2: Similarity

1. Discuss these questions with your class.

   a. If 1 side of a pentagon (five-sided polygon) equals 1 side of another pentagon, are the pentagons similar?

   b. If 2 sides of a pentagon equal 2 sides of another pentagon, are the pentagons similar?

   c. If 3 sides of a pentagon equal 3 sides of another pentagon, are the pentagons similar?

   d. If 4 sides of a pentagon equal 4 sides of another pentagon, are the pentagons similar?

   e. If 5 sides of a pentagon equal 5 sides of another pentagon, are the pentagons similar?

2. Conduct a geometric mean bee (similar to a spelling bee) in which two numbers are said to each student in turn and the student finds the geometric mean between the two numbers. Or, the mean and one number may be given, and the student finds the missing number. Pencils and paper or a chalkboard may be used.

3. Observe your classroom, school, church, home, or other building for similar polygons. Tell how you know the polygons are similar based on definitions, postulates, and theorems.

4. Research the history and development of the Pythagorean Theorem.

Section 3: Right Triangles

1. Have the class draw the following figure to demonstrate proof of the Pythagorean Theorem.

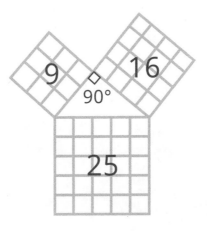

2. Two students may work together on this activity. Let the students go outside and locate or place a small marker on the ground at a distance of no more than 15 or 20 feet from the school building. Measure this distance. Draw a diagram and write each of the measurements on it (the diagram will probably be similar to the one in Problem 3.85 in the LIFEPAC). Then one student stands at a distance of no more than 10 or 15 feet past the marker (away from the school building). The other student measures this distance and writes it on the diagram. The first student measures the height of the student standing past the marker and writes it on the diagram. Then the students use similar triangles to compute the height of the school building.

3. This activity is an outside activity to be done at the student's home. Place a marker on the ground at a distance of no more than 15 or 20 feet from the house. Measure this distance. Draw a diagram and write each of the measurements on it (you may use the diagram in Problem 3.85 in the LIFEPAC as an example). Measure a distance of no more than 10 feet past the marker (away from the house). Write this distance and your height on the diagram. Then use similar triangles to compute the height of your house.

4. Measure the length of the shadow of a tree, school building, or any other object. Then measure the length of your shadow (you may need someone to measure for you). Use these measures and your height to find the height of the object.

Administer the LIFEPAC Test.

The test is to be administered in one session. Give no help except with directions.
Evaluate the tests and review areas where the students have done poorly.
Review the pages and activities that stress the concepts tested.
If necessary, administer the Alternate LIFEPAC Test

ANSWER KEYS

SECTION 1

1.1 $\dfrac{1}{2}$

1.2 $\dfrac{2}{3}$

1.3 $\dfrac{18}{29}$

1.4 $\dfrac{1}{2}$

1.5 $\dfrac{3}{4}$

1.6 $\dfrac{5}{9}$

1.7 $\dfrac{1}{2}$

1.8 3:5:7

1.9 $\dfrac{3}{5}$

1.10 $\dfrac{5}{3}$

1.11 $\dfrac{3}{3+5} = \dfrac{3}{8}$

1.12 $\dfrac{5}{3+5} = \dfrac{5}{8}$

1.13 $\dfrac{4}{5}$

1.14 $\dfrac{5}{4}$

1.15 $\dfrac{5}{4+5} = \dfrac{5}{9}$

1.16 $\dfrac{5-4}{5+4} = \dfrac{1}{9}$

1.17 $\dfrac{12}{6} = \dfrac{2}{1}$

1.18 $\dfrac{12}{12+6} = \dfrac{12}{18} = \dfrac{2}{3}$

1.19 $\dfrac{6}{12+6} = \dfrac{6}{18} = \dfrac{1}{3}$

1.20 $\dfrac{14}{14+7} = \dfrac{14}{21} = \dfrac{2}{3}$

1.21 $\dfrac{14+7}{14} = \dfrac{21}{14} = \dfrac{3}{2}$

1.22 $\dfrac{7}{14+7} = \dfrac{7}{21} = \dfrac{1}{3}$

1.23 $\dfrac{6}{10} = \dfrac{3}{5}$

1.24 $\dfrac{6}{6+10} = \dfrac{6}{16} = \dfrac{3}{8}$

1.25 $\dfrac{10}{6+10} = \dfrac{10}{16} = \dfrac{5}{8}$

1.26 $\dfrac{15}{9} = \dfrac{5}{3}$

1.27 $\dfrac{15}{9+15} = \dfrac{15}{24} = \dfrac{5}{8}$

1.28 $\dfrac{9+15}{6+10} = \dfrac{24}{16} = \dfrac{3}{2}$

1.29 Let x = first $\angle$
$2x$ = second $\angle$
$3x$ = third $\angle$

$x + 2x + 3x = 180$
$6x = 180$
$x = 30°$
$2x = 60°$
$3x = 90°$

1.30 60 feet = 720 inches
10 yards = 360 inches
$AB:BC:CD = 720:360:20 = 36:18:1$

1.31 means: 4, 15
extremes: 3, 20

1.32 means: 7, 20
extremes: 5, 28

1.33 means: 11, x
extremes: 6, y

1.34 means: 9, 2
extremes: 3, 6

1.35 means: 2, 4
extremes: 1, 8

1.36 means: y, 3
extremes: x, 7

1.37 $\dfrac{x}{25} = \dfrac{2}{5}$
$5x = 50$
$x = 10$

1.38 $\dfrac{x}{6} = \dfrac{3}{2}$
$2x = 18$
$x = 9$

1.39 $\dfrac{9}{x} = \dfrac{3}{12}$
$3x = 108$
$x = 36$

1.40 $\dfrac{10}{7} = \dfrac{x}{5}$
$7x = 50$
$x = \dfrac{50}{7}$

1.41 $\dfrac{9}{x} = \dfrac{x}{4}$

$x^2 = 36$

$x = 6$ (only use positive values in ratios)

1.42 $\dfrac{\frac{1}{2}}{x} = \dfrac{\frac{2}{3}}{\frac{3}{4}}$

$\dfrac{2}{3}x = \dfrac{3}{8}$

$2x = \dfrac{9}{8}$

$x = \dfrac{9}{16}$

1.43 $\dfrac{x+3}{6} = \dfrac{5}{4}$

$4x + 12 = 30$

$4x = 18$

$x = \dfrac{18}{4} = \dfrac{9}{2}$

1.44 $\dfrac{x+1}{x+2} = \dfrac{2}{3}$

$2x + 4 = 3x + 3$

$2x + 1 = 3x$

$1 = x$

$x = 1$

1.45 $\dfrac{3}{2} = \dfrac{x}{4}$

$2x = 12$

$x = 6$

1.46 $2x = 3y$

$\dfrac{2x}{y} = 3$

$\dfrac{x}{y} = \dfrac{3}{2}$

1.47 $5x = 7y$

$\dfrac{5x}{y} = 7$

$\dfrac{x}{y} = \dfrac{7}{5}$

1.48 $\dfrac{x}{3} = \dfrac{y}{2}$

$2x = 3y$

$\dfrac{2x}{y} = 3$

$\dfrac{x}{y} = \dfrac{3}{2}$

1.49 $2x - 3y = 0$

$2x = 3y$

$\dfrac{2x}{y} = 3$

$\dfrac{x}{y} = \dfrac{3}{2}$

1.50 $x - 5y = 0$

$x = 5y$

$\dfrac{x}{y} = \dfrac{3}{2}$

1.51 Let x = first $\angle$

$5x$ = second $\angle$

$x + 5x = 90°$

$6x = 90°$

$x = 15°$

$5x = 75°$

1.52 Let $3x$ = first $\angle$

$7x$ = second $\angle$

$3x + 7x = 180$

$10x = 180$

$x = 18°$

$3x = 54°$

$7x = 126°$

1.53 Let $3x$ = first part

$5x$ = second part

$3x + 5x = 30$ in.

$8x = 30$ in.

$x = \dfrac{30}{8} = \dfrac{15}{4}$

$3x = 3(\dfrac{15}{4}) = \dfrac{45}{4} = 11\dfrac{1}{4}$ in.

$5x = 5(\dfrac{15}{4}) = \dfrac{75}{4} = 18\dfrac{3}{4}$ in.

1.54 Let $3x$ = first side

$4x$ = second side

$5x$ = third side

$3x + 4x + 5x = 48$ in.

$12x = 48$ in.

$x = 4$

$3x = 12$ in.

$4x = 16$ in.

$5x = 20$ in.

1.55 Let $2x$ = second side

$3x$ = third side

$8 + 2x + 3x = 18$ in.

$8 + 5x = 18$ in.

$5x = 10$ in.

$x = 2$

$2x = 4$ in.

$3x = 6$ in.

1.56 Denominator Sum

1.57 Cross Product

1.58 Numerator-Denominator Sum

1.59 Equivalent Forms

1.60 Denominator Difference

1.61 Cross Product

1.62 $\dfrac{x}{a} = \dfrac{b}{y}$ or $\dfrac{x}{b} = \dfrac{a}{y}$

1.63 $\dfrac{a}{x} = \dfrac{y}{b}$ or $\dfrac{b}{x} = \dfrac{y}{a}$

1.64 $\dfrac{x}{a} = \dfrac{b}{y}$ or $\dfrac{y}{a} = \dfrac{b}{x}$

1.65 $\dfrac{b}{x} = \dfrac{y}{a}$ or $\dfrac{b}{y} = \dfrac{x}{a}$

1.66 $\dfrac{y}{a} = \dfrac{b}{x}$ or $\dfrac{x}{a} = \dfrac{b}{y}$

1.67 $\dfrac{2}{x} = \dfrac{5}{y} = \dfrac{3}{5}$

$\dfrac{2}{x} = \dfrac{3}{5}$

$3x = 10$

$x = \dfrac{10}{3}$

$\dfrac{5}{y} = \dfrac{3}{5}$

$3y = 25$

$y = \dfrac{25}{3}$

1.68 $\dfrac{2}{x} = \dfrac{y}{4} = \dfrac{1}{4}$

$\dfrac{2}{x} = \dfrac{1}{4}$

$x = 8$

$\dfrac{y}{4} = \dfrac{1}{4}$

$4y = 4$

$y = 1$

1.69 $\dfrac{2}{3} = \dfrac{x}{6} = \dfrac{9}{y}$

$\dfrac{2}{3} = \dfrac{x}{6}$

$3x = 12$

$x = 4$

$\dfrac{2}{3} = \dfrac{9}{y}$

$2y = 27$

$y = \dfrac{27}{2}$

1.70 $\dfrac{2}{3} = \dfrac{4}{y}$

$2x = 12$

$x = 6$

1.71 $\dfrac{6}{2} = \dfrac{8}{x}$

$6x = 16$

$x = \dfrac{16}{6} = \dfrac{8}{3}$

1.72 $\dfrac{\frac{1}{2}}{\frac{2}{3}} = \dfrac{\frac{3}{4}}{x}$

$\dfrac{1}{2}x = \dfrac{1}{2}$

$x = 1$

1.73 $\dfrac{a+1}{4} = \dfrac{2}{3}$

$3a + 3 = 8$

$3a = 5$

$a = \dfrac{5}{3}$

1.74 $\dfrac{a-2}{3} = \dfrac{a}{4}$

$4a - 8 = 3a$

$a - 8 = 0$

$a = 8$

1.75 $\dfrac{a}{4} = \dfrac{9}{a}$

$a^2 = 36$

$a = 6$ (only use the positive value)

1.76 $\dfrac{XC}{AC}$

1.77 $\dfrac{AB + AC}{AC}$

1.78 $\dfrac{AB}{BX}$

1.79 $\dfrac{XC}{BX}$

1.80 $\dfrac{AX}{XB} = \dfrac{AY}{YC}$

$\dfrac{3}{4} = \dfrac{6}{YC}$

$3YC = 24$

$YC = 8$

1.81 $\dfrac{AX}{XB} = \dfrac{AY}{YC}$

$\dfrac{5}{4} = \dfrac{AY}{6}$

$4AY = 30$

$AY = \dfrac{30}{4} = \dfrac{15}{2}$

1.82 $\dfrac{AX}{XB} = \dfrac{AY}{YC}$

$\dfrac{AX}{4} = \dfrac{4}{8}$

$8AX = 16$

$AX = 2$

1.83 $\dfrac{AX}{XB} = \dfrac{AY}{YC}$

$\dfrac{7}{XB} = \dfrac{14}{4}$

$14XB = 28$

$XB = 2$

1.84 $\dfrac{4}{3}$

1.85 $\dfrac{5+7}{7} = \dfrac{12}{7}$

1.86 $\dfrac{5+7}{5} = \dfrac{12}{5}$

1.87 $\dfrac{3+4}{3} = \dfrac{7}{3}$

1.88 $\dfrac{2(3)}{3(4)} = \dfrac{6}{12} = \dfrac{1}{2}$

1.89 $\dfrac{4}{3}$

SELF TEST 1

1.01 division

1.02 $\dfrac{3}{4}$

1.03 3:4

1.04 same

1.05 are not

1.06 ratios

1.07 Cross Product

1.08 Numerator-Denominator Sum

1.09 p

1.010 Either order:

a. 6

b. 10

1.011 $\dfrac{6}{3} = \dfrac{2}{1}$

1.012 7 yards = 21 feet

$\dfrac{21}{6} = \dfrac{7}{2}$

1.013 $\dfrac{12}{100} = \dfrac{3}{25}$

1.014 $\dfrac{3}{9} = \dfrac{1}{3}$

1.015 $\dfrac{9}{3+9} = \dfrac{9}{12} = \dfrac{3}{4}$

1.016 $\dfrac{x}{7} = \dfrac{3}{5}$

$5x = 21$

$x = \dfrac{21}{5}$

1.017 $\dfrac{3}{8} = \dfrac{x}{32}$

$8x = 96$

$x = 12$

1.018 $\dfrac{5}{2x} = \dfrac{25}{4}$

$50x = 20$

$x = \dfrac{20}{50} = \dfrac{2}{5}$

1.019 $\dfrac{x}{3} = \dfrac{x+2}{5}$

$5x = 3x + 6$

$2x = 6$

$x = 3$

1.020 $\dfrac{16}{x} = \dfrac{x}{4}$

$x^2 = 64$

$x = 8$

1.021 $\dfrac{x+2}{2} = \dfrac{6+2}{2}$

$\dfrac{x+2}{2} = \dfrac{8}{2}$

$2x + 4 = 16$

$2x = 12$

$x = 6$

1.022 $\dfrac{TU}{TR} = \dfrac{UW}{RS}$

$\dfrac{3}{9} = \dfrac{UW}{15}$

$9UW = 45$

$UW = 5$

1.023 $\dfrac{TU}{TR} = \dfrac{WT}{ST}$

$\dfrac{3}{9} = \dfrac{4}{ST}$

$3ST = 36$

$ST = 12$

1.024 $WS = ST - WT$

$WS = 12 - 4$

$WS = 8$

1.025 $UR = TR - TU$

$UR = 9 - 3$

$UR = 6$

SECTION 2

2.1   1. **STATEMENT**
$\triangle ABC \sim \triangle RST$
$\triangle DEF \sim \triangle RST$
REASON
Given

2. **STATEMENT**
$\angle A = \angle R,\ \angle D = \angle R$
$\angle C = \angle T,\ \angle F = \angle T$
REASON
Definition of $\sim$ $\triangle$'s

3. **STATEMENT**
$\angle A = \angle D,\ \angle C = \angle F$
REASON
Transitive

4. **STATEMENT**
$\triangle ABC \sim \triangle DEF$
REASON
AA

2.2 $\triangle BAC$

2.3   a. $\dfrac{BC}{DE}$

b. $\dfrac{AC}{AE}$

2.4 $\angle DEA$
2.5 $\angle ABC$
2.6 c and h; a and d; e and f
2.7   yes
2.8   no
2.9   no
2.10   yes
2.11   no

2.12   1. **STATEMENT**
$k \,||\, l$
REASON
Given

2. **STATEMENT**
$\angle ADF = \angle EDB$
REASON
Vertical $\angle$'s =

3. **STATEMENT**
$\angle FBE = \angle AFB$
REASON
If lines $||$, alternate interior $\angle$'s =

4. **STATEMENT**
$\triangle ADF \sim \triangle EDC$
REASON
AA theorem

2.13 1. **STATEMENT**
$k \mid \mid l$
REASON
Given

2. **STATEMENT**
$\angle C = \angle C$
REASON
Reflexive

3. **STATEMENT**
$\angle AFC = \angle BDC$
REASON
If lines $\mid \mid$, corresponding $\angle$'s are =

4. **STATEMENT**
$\triangle BCD \sim \triangle ACF$
REASON
AA theorem

2.14 1. **STATEMENT**
$\overline{DC} \perp \overline{CT}$
$\overline{PB} \perp \overline{CT}$
REASON
Given

2. **STATEMENT**
$\overline{DC} \mid \mid \overline{PB}$
REASON
Two lines $\perp$ to same line are $\mid \mid$

3. **STATEMENT**
$\angle 1 = \angle 2$
REASON
If lines $\mid \mid$, alternate interior $\angle$'s are =.

4. **STATEMENT**
$\angle R = \angle R$
REASON
Reflexive

5. **STATEMENT**
$\angle 2 = \angle DVR$
REASON
Vertical $\angle$'s are =

6. **STATEMENT**
$\angle 1 = \angle DVR$
REASON
Substitution

7. **STATEMENT**
$\triangle SPR \sim \triangle VDR$
REASON
AA theorem

2.15 yes; SAS
2.16 no
2.17 no

2.18 yes; SSS
2.19 yes; SSS
2.20 no

2.21 1. **STATEMENT**
$\dfrac{BC}{CD} = \dfrac{AC}{CE}$
REASON
Given

2. **STATEMENT**
$\angle BCA = \angle ECD$
REASON
Vertical $\angle$'s are =

3. **STATEMENT**
$\triangle ACB \sim \triangle ECD$
REASON
SAS

2.22 1. **STATEMENT**
$\angle A = \angle D$
REASON
Given

2. **STATEMENT**
$\angle BCA = \angle ECD$
REASON
Vertical $\angle$'s are =

3. **STATEMENT**
$\triangle ACB \sim \triangle DCE$
REASON
AA theorem

2.23 1. **STATEMENT**
$GF = \dfrac{1}{2}GC$, $GE = \dfrac{1}{2}GD$
$EF = \dfrac{1}{2}DC$
REASON
Given

2. **STATEMENT**
$\dfrac{GF}{GC} = \dfrac{GE}{GD} = \dfrac{EF}{DC} = \dfrac{1}{2}$
REASON
Multiplication property of equality;
Substitution

3. **STATEMENT**
$\triangle GFE \sim \triangle GCD$
REASON
SSS

2.24 1. **STATEMENT**
$\overline{YZ} \mid \mid \overline{UV}$
REASON
Given

2. **STATEMENT**
$\angle YXZ = \angle VXU$
REASON
Vertical $\angle$'s are =

3. **STATEMENT**
$\angle YZV = \angle UVZ$
REASON
If lines ||, alternate interior $\angle$'s are =.

4. **STATEMENT**
$\triangle XYZ \sim \triangle XUV$
REASON
AA theorem

5. **STATEMENT**
$\dfrac{XY}{XU} = \dfrac{YZ}{VU}$
REASON
Definition of similar polygons

2.25

$\dfrac{y}{5} = \dfrac{x}{4} = \dfrac{9}{3}$

$\dfrac{x}{4} = \dfrac{9}{3}$

$3x = 36$

$x = 12$

$\dfrac{y}{5} = \dfrac{9}{3}$

$3y = 45$

$y = 15$

2.26

$\dfrac{P_1}{P_2} = \dfrac{2}{3} = \dfrac{s_1}{s_2}$

$\dfrac{2}{3} = \dfrac{4}{x}$

$2x = 12$

$x = 6$

$\dfrac{2}{3} = \dfrac{6}{y}$

$2y = 18$

$y = 9$

2.27 $P_1 = 20$

$P_2 = 28$

$\dfrac{P_1}{P_2} = \dfrac{s_1}{s_2}$

$\dfrac{20}{28} = \dfrac{4}{s_2}$

$20s_2 = 112$

$s_2 = \dfrac{112}{20} = \dfrac{28}{5} = 5\dfrac{3}{5}$

2.28 $\dfrac{P_1}{P_2} = \dfrac{s_1}{s_2}$

$\dfrac{30}{P_2} = \dfrac{12}{15}$

$12P_2 = 450$

$P_2 = 37\dfrac{1}{2}$

2.29 yes; symmetric property of similar polygons

2.30 a. $\dfrac{P_1}{P_2} = \dfrac{s_1}{s_2}$

$\dfrac{P_1}{P_2} = \dfrac{3}{9}$

$\dfrac{P_1}{P_2} = \dfrac{1}{3}$

b. $\dfrac{5}{x} = \dfrac{1}{3}$

$x = 15$

$\dfrac{4}{y} = \dfrac{1}{3}$

$y = 12$

$\dfrac{6}{z} = \dfrac{1}{3}$

$z = 18$

2.31 $P_1 = 3 + 5 + 6 + 8 + 10 = 32$

$\dfrac{P_1}{P_2} = \dfrac{32}{40} = \dfrac{4}{5}$

$\dfrac{4}{5} = \dfrac{3}{v}$

$4v = 15$

$v = \dfrac{15}{4}$

$\dfrac{4}{5} = \dfrac{5}{w}$

$4w = 25$

$w = \dfrac{25}{4}$

$\dfrac{4}{5} = \dfrac{6}{x}$

$4x = 30$

$x = \dfrac{30}{4} = \dfrac{15}{2}$

$\dfrac{4}{5} = \dfrac{8}{y}$

$4y = 40$

$y = 10$

$\dfrac{4}{5} = \dfrac{10}{z}$

$4z = 50$

$z = \dfrac{50}{4} = \dfrac{25}{2}$

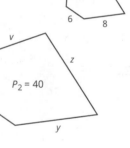

2.32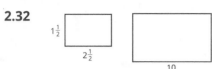

$$\frac{P_1}{P_2} = \frac{2\frac{1}{2}}{10}$$

$$\frac{8}{P_2} = \frac{2\frac{1}{2}}{10}$$

$$\frac{5}{2}P_2 = 80$$

$$P_2 = \frac{2}{5}(80)$$

$$P_2 = 32$$

2.33 $\dfrac{BC}{BX} = \dfrac{CD}{XY}$

$$\frac{10}{6} = \frac{CD}{4}$$

$$6CD = 40$$

$$CD = \frac{40}{6} = \frac{20}{3}$$

2.34 $\dfrac{ZY}{XY} = \dfrac{BC}{DC}$

$$BC = BX + XC$$

$$BC = ZY + XC$$

$$BC = 5 + 3$$

$$BC = 8$$

$$\frac{5}{XY} = \frac{8}{4}$$

$$8XY = 20$$

$$XY = \frac{20}{4} = \frac{5}{2}$$

2.35 $\dfrac{BX}{BZ} = \dfrac{BC}{DC}$

$$\frac{8}{3} = \frac{BC}{5}$$

$$3BC = 40$$

$$BC = \frac{40}{3}$$

$$XC = BC - BX$$

$$XC = \frac{40}{3} - 8$$

$$XC = \frac{40}{3} - \frac{24}{3}$$

$$XC = \frac{16}{3}$$

2.36 $\dfrac{BC}{BX} = \dfrac{BA}{BZ}$

$$\frac{12}{BX} = \frac{8}{3}$$

$$8BX = 36$$

$$BX = \frac{36}{8} = \frac{9}{2}$$

2.37 $\dfrac{BC}{YC} = \dfrac{AC}{XC}$

$$BC = BY + YC$$

$$BC = 4 + 7$$

$$BC = 11$$

$$\frac{11}{7} = \frac{AC}{10}$$

$$7AC = 110$$

$$AC = \frac{110}{7}$$

2.38 $\dfrac{BY}{YC} = \dfrac{AX}{XC}$

$$\frac{6}{10} = \frac{18}{XC}$$

$$6XC = 180$$

$$XC = 30$$

2.39 $\dfrac{BC}{YC} = \dfrac{AC}{XC}$

$$YC = BC - BY$$

$$YC = 20 - 5$$

$$YC = 15$$

$$\frac{20}{15} = \frac{18}{XC}$$

$$20XC = 270$$

$$XC = \frac{27}{2}$$

2.40 $\dfrac{BC}{AB} = \dfrac{YC}{XY}$

$$\frac{6}{AB} = \frac{4}{5}$$

$$4AB = 30$$

$$AB = \frac{30}{4} = \frac{15}{2}$$

2.41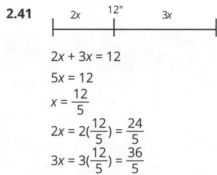

$$2x + 3x = 12$$

$$5x = 12$$

$$x = \frac{12}{5}$$

$$2x = 2(\frac{12}{5}) = \frac{24}{5}$$

$$3x = 3(\frac{12}{5}) = \frac{36}{5}$$

2.42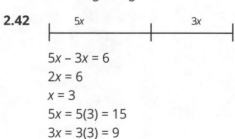

$$5x - 3x = 6$$

$$2x = 6$$

$$x = 3$$

$$5x = 5(3) = 15$$

$$3x = 3(3) = 9$$

2.43 $\dfrac{CR}{RA} = \dfrac{CS}{SB}$

$\dfrac{3}{5} = \dfrac{4}{SB}$

$3SB = 20$

$SB = \dfrac{20}{3}$

2.44 $\dfrac{CR}{RA} = \dfrac{CS}{SB}$

$\dfrac{2}{3} = \dfrac{CS}{10 - CS}$

$3CS = 20 - 2CS$

$5CS = 20$

$CS = 4$

2.45 $\dfrac{CR}{CA} = \dfrac{RS}{AB}$

$\dfrac{4}{10} = \dfrac{10}{AB}$

$4AB = 100$

$AB = 25$

2.46 $\dfrac{CR}{RA} = \dfrac{CS}{SB}$

$\dfrac{CR}{4} = \dfrac{9}{CR}$

$(CR)^2 = 36$

$CR = 6$

2.47 a. $\dfrac{AD}{DB} = \dfrac{AC}{BC}$

$\dfrac{AD}{7 - AD} = \dfrac{3}{5}$

$21 - 3AD = 5AD$

$21 = 8AD$

$\dfrac{21}{8} = AD$

$2\dfrac{5}{8} = AD$

b. $DB = AB - AD$

$DB = 7 - 2\dfrac{5}{8}$

$DB = 4\dfrac{3}{8}$

2.48 a. $\dfrac{AD}{DB} = \dfrac{AC}{BC}$

$\dfrac{AD}{10 - AD} = \dfrac{6}{6}$

$6AD = 60 - 6AD$

$12AD = 60$

$AD = 5$

b. $DB = AB - AD$

$DB = 10 - 5$

$DB = 5$

2.49 a. $\dfrac{AD}{DB} = \dfrac{AC}{BC}$

$\dfrac{AD}{10 - AD} = \dfrac{4}{8}$

$8AD = 40 - 4AD$

$12AD = 40$

$AD = \dfrac{40}{12} = \dfrac{10}{3} = 3\dfrac{1}{3}$

b. $DB = AB - AD$

$DB = 10 - 3\dfrac{1}{3}$

$DB = 6\dfrac{2}{3}$

2.50 a. $\dfrac{AD}{DB} = \dfrac{AC}{BC}$

$\dfrac{AD}{12 - AD} = \dfrac{3}{5}$

$5AD = 36 - 3AD$

$8AD = 36$

$AD = \dfrac{36}{8} = \dfrac{9}{2} = 4\dfrac{1}{2}$

b. $DB = AB - AD$

$DB = 12 - 4\dfrac{1}{2}$

$DB = 7\dfrac{1}{2}$

2.51 $\dfrac{6}{8} = \dfrac{9}{x}$

$6x = 72$

$x = 12$

$\dfrac{6}{14} = \dfrac{y}{21}$

$14y = 126$

$y = 9$

2.52 $\dfrac{12}{x} = \dfrac{10}{15}$

$10x = 180$

$x = 18$

$\dfrac{10}{25} = \dfrac{y}{20}$

$25y = 200$

$y = 8$

2.53 $\dfrac{x}{10} = \dfrac{30}{15}$

$15x = 300$

$x = 20$

$\dfrac{y}{12} = \dfrac{45}{15}$

$15y = 540$

$y = 36$

2.54 $\dfrac{x}{9} = \dfrac{4}{12}$

$12x = 36$

$x = 3$

$\dfrac{y}{12} = \dfrac{4}{16}$

$16y = 48$

$y = 3$

2.55 $\dfrac{x}{16} = \dfrac{6}{12}$

$12x = 96$

$x = 8$

$\dfrac{15}{y} = \dfrac{18}{12}$

$18y = 180$

$y = 10$

2.56 $\dfrac{x}{27} = \dfrac{16}{36}$

$36x = 432$

$x = 12$

$\dfrac{x}{y} = \dfrac{16}{20}$

$\dfrac{12}{y} = \dfrac{16}{20}$

$16y = 240$

$y = 15$

2.57 $\dfrac{x}{12} = \dfrac{x + 6}{16}$

$16x = 12x + 72$

$4x = 72$

$x = 18$

2.58 $\dfrac{x}{x + 7} = \dfrac{16}{22}$

$22x = 16x + 112$

$6x = 112$

$x = \dfrac{112}{6} = \dfrac{56}{3} = 18\dfrac{2}{3}$

2.59

1. **STATEMENT**
$\overline{XA} \perp \overrightarrow{RS}$, $\angle 1 = \angle 2$
REASON
Given

2. **STATEMENT**
$\angle 1$, $\angle 3$ are complementary
$\angle 2$, $\angle 4$ are complementary
REASON
Adjacent $\angle$'s with exterior sides in $\perp$'s are complementary

3. **STATEMENT**
$\angle 3 = \angle 4$
REASON
Two $\angle$'s complementary to equal angles are equal

4. **STATEMENT**
$\dfrac{BX}{XC} = \dfrac{AB}{AC}$
REASON
$\angle$ bisector proportion theorem

2.60

1. **STATEMENT**
$\overline{XZ} \parallel \overline{BC}$, $\angle 1 = \angle 2$
REASON
Given

2. **STATEMENT**
$YC = ZC$
REASON
Sides opposite = $\angle$'s are =

3. **STATEMENT**
$\dfrac{AX}{XB} = \dfrac{AY}{YC}$
REASON
Segment $\parallel$ to side of $\triangle$ divides other sides proportionally

4. **STATEMENT**
$\dfrac{AX}{XB} = \dfrac{AY}{ZC}$
REASON
Substitution

2.61

1. **STATEMENT**
$\overline{RS} \parallel \overline{BC}$, $\angle 1 = \angle 2$
REASON
Given

2. **STATEMENT**
$\angle 2 = \angle 3$
REASON
If lines $\parallel$, alternate interior $\angle$'s =

3. **STATEMENT**
$\angle 1 = \angle 3$
REASON
Substitution

4. **STATEMENT**
$BR = RS$
REASON
Sides opposite $= \angle$'s are $=$

5. **STATEMENT**
$\dfrac{AR}{RB} = \dfrac{AS}{SC}$
REASON
Segment $||$ to side of $\triangle$ divides other sides proportionally

6. **STATEMENT**
$\dfrac{AR}{RS} = \dfrac{AS}{SC}$
REASON
Substitution

2.62 $\dfrac{2}{x} = \dfrac{x}{9}$
$x^2 = 18$
$\sqrt{x^2} = \sqrt{18}$
$x = 3\sqrt{2}$

2.63 $\dfrac{6}{x} = \dfrac{x}{3}$
$x^2 = 18$
$\sqrt{x^2} = \sqrt{18}$
$x = 3\sqrt{2}$

2.64 $\dfrac{8}{x} = \dfrac{x}{2}$
$x^2 = 16$
$\sqrt{x^2} = \sqrt{16}$
$x = 4$

2.65 $\dfrac{2}{x} = \dfrac{x}{6}$
$x^2 = 12$
$\sqrt{x^2} = \sqrt{12}$
$x = 2\sqrt{3}$

2.66 $\dfrac{x}{4} = \dfrac{5}{x}$
$x^2 = 20$
$\sqrt{x^2} = \sqrt{20}$
$x = 2\sqrt{5}$

2.67 $\dfrac{x}{3} = \dfrac{3}{x}$
$x^2 = 9$
$\sqrt{x^2} = \sqrt{9}$
$x = 3$

2.68 $\dfrac{2}{\sqrt{6}} = \dfrac{\sqrt{6}}{x}$
$2x = (\sqrt{6})^2$
$2x = 6$
$x = 3$

2.69 $\dfrac{12}{\sqrt{6}} = \dfrac{\sqrt{6}}{x}$
$12x = (\sqrt{6})^2$
$12x = 6$
$x = \dfrac{6}{12} = \dfrac{1}{2}$

2.70 $\dfrac{6}{\sqrt{6}} = \dfrac{\sqrt{6}}{x}$
$6x = (\sqrt{6})^2$
$6x = 6$
$x = 1$

2.71 $\dfrac{4}{\sqrt{6}} = \dfrac{\sqrt{6}}{x}$
$4x = (\sqrt{6})^2$
$4x = 6$
$x = \dfrac{6}{4} = \dfrac{3}{2}$

2.72 $\dfrac{2}{BD} = \dfrac{BD}{8}$
$(BD)^2 = 16$
$\sqrt{(BD)^2} = \sqrt{16}$
$BD = 4$

2.73 $\dfrac{3}{AB} = \dfrac{AB}{9}$
$(AB)^2 = 27$
$\sqrt{(AB)^2} = \sqrt{27}$
$AB = 3\sqrt{3}$

2.74 $\dfrac{DC}{BC} = \dfrac{BC}{DC + AD}$
$\dfrac{DC}{6} = \dfrac{6}{DC + 5}$
$(DC)^2 + 5DC = 36$
$(DC)^2 + 5DC - 36 = 0$
$(DC + 9)(DC - 4) = 0$
$DC + 9 = 0$ or $DC - 4 = 0$
$DC = -9, DC = 4$
$\therefore DC = 4$

2.75 $\dfrac{AD}{DB} = \dfrac{DB}{DC}$

$\dfrac{AD}{4} = \dfrac{4}{6}$

$6AD = 16$

$AD = \dfrac{16}{6} = \dfrac{8}{3} = 2\dfrac{2}{3}$

2.76 $\dfrac{AD}{AB} = \dfrac{AB}{AC}$

$AD = AC - DC$

$AD = 12 - 8$

$AD = 4$

$\dfrac{4}{AB} = \dfrac{AB}{12}$

$(AB)^2 = 48$

$\sqrt{(AB)^2} = \sqrt{48}$

$AB = 4\sqrt{3}$

2.77 $\dfrac{9}{x} = \dfrac{x}{4}$

$x^2 = 36$

$\sqrt{x^2} = \sqrt{36}$

$x = 6$

2.78 $\dfrac{4}{y} = \dfrac{y}{5}$

$y^2 = 20$

$\sqrt{y^2} = \sqrt{20}$

$y = 2\sqrt{5}$

2.79 $\dfrac{9}{z} = \dfrac{z}{5}$

$z^2 = 45$

$\sqrt{z^2} = \sqrt{45}$

$z = 3\sqrt{5}$

2.80 $\dfrac{4}{6} = \dfrac{6}{a}$

$4a = 36$

$a = 9$

2.81 $\dfrac{9}{b} = \dfrac{b}{4 + 9}$

$\dfrac{9}{b} = \dfrac{b}{13}$

$b^2 = 117$

$\sqrt{b^2} = \sqrt{117}$

$b = 3\sqrt{13}$

2.82 $\dfrac{4}{c} = \dfrac{c}{4 + 9}$

$\dfrac{4}{c} = \dfrac{c}{13}$

$c^2 = 52$

$\sqrt{c^2} = \sqrt{52}$

$c = 2\sqrt{13}$

2.83 $\overline{ST}$

2.84 S

2.85 $\overline{UT}$

2.86 $\overline{QU}$

2.87 $\overline{RS}$

2.88 1. **STATEMENT**
$\overline{DB} \perp \overline{AC}$, $DB = n$
REASON
Given

2. **STATEMENT**
$\dfrac{AB}{DB} = \dfrac{DB}{BC}$
REASON
Altitude is geometric mean

3. **STATEMENT**
$\dfrac{AB}{n} = \dfrac{n}{BC}$
REASON
Substitution

4. **STATEMENT**
$AB \cdot BC = n^2$
REASON
POP

2.89 1. **STATEMENT**
$\overline{SU} \perp \overline{RT}$, $RS = \sqrt{15}$
REASON
Given

2. **STATEMENT**
$\dfrac{RU}{RS} = \dfrac{RS}{RT}$
REASON
Leg of rt. $\triangle$ is geometric mean

3. **STATEMENT**
$\dfrac{RU}{\sqrt{15}} = \dfrac{\sqrt{15}}{RT}$
REASON
Substitution

4. **STATEMENT**
$RU \cdot RT = 15$
REASON
POP

2.90 $x^2 = 4^2 + 7^2$

2.91 $y^2 = 3^2 + 3^2$

2.92 $9^2 = a^2 + 5^2$

2.93 $8^2 = 4^2 + b^2$

2.94

$3^2 + 4^2$	?	5^2
$9 + 16$	?	25
25	=	25 yes

2.95

$4^2 + 5^2$	?	6^2
$16 + 25$	?	36
41	≠	36 no

2.96

$6^2 + 8^2$	?	10^2
$36 + 64$	?	100
100	=	100 yes

2.97

$3^2 + 3^2$	?	$(3\sqrt{2})^2$
$9 + 9$	?	18
18	=	18 yes

2.98

$5^2 + 12^2$	=	c^2
$25 + 144$	=	c^2
169	=	c^2
$\sqrt{169}$	=	$\sqrt{c^2}$
13	=	c

2.99

$4^2 + 4^2$	=	c^2
$16 + 16$	=	c^2
32	=	c^2
$\sqrt{32}$	=	$\sqrt{c^2}$
$4\sqrt{2}$	=	c

2.100

$40^2 + b^2$	=	41^2
$1{,}600 + b^2$	=	$1{,}681$
b^2	=	81
$\sqrt{b^2}$	=	$\sqrt{81}$
b	=	9

2.101

$a^2 + 9^2$	=	16^2
$a^2 + 81$	=	256
a^2	=	175
$\sqrt{a^2}$	=	$\sqrt{175}$
a	=	$5\sqrt{7}$

2.102

$8^2 + 15^2$	=	c^2
$64 + 225$	=	c^2
289	=	c^2
$\sqrt{289}$	=	$\sqrt{c^2}$
17	=	c

2.103

$5^2 + 10^2$	=	c^2
$25 + 100$	=	c^2
125	=	c^2
$\sqrt{125}$	=	$\sqrt{c^2}$
$5\sqrt{5}$	=	c

2.104

$16^2 + b^2$	=	20^2
$256 + b^2$	=	400
b^2	=	144
$\sqrt{b^2}$	=	$\sqrt{144}$
b	=	12

2.105

$a^2 + 8^2$	=	12^2
$a^2 + 64$	=	144
a^2	=	80
$\sqrt{a^2}$	=	$\sqrt{80}$
a	=	$4\sqrt{5}$

2.106

$11^2 + 6^2$	=	x^2
$121 + 36$	=	x^2
157	=	x^2 same as
$\sqrt{157}$	=	$\sqrt{x^2}$
x	=	$\sqrt{157}$ miles

2.107

$x^2 + 4^2$	=	6^2
$x^2 + 16$	=	36
x^2	=	20
$\sqrt{x^2}$	=	$\sqrt{20}$
x	=	$2\sqrt{5}$ in.

2.108

$x^2 + 3^2$	=	6^2
$x^2 + 9$	=	36
x^2	=	27
$\sqrt{x^2}$	=	$\sqrt{27}$
x	=	$3\sqrt{3}$ ft.

2.109

$x^2 + x^2$	=	6^2
$2x^2$	=	36
x^2	=	18
$\sqrt{x^2}$	=	$\sqrt{18}$
x	=	$3\sqrt{2}$ yd.

2.110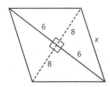

$$x^2 = 6^2 + 8^2$$
$$x^2 = 36 + 64$$
$$x^2 = 100$$
$$\sqrt{x^2} = \sqrt{100}$$
$$x = 10$$
$$P = 4(10) = 40$$

2.111 a. $5\sqrt{3}$

b. $2(5) = 10$

2.112 a. $\dfrac{2\sqrt{3}}{\sqrt{3}} = 2$

b. $2(2) = 4$

2.113 a. $\dfrac{12}{2} = 6$

b. $6\sqrt{3}$

2.114 a. $\dfrac{10}{2} = 5$

b. $5\sqrt{3}$

2.115 a. $7\sqrt{3}$

b. $2(7) = 14$

2.116 a. $\dfrac{3}{\sqrt{3}} = \dfrac{3}{\sqrt{3}} \cdot \dfrac{\sqrt{3}}{\sqrt{3}} = \dfrac{3\sqrt{3}}{3} = \sqrt{3}$

b. $2\sqrt{3}$

2.117 a. $\dfrac{8}{2} = 4$

b. $\dfrac{4}{2}\sqrt{3} = 2\sqrt{3}$

c. $AD = AB - DB$

$DB = \dfrac{4}{2} - 2$

$AD = 8 - 2 = 6$

d. $\dfrac{4}{2} = 2$

e. AC is hypotenuse of $\triangle ACD$.
$AC = 2(2\sqrt{3}) = 4\sqrt{3}$

2.118 a. $2(2) = 4$

b. $CD = \sqrt{3}DB$

$DB = \dfrac{CB}{2}$

$DB = \dfrac{2}{2} = 1$

$CD = \sqrt{3}(1) = \sqrt{3}$

c. $AD = AB - DB$

$AD = 4 - 1$

$AD = 3$

d. $\dfrac{2}{2} = 1$

e. AC is hypotenuse of $\triangle ACD$.
$AC = 2\sqrt{3}$

2.119 a. $AB = AD + DB$

$AD = \sqrt{3}(4\sqrt{3}) = 4(3) = 12$

$DB = \dfrac{4\sqrt{3}}{\sqrt{3}} = 4$

$AB = 12 + 4 = 16$

b. $2(4) = 8$

c. $\sqrt{3}(4\sqrt{3}) = 12$

d. $\dfrac{4\sqrt{3}}{\sqrt{3}} = 4$

e. AC is hypotenuse of $\triangle ACD$.
$AC = 2(4\sqrt{3}) = 8\sqrt{3}$

2.120 $CD = \dfrac{9}{\sqrt{3}} = \dfrac{9}{\sqrt{3}} \cdot \dfrac{\sqrt{3}}{\sqrt{3}} = \dfrac{9\sqrt{3}}{3} = 3\sqrt{3}$

$DB = \dfrac{3\sqrt{3}}{\sqrt{3}} = 3$

$BC = 2(3) = 6$

$AC = 2(3\sqrt{3}) = 6\sqrt{3}$

$AB = AD + DB = 9 + 3 = 12$

a. 12

b. 6

c. $3\sqrt{3}$

d. 3

e. $6\sqrt{3}$

2.121 $CD = \sqrt{3}(10\sqrt{3}) = 10(3) = 30$

$BC = 2(10\sqrt{3}) = 20\sqrt{3}$

$AD = 30\sqrt{3}$

$AC = 2(30) = 60$

$AB = 30\sqrt{3} + 10\sqrt{3} = 40\sqrt{3}$

a. $40\sqrt{3}$

b. $20\sqrt{3}$

c. 30

d. $30\sqrt{3}$

e. 60

2.122 $CD = \dfrac{8\sqrt{3}}{2} = 4\sqrt{3}$

$AD = \sqrt{3}(4\sqrt{3}) = 12$

$DB = \dfrac{4\sqrt{3}}{\sqrt{3}} = 4$

$BC = 2(4) = 8$

$AB = 12 + 4 = 16$

   a. 16

   b. 8

   c. $4\sqrt{3}$

   d. 12

   e. 4

2.123 $6\sqrt{2}\,''$

2.124 $3\sqrt{2}(\sqrt{2}) = 6''$

2.125 $8\sqrt{2}\,''$

2.126 $6\sqrt{2}(\sqrt{2}) = 12''$

2.127 $\dfrac{12}{\sqrt{2}} = \dfrac{12}{\sqrt{2}} \cdot \dfrac{\sqrt{2}}{\sqrt{2}} = \dfrac{12\sqrt{2}}{2} = 6\sqrt{2}$ cm

2.128 $\dfrac{6\sqrt{2}}{\sqrt{2}} = 6$ cm

2.129 $\dfrac{8}{\sqrt{2}} = \dfrac{8}{\sqrt{2}} \cdot \dfrac{\sqrt{2}}{\sqrt{2}} = \dfrac{8\sqrt{2}}{2} = 4\sqrt{2}$ cm

2.130 $\dfrac{5\sqrt{6}}{\sqrt{2}} = \dfrac{5\sqrt{6}}{\sqrt{2}} \cdot \dfrac{\sqrt{2}}{\sqrt{2}} = \dfrac{5\sqrt{12}}{2} = \dfrac{5(2\sqrt{3})}{2} = 5\sqrt{3}$ cm

2.131 $16\sqrt{2}\,''$

2.132 $7\sqrt{3}(\sqrt{2}) = 7\sqrt{6}$

2.133 $5\sqrt{2}\,''$

2.134 $3\sqrt{2}(\sqrt{2}) = 2(3) = 6$

2.135 $\dfrac{12\sqrt{10}}{\sqrt{2}} = \dfrac{12\sqrt{10}}{\sqrt{2}} \cdot \dfrac{\sqrt{2}}{\sqrt{2}} = \dfrac{12\sqrt{20}}{2} = \dfrac{12(2\sqrt{5})}{2} =$ $12\sqrt{5}$ ft.

2.136 $\dfrac{15\sqrt{2}}{\sqrt{2}} = 15$ cm

2.137 $\dfrac{8}{\sqrt{2}} = \dfrac{8}{\sqrt{2}} \cdot \dfrac{\sqrt{2}}{\sqrt{2}} = \dfrac{8\sqrt{2}}{2} = 4\sqrt{2}$ miles

2.138 $\dfrac{\frac{1}{2}}{\sqrt{2}} = \dfrac{1}{2} \cdot \dfrac{1}{\sqrt{2}} = \dfrac{1}{2\sqrt{2}} = \dfrac{1}{2\sqrt{2}} \cdot \dfrac{\sqrt{2}}{\sqrt{2}} = \dfrac{\sqrt{2}}{2(2)} = \dfrac{\sqrt{2}}{4}\,''$

or $\dfrac{1}{4}\sqrt{2}\,''$

SELF TEST 2

2.01 equal

2.02 proportional

2.03 If two sides of one $\triangle$ are proportional to two sides of another and included $\angle$'s are =, then the $\triangle$'s are similar.

2.04 If three corresponding sides of one $\triangle$ are proportional to three sides of another, then the $\triangle$'s are similar.

2.05 the ratio of corresponding sides

2.06 proportionally

2.07 the ratio of corresponding sides

2.08 point

2.09 Pythagorean

2.010 twice

2.011 $\dfrac{4}{\sqrt{2}} = \dfrac{4}{\sqrt{2}} \cdot \dfrac{\sqrt{2}}{\sqrt{2}} = \dfrac{4\sqrt{2}}{2} = 2\sqrt{2}$

2.012 c

$$\begin{aligned}
4^2 + (3\sqrt{3})^2 &= (\sqrt{43})^2 \\
16 + 27 &= 43 \\
43 &= 43
\end{aligned}$$

2.013 Either order:

   a. $\triangle TSX$

   b. $\triangle RST$

2.014 $\dfrac{RX}{XT} = \dfrac{XT}{XS}$

$\dfrac{4}{XT} = \dfrac{XY}{9}$

$(XT)^2 = 36$

$\sqrt{(XT)^2} = \sqrt{36}$

$XT = 6$

2.015 $\dfrac{RX}{RT} = \dfrac{RT}{RS}$

$\dfrac{RX}{6} = \dfrac{6}{9}$

$9RX = 36$

$RX = 4$

2.016

$$\begin{aligned}
4^2 + 6^2 &= c^2 \\
16 + 36 &= c^2 \\
52 &= c^2 \\
\sqrt{52} &= \sqrt{c^2} \\
2\sqrt{13} &= c
\end{aligned}$$

2.017

$$\begin{aligned}
3^2 + b^2 &= 6^2 \\
9 + b^2 &= 36 \\
b^2 &= 27 \\
\sqrt{b^2} &= \sqrt{27} \\
b &= 3\sqrt{3}
\end{aligned}$$

2.018
$$a^2 + 2^2 = (3\sqrt{2})^2$$
$$a^2 + 4 = 18$$
$$a^2 = 14$$
$$\sqrt{a^2} = \sqrt{14}$$
$$a = \sqrt{14}$$

2.019
$RT = 2RX$
$RT = 2(3)$
$RT = 6$

2.020
$RX = \dfrac{RT}{2}$

$RX = \dfrac{8}{2}$

$RX = 4$
$TX = 4\sqrt{3}$

2.021
$TX = \sqrt{3}RX$
$TX = \sqrt{3}(2\sqrt{3})$
$TX = 2(3)$
$TX = 6$

2.022
$\dfrac{RX}{XS} = \dfrac{RT}{ST}$

$\dfrac{RX}{10 - RX} = \dfrac{4}{8}$

$8RX = 40 - 4RX$

$12RX = 40$

$RX = \dfrac{40}{12} = \dfrac{10}{3} = 3\dfrac{1}{3}$

2.023
$\dfrac{3}{XR} = \dfrac{TY}{6}$

$\dfrac{3}{XR} = \dfrac{XR}{6}$

$(XR)^2 = 18$
$\sqrt{(XR)^2} = \sqrt{18}$
$XR = 3\sqrt{2}$

2.024
$\dfrac{x - 4}{4} = \dfrac{3}{x}$

$x^2 - 4x = 12$
$x^2 - 4x - 12 = 0$
$(x + 2)(x - 6) = 0$
$x + 2 = 0 \text{ or } x - 6 = 0$
$x = -2, x = 6$
$\therefore x = 6$

2.025
$\dfrac{2}{x} = \dfrac{x}{8}$

$x^2 = 16$
$\sqrt{x^2} = \sqrt{16}$
$x = 4$

SECTION 3

3.1 6
3.2 $\overline{QR}, \overline{TS}, \overline{BR}, \overline{CS}$
3.3 $\overline{AS}, \overline{BT}, \overline{CQ}, \overline{DR}$
3.4 90°
3.5 $\overline{QR}, \overline{TS}, \overline{DC}$
3.6 $QN = SL = 4$
3.7 $QT = RS = 6$
3.8 $KN = ST = 3$

3.9
$$(QS)^2 = (QR)^2 + (RS)^2$$
$$(QS)^2 = 3^2 + 6^2$$
$$(QS)^2 = 9 + 36$$
$$(QS)^2 = 45$$
$$\sqrt{(QS)^2} = \sqrt{45}$$
$$QS = 3\sqrt{5}$$

3.10
$$(SM)^2 = (ST)^2 + (TM)^2$$
$$(SM)^2 = 3^2 + 4^2$$
$$(SM)^2 = 9 + 16$$
$$(SM)^2 = 25$$
$$\sqrt{(SM)^2} = \sqrt{25}$$
$$SM = 5$$

3.11
$$(RL)^2 = (RS)^2 + (SL)^2$$
$$(RL)^2 = 6^2 + 4^2$$
$$(RL)^2 = 36 + 16$$
$$(RL)^2 = 52$$
$$\sqrt{(RL)^2} = \sqrt{52}$$
$$RL = 2\sqrt{13}$$

3.12
$$(NS)^2 = (NQ)^2 + (QS)^2$$
$$(NS)^2 = 4^2 + (3\sqrt{5})^2$$
$$(NS)^2 = 16 + 45$$
$$(NS)^2 = 61$$
$$\sqrt{(NS)^2} = \sqrt{61}$$
$$NS = \sqrt{61}$$

3.13
$$(KT)^2 = (KR)^2 + (RT)^2$$
$$(KT)^2 = 4^2 + [(RS)^2 + (ST)^2]$$
$$(KT)^2 = 4^2 + 6^2 + 3^2$$
$$(KT)^2 = 16 + 36 + 9$$
$$(KT)^2 = 61$$
$$\sqrt{(KT)^2} = \sqrt{61}$$
$$KT = \sqrt{61}$$

3.14
$d = \sqrt{2^2 + 3^2 + 6^2}$
$d = \sqrt{4 + 9 + 36}$
$d = \sqrt{49}$
$d = 7$

3.15　$d = \sqrt{5^2 + 4^2 + 2^2}$
$d = \sqrt{25 + 16 + 4}$
$d = \sqrt{45}$
$d = 3\sqrt{5}$

3.16　$d = \sqrt{3^2 + 3^2 + 2^2}$
$d = \sqrt{9 + 9 + 4}$
$d = \sqrt{22}$

3.17　$d = \sqrt{18^2 + 10^2 + 2^2}$
$d = \sqrt{324 + 100 + 4}$
$d = \sqrt{428}$
$d = 2\sqrt{107}$

3.18　$d = \sqrt{3^2 + 5^2 + 5^2}$
$d = \sqrt{9 + 25 + 25}$
$d = \sqrt{59}$

3.19　$d = e\sqrt{3}$
$d = 3\sqrt{3}$

3.20　$d = \sqrt{2^2 + 3^2 + 5^2}$
$d = \sqrt{4 + 9 + 25}$
$d = \sqrt{38}$

3.21　$\overline{PA}, \overline{PB}, \overline{PC}, \overline{PD}$
3.32　yes
3.23　yes
3.24　yes
3.25　yes
3.26　yes

3.27　$XY = \frac{1}{2}RS = \frac{1}{2}(6) = 3$

3.28　$PY = \sqrt{(PX)^2 + (XY)^2}$
$PY = \sqrt{4^2 + 3^2}$
$PY = \sqrt{16 + 9}$
$PY = \sqrt{25}$
$PY = 5$

3.29　$SY = \frac{1}{2}ST = \frac{1}{2}RS = \frac{1}{2}(6) = 3$

3.30　$ST = RS = 6$

3.31　$PS = \sqrt{(PY)^2 + (SY)^2}$
$PS = \sqrt{5^2 + 3^2}$
$PS = \sqrt{25 + 9}$
$PS = \sqrt{34}$

3.32　$PT = PS = \sqrt{34}$
3.33　$QS = RS\sqrt{2}$
$QS = 6\sqrt{2}$

3.34　$XT = XY\sqrt{2}$
$XT = 3\sqrt{2}$

3.35　$\frac{3}{5}$

3.36　$\frac{12}{13}$

3.37　$\frac{15}{17}$

3.38　$\frac{20}{29}$

3.39　a.　$\frac{a}{c}$

　　　b.　$\frac{b}{c}$

3.40　a.　$\frac{5}{10} = \frac{1}{2}$

　　　b.　$\frac{1}{2}\sqrt{3}$

3.41　a.　$\frac{1}{2}\sqrt{2}$

　　　b.　$\frac{1}{2}\sqrt{2}$

3.42　$\sin 40° = \frac{x}{13}$

3.43　$\sin 25° = \frac{x}{18}$

3.44　$\sin 40° = \frac{x}{15}$

3.45　$\sin 20° = \frac{5}{x}$

3.46　$\sin 25° = \frac{6}{x}$

3.47　$\sin 80° = \frac{15}{x}$

3.48　$\sin 20° = \frac{x}{8}$

　　　$0.342 = \frac{x}{8}$
　　　$x = 8(0.342)$
　　　$x = 2.736$
　　　$x \doteq 2.7$

3.49　$\sin 50° = \frac{x}{12}$

　　　$0.766 = \frac{x}{12}$
　　　$x = 12(0.766)$
　　　$x = 9.192$
　　　$x \doteq 9.2$

3.50　$\sin 70° = \frac{x}{10}$

　　　$0.9397 = \frac{x}{10}$
　　　$x = 10(0.9397)$
　　　$x = 9.397$
　　　$x \doteq 9.4$

3.51 $\sin 48° = \dfrac{10}{x}$

$0.7431 = \dfrac{10}{x}$

$0.7431x = 10$

$x = \dfrac{10}{0.7431}$

$x = 13.4571...$

$x \doteq 13.5$

3.52 $\sin 15° = \dfrac{12}{x}$

$0.2588 = \dfrac{12}{x}$

$0.2588x = 12$

$x = \dfrac{12}{0.2588}$

$x = 46.3678...$

$x \doteq 46.4$

3.53 $\sin 35° = \dfrac{8}{x}$

$0.5736 = \dfrac{8}{x}$

$0.5736x = 8$

$x = \dfrac{8}{0.5736}$

$x = 13.947...$

$x \doteq 13.9$

3.54 $\sin \angle A = \dfrac{7}{10}$

$= 0.7000$

$\angle A \doteq 45°$

3.55 $\sin \angle A = \dfrac{3}{9}$

$= 0.3333$

$\angle A \doteq 19°$

3.56 $\sin \angle A = \dfrac{4}{20}$

$= 0.2000$

$\angle A \doteq 12°$

3.57 $\sin \angle A = \dfrac{12}{60}$

$= 0.2000$

$\angle A \doteq 12°$

3.58 $\sin \angle A = \dfrac{5}{7}$

$= 0.7143$

$\angle A \doteq 46°$

3.59 $\sin \angle A = \dfrac{2}{20}$

$= 0.1000$

$\angle A \doteq 6°$

3.60 $\cos 55° = \dfrac{x}{223}$

$0.5736 = \dfrac{x}{223}$

$x = 223(0.5736)$

$x = 127.9128$

$x \doteq 127.9$

3.61 $\cos 52° = \dfrac{x}{119}$

$0.6157 = \dfrac{x}{119}$

$x = 119(0.6157)$

$x = 73.2683$

$x \doteq 73.3$

3.62 $\cos 33° = \dfrac{1.2}{x}$

$0.8387 = \dfrac{1.2}{x}$

$0.8387x = 1.2$

$x = \dfrac{1.2}{0.8387}$

$x = 1.4307...$

$x \doteq 1.4$

3.63 $\cos 40° = \dfrac{x}{0.9}$

$0.766 = \dfrac{x}{0.9}$

$x = 0.9(0.766)$

$x = 0.6894$

$x \doteq 0.7$

3.64 $\cos 70° = \dfrac{x}{12.4}$

$0.342 = \dfrac{x}{12.4}$

$x = 12.4(0.342)$

$x = 4.2408$

$x \doteq 4.2$

3.65 $\cos 38° = \dfrac{24}{x}$

$0.788 = \dfrac{24}{x}$

$0.788x = 24$

$x = \dfrac{24}{0.788}$

$x = 30.4568...$

$x \doteq 30.5$

3.66 $\cos \angle A = \dfrac{14}{26}$

$= 0.5385$

$\angle A \doteq 57°$

3.67 $\cos \angle A = \dfrac{0.91}{1.2}$

$= 0.7583$

$\angle A \doteq 41°$

3.68 $\cos \angle A = \dfrac{75.5}{100}$

$= 0.7550$

$\angle A \doteq 41°$

3.69 $\cos \angle A = \dfrac{267}{391}$

$= 0.6829$

$\angle A \doteq 47°$

3.70 $\tan 20° = \dfrac{x}{10}$

$0.364 = \dfrac{x}{10}$

$x = 10(0.364)$

$x = 3.64$

$x \doteq 3.6$

3.71 $\tan 15° = \dfrac{5}{x}$

$0.2679 = \dfrac{5}{x}$

$0.2679x = 5$

$x = \dfrac{5}{0.2679}$

$x = 18.6636...$

$x \doteq 18.7$

3.72 $\tan 50° = \dfrac{x}{12}$

$1.1918 = \dfrac{x}{12}$

$x = 12(1.1918)$

$x = 14.3016$

$x \doteq 14.3$

3.73 $\tan 80° = \dfrac{x}{3}$

$5.6713 = \dfrac{x}{3}$

$x = 3(5.6713)$

$x = 17.0139$

$x \doteq 17.0$

3.74 $\tan 60° = \dfrac{x}{4}$

$0.7321 = \dfrac{x}{4}$

$x = 4(1.7321)$

$x = 6.9284$

$x \doteq 6.9$

3.75 $\tan 45° = \dfrac{6}{x}$

$1 = \dfrac{6}{x}$

$x = 6.0$

3.76 $\tan \angle A = \dfrac{3}{8}$

$= 0.3750$

$\angle A \doteq 21°$

3.77 $\tan \angle A = \dfrac{5}{8}$

$= 0.6250$

$\angle A \doteq 32°$

3.78 $\tan \angle A = \dfrac{6}{8}$

$= 0.7500$

$\angle A \doteq 37°$

3.79 $\tan \angle A = \dfrac{14}{7}$

$= 2.000$

$\angle A \doteq 63°$

3.80 $\tan \angle A = \dfrac{6}{6}$

$= 1.000$

$\angle A \doteq 45°$

3.81

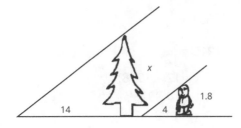

$$\frac{x}{1.8} = \frac{14}{4}$$

$4x = 25.2$

$x = 6.3$ m

3.82

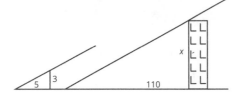

$$\frac{3}{x} = \frac{5}{110}$$

$5x = 330$

$x = 66$ m

3.83

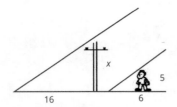

$$\frac{x}{5} = \frac{16}{6}$$

$6x = 80$

$x = \frac{80}{6} = \frac{40}{3} = 13\frac{1}{3}$ ft.

3.84 $\dfrac{a}{c} = \dfrac{b}{x} = \dfrac{d}{y}$

$$\frac{9}{12} = \frac{15}{x} = \frac{7}{y}$$

$$\frac{9}{12} = \frac{15}{x}$$

$9x = 180$

$x = 20$ ft.

$$\frac{9}{12} = \frac{7}{y}$$

$9y = 84$

$y = \frac{84}{9} = \frac{28}{3} = 9\frac{1}{3}$ ft.

3.85 $\dfrac{6}{x} = \dfrac{8}{16}$

$8x = 96$

$x = 12$ ft.

3.86

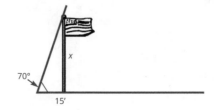

$\tan 70° = \dfrac{x}{15}$

$2.7475 = \dfrac{x}{15}$

$x = 15(2.7475)$

$x = 41.2125$

$x \doteq 41.2$ ft.

3.87

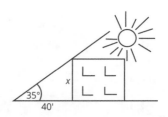

$\tan 35° = \dfrac{x}{40}$

$0.7002 = \dfrac{x}{40}$

$x = 40(0.7002)$

$x = 28.008$

$x \doteq 28$ ft.

3.88

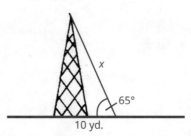

$\cos 65° = \dfrac{10}{x}$

$0.4226 = \dfrac{10}{x}$

$0.4226x = 10$

$x = \dfrac{10}{0.4226}$

$x = 23.663...$

$x \doteq 23.7$ yds.

3.89

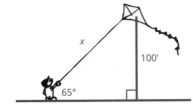

$$\sin 65° = \frac{100}{x}$$

$$0.9063 = \frac{100}{x}$$

$$0.9063x = 100$$

$$x = \frac{100}{0.9063}$$

$$x = 110.3387...$$

$$x \doteq 110.3 \text{ ft.}$$

3.90

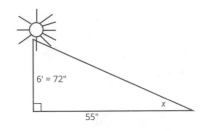

$$\tan x = \frac{72}{55}$$

$$\tan x = 1.3091$$

$$x \doteq 53°$$

3.91

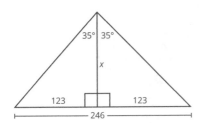

$$\tan 35° = \frac{123}{x}$$

$$0.7002 = \frac{123}{x}$$

$$0.7002x = 123$$

$$x = \frac{123}{0.7002}$$

$$x = 175.6641$$

$$x \doteq 175.7$$

3.92

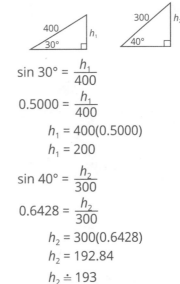

$$\sin 30° = \frac{h_1}{400}$$

$$0.5000 = \frac{h_1}{400}$$

$$h_1 = 400(0.5000)$$

$$h_1 = 200$$

$$\sin 40° = \frac{h_2}{300}$$

$$0.6428 = \frac{h_2}{300}$$

$$h_2 = 300(0.6428)$$

$$h_2 = 192.84$$

$$h_2 \doteq 193$$

The pilot rising 30° at 400 mph gains altitude 7 mph faster.

3.93

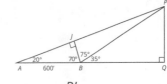

$$\sin 20° = \frac{BJ}{600}$$

$$0.342 = \frac{BJ}{600}$$

$$BJ = 600(0.342)$$

$$BJ = 205.2$$

$$\cos 75° = \frac{205.2}{BP}$$

$$0.2588 = \frac{205.2}{BP}$$

$$0.2588BP = 205.2$$

$$BP = \frac{205.2}{0.2588}$$

$$BP = 792.8902...$$

$$BP \doteq 792.9$$

$$\sin 35° = \frac{PQ}{792.9}$$

$$0.5736 = \frac{PQ}{792.9}$$

$$PQ = 792.9(0.5736)$$

$$PQ = 454.80744$$

$$PQ \doteq 454.8$$

height = 6,500 + 454.8 = 6,954.8 ft.

SELF TEST 3

3.01 never

3.02 sometimes

3.03 never

3.04 sometimes

3.05 always

3.06 never

3.07 always

3.08 sometimes

3.09 never

3.010 sometimes

3.011

$$
\begin{aligned}
8^2 + 10^2 &= x^2 \\
64 + 100 &= x^2 \\
164 &= x^2 \\
\sqrt{164} &= \sqrt{x^2} \\
2\sqrt{41} &= x
\end{aligned}
$$

3.012 $\tan y = \dfrac{8}{10}$

$\tan y = 0.8000$

$y \doteq 39°$

3.013 $\tan z = \dfrac{10}{8}$

$\tan z = 1.2500$

$z \doteq 51°$

3.014 $15 = 2x$

$\dfrac{15}{2} = x$

3.015 $y = \dfrac{\frac{15}{2}}{2}\sqrt{3}$

$y = \dfrac{15}{4}\sqrt{3}$

3.016 $z = \dfrac{15\sqrt{3}}{2}$

3.017 $a = \dfrac{\frac{15}{2}}{2}$

$a = \dfrac{15}{4}$

3.018 $b = 15 - \dfrac{15}{4}$

$b = \dfrac{60}{4} - \dfrac{15}{4}$

$b = \dfrac{45}{4}$

3.019 $d = \sqrt{8^2 + 4^2}$

$d = \sqrt{64 + 16}$

$d = \sqrt{80}$

$d = 4\sqrt{5}$

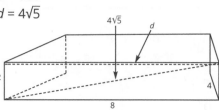

3.020 $d = \sqrt{(4\sqrt{5})^2 + 2^2}$

$d = \sqrt{80 + 4}$

$d = \sqrt{84}$

$d = 2\sqrt{21}$

3.021

$$
\begin{aligned}
(Py)^2 + 3^2 &= 6^2 \\
(Py)^2 + 9 &= 36 \\
(Py)^2 &= 27 \\
\sqrt{(Py)^2} &= \sqrt{27} \\
Py &= 3\sqrt{3}
\end{aligned}
$$

3.022

$$
\begin{aligned}
(Px)^2 + 3^2 &= (3\sqrt{3})^2 \\
(Px)^2 + 9 &= 27 \\
(Px)^2 &= 18 \\
\sqrt{(Px)^2} &= \sqrt{18} \\
Px &= 3\sqrt{2}
\end{aligned}
$$

3.023 $\sin 20° = \dfrac{x}{8}$

$0.342 = \dfrac{x}{8}$

$x = 8(0.342)$

$x = 2.736$

$x \doteq 2.7$

3.024 $\cos 20° = \dfrac{y}{8}$

$0.9397 = \dfrac{y}{8}$

$y = 8(0.9397)$

$y = 7.5176$

$y \doteq 7.5$

3.025 $\dfrac{h}{6} = \dfrac{20}{8}$

$8h = 120$

$h = \dfrac{120}{8}$

$h = 15$

LIFEPAC TEST

1. $\dfrac{5}{15} = \dfrac{1}{3}$

2. 2 hours = 120 minutes

$\dfrac{15}{120} = \dfrac{1}{8}$

3. $\dfrac{30}{6} = \dfrac{5}{1}$

4. $\dfrac{\frac{2}{3}}{\frac{3}{2}} = \dfrac{2}{3}\left(\dfrac{2}{3}\right) = \dfrac{4}{9}$

5. $\dfrac{x}{3} = \dfrac{5}{8}$

$8x = 15$

$x = \dfrac{15}{8} = 1\dfrac{7}{8}$

6. $\dfrac{3}{12} = \dfrac{x}{16}$

$12x = 48$

$x = \dfrac{48}{12}$

$x = 4$

7. $\dfrac{2}{x} = \dfrac{6}{2}$

$6x = 4$

$x = \dfrac{4}{6}$

$x = \dfrac{2}{3}$

8. a. $\dfrac{x}{5} = \dfrac{2}{3}$

$3x = 10$

$x = \dfrac{10}{3} = 3\dfrac{1}{3}$

b. $\dfrac{2}{3} = \dfrac{5}{y}$

$2y = 15$

$y = \dfrac{15}{2} = 7\dfrac{1}{2}$

9. Denominator Sum
10. Numerator-Denominator Sum
11. Cross Product
12. Equivalent Forms
13. a and d
14. a, b, and d

15. b

$4^2 + 5^2 = (\sqrt{41})^2$

$16 + 25 = 41$

$41 = 41$

16. $\dfrac{20}{x} = \dfrac{3}{9}$

$3x = 180$

$x = 60$ ft.

17. $\dfrac{P_1}{P_2} = \dfrac{s_1}{s_2}$

$\dfrac{P_1}{P_2} = \dfrac{3}{9}$

$\dfrac{P_1}{P_2} = \dfrac{1}{3}$

18. $5^2 + 8^2 = x^2$

$25 + 64 = x^2$

$89 = x^2$

$\sqrt{89} = \sqrt{x^2}$

$\sqrt{89} = x$

19. a. $\cos 60° = \dfrac{8}{x}$

$0.5000 = \dfrac{8}{x}$

$0.5000x = 8$

$x = \dfrac{8}{0.5000}$

$x = 16$

b. $\tan 60° = \dfrac{y}{8}$

$\sqrt{3} = \dfrac{y}{8}$

$y = 8\sqrt{3}$ or

$\tan 60° = \dfrac{y}{8}$

$1.7321 = \dfrac{y}{8}$

$y = 8(1.7321)$

$y = 13.8568$

$y \doteq 13.9$

20.

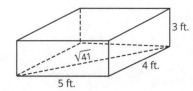

diagonal of base = $\sqrt{5^2 + 4^2}$
$$= \sqrt{25 + 16}$$
$$= \sqrt{41}$$

diagonal of solid = $\sqrt{3^2 + (41)^2}$
$$= \sqrt{9 + 41}$$
$$= \sqrt{50}$$
$$= 5\sqrt{2}$$

21. $3^2 + l^2 = 6^2$
$9 + l^2 = 36$
$l^2 = 27$
$\sqrt{l^2} = \sqrt{27}$
$l = 3\sqrt{3}\,"$

22. a. $\tan 45° = \dfrac{7}{x}$

$1 = \dfrac{7}{x}$

$x = 7$

b. $\sin 45° = \dfrac{7}{y}$

$\dfrac{\sqrt{2}}{2} = \dfrac{7}{y}$

$\dfrac{\sqrt{2}}{2}y = 7$

$y = \dfrac{7}{\frac{\sqrt{2}}{2}}$

$y = \dfrac{7(2)}{\sqrt{2}}$

$y = \dfrac{14}{\sqrt{2}} \cdot \dfrac{\sqrt{2}}{\sqrt{2}}$

$y = \dfrac{14\sqrt{2}}{2}$

$y = 7\sqrt{2}$ or

$\sin 45° = \dfrac{7}{y}$

$0.7071 = \dfrac{7}{y}$

$0.7071y = 7$

$y = \dfrac{7}{0.7071}$

$y = 9.8995$

$y \doteq 9.9$

23. $\tan 70° = \dfrac{x}{800}$

24. $\tan 80° = \dfrac{d}{30}$

25. 2 yards = 72 inches
5 ft. 6 in. = 66 inches
2 ft. = 24 inches

$\dfrac{h}{72} = \dfrac{66}{24}$

$24h = 4{,}752$

$h = \dfrac{4{,}752}{24}$

$h = 198$ in. $= 16\dfrac{1}{2}$ ft.

ALTERNATE LIFEPAC TEST

1. $\dfrac{x}{5} = \dfrac{6}{3}$

    $x(3) = 5(6)$

    $3x = 30$

    $x = \dfrac{30}{3} = 10$

2. $\dfrac{2x}{3} = \dfrac{8}{6}$

    $2x(6) = 3(8)$

    $12x = 24$

    $x = \dfrac{24}{12} = 2$

3. $1:8 = x:24$

    $8(x) = 1(24)$

    $8x = 24$

    $x = \dfrac{24}{8} = 3$

4. $3:x = x:4$

    $x(x) = 3(4)$

    $x^2 = 12$

    $x = \sqrt{12} = 2\sqrt{3}$

    $x = \sqrt{4 \cdot 3} = \sqrt{4} \cdot \sqrt{3} = 2\sqrt{3}$

5. $\dfrac{3}{4} = \dfrac{x + 2}{5}$

    $3(5) = 4(x + 2)$

    $15 = 4x + 8$

    $7 = 4x$

    $x = \dfrac{7}{4}$

6. $\dfrac{8 \div 8}{24 \div 8} = \dfrac{1}{3}$

7. $\dfrac{40 \div 20}{60 \div 20} = \dfrac{2}{3}$

8. 1 foot = 12 inches; $\dfrac{1}{12}$

9. $\dfrac{16 \div 16}{64 \div 16} = \dfrac{1}{4}$

10. $\dfrac{50 \div 5}{5 \div 5} = \dfrac{10}{1}$

11. $\dfrac{AB}{AC} = \dfrac{BE}{CD}$

    $\dfrac{5}{10} = \dfrac{BE}{16}$

    $\dfrac{1}{2} = \dfrac{BE}{16}$

    $16 = 2BE$

    $BE = \dfrac{16}{2} = 8$

12. $\dfrac{AB}{AC} = \dfrac{EA}{DA}$

    $\dfrac{5}{10} = \dfrac{6}{DA}$

    $\dfrac{1}{2} = \dfrac{6}{DA}$

    $DA = 2(6) = 12$

13. $\dfrac{AB}{BC} = \dfrac{AE}{ED}$

    $BC = AC - AB$

    $BC = 10 - 5$

    $BC = 5$

    $\dfrac{5}{5} = \dfrac{6}{ED}$

    $\dfrac{1}{1} = \dfrac{6}{ED}$

    $ED = 6$

14. $BC = AC - AB$

    $BC = 10 - 5$

    $BC = 5$

15. $\triangle ABD \sim \triangle DBC$
16. $\triangle ABD \sim \triangle ADC$
17. $\triangle DBC \sim \triangle ADC$

18. $\dfrac{2}{5} = \dfrac{18}{x}$

    $2x = 5(18)$

    $2x = 90$

    $x = \dfrac{90}{2} = 45$ sq. ft.

19. $6\sqrt{3}$
20. 16
21. diagonal of base $= \sqrt{3^2 + 5^2}$

    $= \sqrt{9 + 25}$

    $= \sqrt{34}$

22. diagonal of rectangular solid

$= \sqrt{3^2 + 5^2 + 2^2}$

$= \sqrt{9 + 25 + 4}$

$= \sqrt{38}$

23.

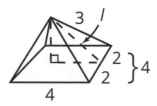

$\sqrt{l^2 + 2^2}$ $=$ 3

$\sqrt{l^2 + 4}$ $=$ 3

$(\sqrt{l^2 + 4})^2$ $=$ 3^2

$l^2 + 4$ $=$ 9

l^2 $=$ $9 - 4$

l^2 $=$ 5

$\sqrt{l^2}$ $=$ $\sqrt{5}$

l $=$ $\sqrt{5}$

24. $\tan 60° = \dfrac{x}{80}$

25. $\tan 75° = \dfrac{x}{8}$

26. $\dfrac{x}{20} = \dfrac{3}{5}$

$x(5) = 20(3)$

$5x = 60$

$x = \dfrac{60}{5} = 12$ ft.

27. diagonal $= 2\sqrt{3} = 5\sqrt{3}''$

28. $\dfrac{3}{x} = \dfrac{x}{12}$

$3(12) = x(x)$

$36 = x^2$

$x^2 = 36$

$\sqrt{x^2} = \sqrt{36}$

$x = 6$

MATH 1005

ALTERNATE LIFEPAC TEST

NAME _____

DATE _____

SCORE _____

67

84

Solve the following proportions for *x* (each answer, 2 points).

1. $\dfrac{x}{5} = \dfrac{6}{3}$ *x* = _____

2. $\dfrac{2x}{3} = \dfrac{8}{6}$ *x* = _____

3. 1:8 = *x*:24   *x* = _____

4. 3:*x* = *x*:4   *x* = _____

5. $\dfrac{3}{4} = \dfrac{x + 2}{5}$ *x* = _____

Express the following ratios in simplest form (each answer, 2 points).

6. $8 to $24   _____

7. 40° to 60°   _____

8. 1 inch to 1 foot   _____

9. 16 to 64   _____

10. 50 to 5   _____

Find the required numbers (each answer, 3 points).

Given: $\dfrac{AB}{AC} = \dfrac{BE}{CD} = \dfrac{EA}{DA}$

$AB = 5$ $CD = 16$ $AE = 6$ $AC = 10$

11. $BE =$ _____

12. $DA =$ _____

13. $ED =$ _____

14. $BC =$ _____

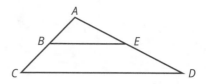

Name three pairs of similar triangles (each answer, 3 points).

15.   _____ ~ _____

16.   _____ ~ _____

17.   _____ ~ _____

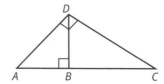

Solve the following questions (each answer, 4 points).

18.   The area of a triangle is 18 square feet. Find the area of a similar larger triangle if corresponding sides are 2 feet and 5 feet.

_____

Given: rt. $\triangle ABC$

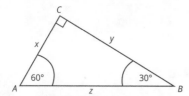

19.   If $x = 6$, then $y =$ _____ .

20.   If $x = 8$, then $z =$ _____ .

21. Find the diagonal of the base of the rectangular solid. _____

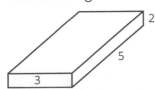

22. Find the diagonal of the rectangular solid. _____

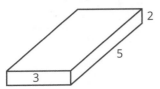

23. Find the slant height of the pyramid. _____

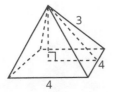

24. Write the equation to use to find the height of the kite. _____

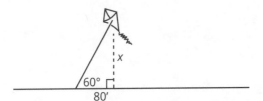

25. Write the equation to use to find the distance to shore. _____

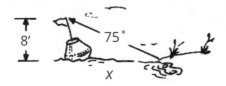

26. Find the height of the tree if the 3-ft. stick has a shadow of 5 ft. and the tree has a shadow of 20 ft. _____

27. Find the diagonal of a cube whose edge is 5". _____

Solve the following problem (each answer, 3 points).

28. Given: $\frac{a}{x} = \frac{x}{b}$, $a = 3$, and $b = 12$

   Find: the geometric mean. _____

MATH 1006

Unit 6: Circles

TEACHER NOTES

MATERIALS NEEDED FOR LIFEPAC	
Required	Suggested
• protractors, compasses, and straightedges	(None)

ADDITIONAL LEARNING ACTIVITIES

Section 1: Circles and Spheres

1. Find Bible verses that refer to circles or spheres. The verses may be direct references to circles or spheres or they may be indirect references (such as a reference to a wheel). For each verse you find write the Bible reference (where the verse is located) and a phrase telling what the verse is about.

Section 2: Tangents, Arcs, and Chords

1. Discuss these questions with your class.

    a. What mechanical devices or machines use the concept of common internal tangents?

    b. What mechanical devices or machines use the concept of common external tangents?

2. Given the following tangent circles, have the students draw seven other systems that maintain a tangency relationship. Note: Relative size of circles may be changed.

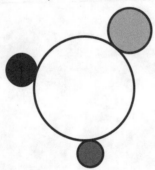

3. Have the students each draw a large circle. Mark off 18 equal arcs. To mark off 18 equal arcs, decide what the measure of each central angle will be. Then use a compass to mark off an arc on the circle. Use a compass to mark off the remaining 17 arcs. Label the end points of the arcs *A, B, C, ... R*. What is the measure of each arc? Have the students draw each of the following sets of chords (one set per circle). Each end point will have two lines drawn to it.

    $\{\overline{AI}, \overline{BJ}, \overline{CK}, ... \overline{RH}\}$

    $\{\overline{AH}, \overline{BI}, \overline{CJ}, ... \overline{RG}\}$

    $\{\overline{AG}, \overline{BH}, \overline{CI}, ... \overline{RF}\}$

    $\{\overline{AF}, \overline{BG}, \overline{CH}, ... \overline{RE}\}$

    $\{\overline{AE}, \overline{BF}, \overline{CG}, ... \overline{RD}\}$

4. Let one student read from the LIFEPAC the "If" part of Theorem 6-1, 6-2, 6-3, 6-4, 6-5, 6-6, 6-7, 6-8, 6-9, or Postulate 16. Then let a second student draw and label an appropriate figure to illustrate the theorem or postulate (representative figures are included in the LIFEPAC with each theorem and postulate). Then let a third student say the "then" part of the theorem or postulate (without using the LIFEPAC). Repeat the procedure with each of the other theorems or the postulate.

Section 3: Special Angles and Segments Related to Circles

1. Have the students draw three externally tangent circles the same size as shown. A straight line connects the centers of the circles. Then have the students find the length of $\overline{DE}$ in terms of $\overline{BC}$.

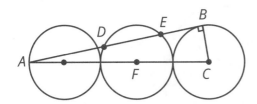

2. Let one student read from the LIFEPAC Theorem 6-10, 6-11, 6-12, 6-13, 6-14, or 6-15. Then let a second student draw and label an appropriate figure to illustrate the theorem (representative figures are included in the LIFEPAC with each theorem). Let a third student write all but one measurement in the figure (use a variable for the missing measurement). Then let a fourth student find the missing measurement by using the stated theorem. Repeat the procedure with each of the other theorems.

Example:	First student:	Theorem 6-10 says "the measure of an inscribed angle is equal to half the measure of its intercepted arc."

Second student: Draws and labels:

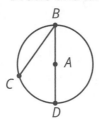

Third student:

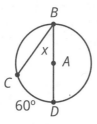

Fourth student: m $\angle CBA$ equals $\frac{1}{2}$ m $\overarc{CD}$;

m $\angle CBA = \frac{1}{2}$ (60°), which equals 30°.

3. Let one student read from the LIFEPAC the "If" part of Theorem 6-16, 6-17, or 6-18.
    Then let a second student draw and label an appropriate figure to illustrate the theorem
    (representative figures are included in the LIFEPAC with each theorem). Let a third student
    say the "then" part of the theorem (without using the LIFEPAC). Then let a fourth student,
    write all but one measurement in the figure (use a variable for the missing measurement).
    Then let a fifth student find the missing measurement by using the stated theorem. Repeat
    the procedure for each of the other theorems.

Example:	First student:	Theorem 6-16 says "if two chords intersect in a circle."
	Second student:	Draws and labels:

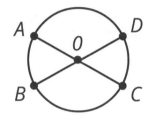

	Third student:	(Then) the product of the lengths of the segments of one chord is equal to the product of the lengths of the other chord.
	Fourth student:	

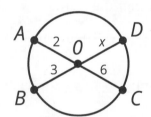

Fifth student: Two times 6 equals 3 times x; 12 equals $3x$; $\dfrac{12}{3} = \dfrac{3x}{3}$, $4 = x$, which is the missing length.

Administer the LIFEPAC Test.

    The test is to be administered in one session. Give no help except with directions.
    Evaluate the tests and review areas where the students have done poorly.
    Review the pages and activities that stress the concepts tested.
    If necessary, administer the Alternate LIFEPAC Test

ANSWER KEYS

SECTION 1

1.1	$\overline{DK}$ and $\overline{DM}$
1.2	$\overline{EF}$
1.3	$\overline{BN}$ and $\overline{BH}$
1.4	C
1.5	$\overline{AE}, \overline{AG}, \overline{AF}$
1.6	5"
1.7	6"
1.8	A and D
1.9	A and D
1.10	none
1.11	$\overline{AB}$
1.12	$\overline{AC}$ or $\overline{AD}$
1.13	E, H, C, D, F, G
1.14	A, B, F, H
1.15	$BD = AC - AB = 6 - 4 = 2$
1.16	E, G
1.17	A
1.18	yes; $6 = 4 + 2$
1.19	$AC = AB + BD$
	$20 = AB + 8$
	$12 = AB$
1.20	$AC = AB + BD$
	$AC = 7 + 7$
	$AC = 14$
	diameter $= 2(14) = 28$
1.21	R, S, T
1.22	$\overline{SD}, \overline{SJ},$ or $\overline{SE}$
1.23	$\overline{TF}, \overline{TH}, \overline{TG}$
1.24	$\overline{AB}$
1.25	S and T
1.26	$2 \cdot 4 = 8$
1.27	isosceles right triangle
1.28	T, I
1.29	A, B, C
1.30	8"

SELF TEST 1

1.01	center
1.02	center
1.03	two
1.04	concentric
1.05	equal
1.06	interior
1.07	sphere
1.08	equal
1.09	radii
1.010	concentric
1.011	$2(2) = 4"$
1.012	A and C
1.013	$1 + 1 = 2"$
1.014	D, X
1.015	$\angle JBM$, or $\angle KCG$
1.016	F, M, J
1.017	$1 + 1 = 2"$
1.018	$FB = MB = JB$
1.019	$2(3) = 6"$
1.020	no

1.021 through 1.025

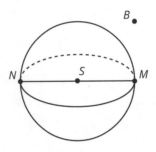

1.026 though 1.030

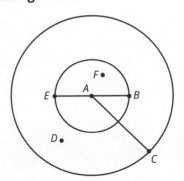

SECTION 2

2.1 *B, C*
2.2 *A, B,* or *A, C*
2.3 *B, C*
2.4 *A, B,* or *A, C*
2.5 no
2.6 a. 2
     b. 1
     c. 0
     d. 0
     e. 0
2.7 a. 2
     b. 2
     c. 2
     d. 1
     e. 0
2.8 a. infinite
     b. infinite
     c. infinite
     d. 1
     e. 0
2.9 a. infinite
     b. infinite
     c. infinite
     d. infinite
     e. 0

2.10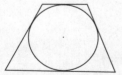

2.11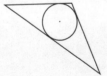

2.12

2.13

2.14 a.

     b. no

2.15 a.

     b. yes

2.16

2.17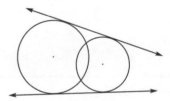

2.18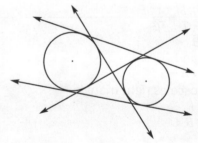

2.19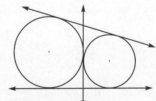

2.20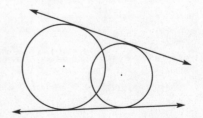

2.21

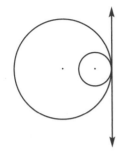

2.22 $\overline{RS}$, $\overline{RM}$, or $\overline{MS}$
2.23 $\overline{BC}$
2.24 M
2.25 It intersects the circle in two points.
2.26 $OP = 4 + 2 = 6$
2.27 a. 3
 b. 4
 c. $AB = OP - (OA + BP)$
 $AB = 9 - (4 + 3)$
 $AB = 9 - 7$
 $AB = 2$

2.28 4
2.29 $(AP)^2 + (OA)^2 = (OP)^2$
 $(AP)^2 + 6^2 = (6 + 4)^2$
 $(AP)^2 + 36 = 100$
 $(AP)^2 = 64$
 $\sqrt{(AP)^2} = \sqrt{64}$
 $AP = 8$

2.30 $(ON)^2 + (PN)^2 = (OP)^2$
 $(ON)^2 + 15^2 = 17^2$
 $(ON)^2 + 225 = 289$
 $(ON)^2 = 64$
 $\sqrt{(ON)^2} = \sqrt{64}$
 $ON = 8$

2.31 no
2.32 no
2.33 90°
2.34 360° − 90° = 270°
2.35 $\overset{\frown}{ABC}$, $\overset{\frown}{ATC}$
2.36 $\overset{\frown}{AB}$, $\overset{\frown}{BR}$, $\overset{\frown}{RC}$, or $\overset{\frown}{BC}$
2.37 $\overset{\frown}{ATB}$, $\overset{\frown}{BAR}$, $\overset{\frown}{RAC}$, or $\overset{\frown}{BAC}$
2.38 a. $\overset{\frown}{AB}$
 b. $\overset{\frown}{ACB}$
2.39 The triangle is equilateral, therefore, the segment is 8".

2.40

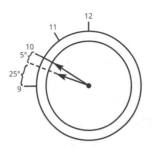

At 9:50 the hour hand is $\dfrac{50}{60} = \dfrac{5}{6}$ of the way from 9 to 10. The minute hand is on the 10.
$\dfrac{5}{6}$ of 30° = 25°
30° − 25° = 5°

2.41

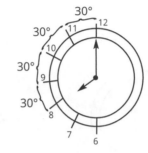

4(30°) = 120°

2.42

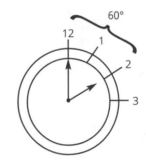

2(30°) = 60°

2.43

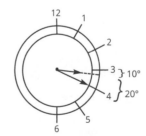

At 3:20 the hour hand is $\dfrac{20}{60} = \dfrac{1}{3}$ of the way from 3 to 4. The minute hand is on the 4.
$\dfrac{1}{3}$ of 30° = 10°
30° − 10° = 20°

2.44

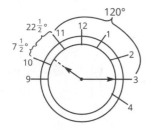

At 10:15 the hour hand has moved $\frac{15}{60} = \frac{1}{4}$ of the way from 10 to 11. The minute hand is on the 3.

$\frac{1}{4}$ of 30° = $7\frac{1}{2}$°

$30° - 7\frac{1}{2}° = 22\frac{1}{2}°$

$120° + 22\frac{1}{2}° = 142\frac{1}{2}°$

2.45

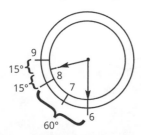

At 8:30 the hour hand is halfway between 8 and 9. The minute hand is on the 6.

$\frac{1}{2}$ of 30° = 15°

$60° + 15° = 75°$

2.46

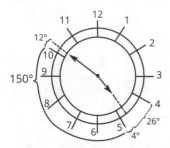

At 4:52 the hour hand is $\frac{52}{60} = \frac{13}{15}$ of the way from 4 to 5. The minute hand is $\frac{2}{5}$ of the way from 10 to 11.

$\frac{13}{15}$ of 30° = 26°

$30° - 26° = 4°$

$\frac{2}{5}$ of 30° = 12°

$150° + 4° + 12° = 166°$

2.47

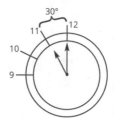

2.48

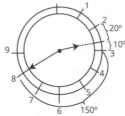

At 2:40 the hour hand is $\frac{40}{60} = \frac{2}{3}$ of the way from 2 to 3. The minute hand is on the 8.

$\frac{2}{3}$ of 30° = 20°

$30° - 20° = 10°$

$150° + 10° = 160°$

2.49

At 10:50 the hour hand is $\frac{50}{60} = \frac{5}{6}$ of the way from 10 to 11. The minute hand is on the 10.

$\frac{5}{6}$ of 30° = 25°

2.50

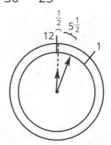

At 12:01 the hour hand is $\frac{1}{60}$ of the way from 12 to 1. The minute hand is $\frac{1}{5}$ of the way from 12 to 1.

$\frac{1}{60}$ of 30° = $\frac{1}{2}$°

$\frac{1}{5}$ of 30° = 6°

$6° - \frac{1}{2}° = 5\frac{1}{2}°$

2.51 m ∠2 = 180° – m ∠1
= 180° – 100°
= 80°

2.52 m ∠3 = m $\overset{\frown}{BC}$ = 30°

2.53 m ∠4 = 180° – m ∠3
= 180° – 30°
= 150°

2.54 m $\overset{\frown}{AD}$ = m ∠1 = 100°

2.55 m $\overset{\frown}{AC}$ = m AB + m BC
= m ∠2 + m ∠BC
= 80° + 30°
= 110°

2.56 m $\overset{\frown}{DC}$ = m ∠4 = 150°

2.57 m $\overset{\frown}{ADB}$ = 360° – m ∠2
= 360° – 80°
= 280°

2.58 180°

2.59 m $\overset{\frown}{DAC}$ = 360° – m ∠4
= 360° – 150°
= 210°

2.60 m $\overset{\frown}{CAB}$ = 360° – m ∠3
= 360° – 30°
= 330°

2.61 $\overline{RS}$, $\overline{WR}$, $\overline{WS}$, $\overline{SV}$, $\overline{WT}$, $\overline{RU}$

2.62 $\overline{WT}$, $\overrightarrow{VS}$

2.63 none

2.64 no

2.65 yes

2.66 $\overline{VS}$, $\overline{RU}$

2.67 $\overline{AS}$, $\overline{AR}$, $\overline{AV}$, $\overline{AU}$

2.68 Any three:
$\overline{MG}$, $\overline{MT}$, $\overline{MH}$, or $\overline{MC}$

2.69 Any three:
$\overline{HG}$, $\overline{JS}$, $\overline{CD}$, or $\overline{CT}$

2.70 $\overline{JS}$, $\overline{CD}$

2.71 $\overline{HG}$ or $\overline{CT}$

2.72 l

2.73 A polygon inscribed in a sphere is a polygon each of whose vertices is a point of the sphere.

2.74 Example:

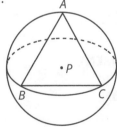

2.75 inscribed in the circle

2.76 circumscribed about the circle

2.77 neither

2.78 neither

2.79 neither

2.80 1. **STATEMENT**
$\overline{AB}$ is the diameter of circle O
$\overrightarrow{AC}$ and $\overrightarrow{BD}$ are tangents
REASON
Given

2. **STATEMENT**
$\overline{AB}$ ⊥ $\overrightarrow{AC}$
$\overline{AB}$ ⊥ $\overrightarrow{BD}$
REASON
Radius ⊥ to tangent

3. **STATEMENT**
$\overrightarrow{AC}$ || $\overrightarrow{BD}$
REASON
Two lines ⊥ to same line are ||.

2.81 1. **Given**

2. **STATEMENT**
$\overline{AR}$ ⊥ $\overrightarrow{RS}$
$\overline{BS}$ ⊥ $\overrightarrow{RS}$
REASON
Radius ⊥ to tangent

3. **STATEMENT**
$\overline{AR}$ || $\overline{BS}$
REASON
Two lines ⊥ to same line are ||.

2.82 1. **Given**

2. **STATEMENT**
Draw $\overline{RA}$, $\overline{RB}$, $\overline{RP}$
REASON
Auxiliary lines

3. **STATEMENT**
RA = RB
REASON
Radii of same ⊙ are =.

4. **STATEMENT**
$\overline{RP}$ = $\overline{RP}$
REASON
Reflexive

5. **STATEMENT**
$\overline{RA}$ ⊥ $\overline{AP}$, $\overline{RB}$ ⊥ $\overline{PB}$
REASON
Radii ⊥ to tangent

6. **STATEMENT**
rt. △RAP ≅ rt. △RBP
REASON
HL

7. **STATEMENT**
$PA = PB$
REASON
CPCTE

2.83 1. **Given**

2. **STATEMENT**
$\overline{RA} \perp \overline{AE}, \overline{SE} \perp \overline{AE}$
REASON
Radii $\perp$ to tangent

3. **STATEMENT**
$\overline{RA} \,||\, \overline{SE}$
REASON
Two lines $\perp$ to same line are $||$.

4. **STATEMENT**
$\angle R = \angle S$
REASON
If lines $||$, alternate interior $\angle$'s are =.

2.84 1. **Given**

2. **STATEMENT**
Draw $\overline{OA}, \overline{OB}$
REASON
Auxiliary lines

3. **STATEMENT**
$\overline{OR} \perp \overline{AB}$
REASON
Radius $\perp$ to tangent

4. **STATEMENT**
$OR = OR$
REASON
Reflexive

5. **STATEMENT**
$OA = OB$
REASON
Radii of same $\odot$ are =.

6. **STATEMENT**
rt. $\triangle AOR \cong$ rt. $\triangle BOR$
REASON
HL

7. **STATEMENT**
$AR = RB$
REASON
CPCTE

2.85 1. **Given**

2. **STATEMENT**
m $\overset{\frown}{RS}$ + m $\overset{\frown}{ST}$ = m $\overset{\frown}{RT}$
m $\overset{\frown}{RT}$ + m $\overset{\frown}{TQ}$ = m $\overset{\frown}{RQ}$
REASON
Arc addition

3. **STATEMENT**
m $\overset{\frown}{RS}$ + m $\overset{\frown}{ST}$ + m $\overset{\frown}{TQ}$ = m $\overset{\frown}{RQ}$
REASON
Substitution

2.86 1. **Given**

2. **STATEMENT**
$OD = OC$; $OB = OA$
REASON
Radii of same $\odot$ are =.

3. **STATEMENT**
m $\angle DOB$ = m $\angle COA$
REASON
Vertical $\angle$'s are =.

4. **STATEMENT**
$\triangle DOB \cong \triangle COA$
REASON
SAS

5. **STATEMENT**
$BD = CA$
REASON
CPCTE

2.87 1. **STATEMENT**
m $\angle XOY$ = m $\angle WOV$, m $\overset{\frown}{YZ}$ = m $\overset{\frown}{ZW}$
REASON
Given

2. **STATEMENT**
m $\angle YOZ$ = m $\angle ZOW$
REASON
Central $\angle$'s = arcs.

3. **STATEMENT**
m $\angle XOY$ + m $\angle YOZ$ = m $\angle WOV$ + m $\angle ZOW$
REASON
Addition property of equality

4. **STATEMENT**
m $\angle XOZ$ = m $\angle ZOV$
REASON
Angle addition

5. **STATEMENT**
m $\overset{\frown}{XZ}$ = m $\overset{\frown}{ZV}$
REASON
Measure of arc = measure of central $\angle$.

2.88 1. **STATEMENT**
m $\overset{\frown}{TS}$ = 30°
REASON
Given

2. **STATEMENT**
m $\angle SRT$ = 30°
REASON
Central $\angle$ = arc.

3. **STATEMENT**
   ∠T = ∠W
   REASON
   Base ∠ of isosceles △'s are =.

4. **STATEMENT**
   m ∠SRT = m ∠T + m ∠W
   REASON
   Exterior ∠ = sum of remote interior ∠'s.

5. **STATEMENT**
   30° = 2(m ∠T)
   REASON
   Substitution

6. **STATEMENT**
   m ∠T = 15°
   REASON
   Division

2.89 a. minor arc
   b. m $\widehat{QR}$ = 180° – 48°
       = 132°

2.90 a. major arc
   b. m $\widehat{QSP}$ = m $\widehat{QR}$ + m $\widehat{RS}$ + m $\widehat{SP}$
       = 132° + 48° + 132°
       = 312°

2.91 a. semicircle
   b. 180°

2.92 a. minor arc
   b. m $\widehat{PQ}$ = m $\widehat{RS}$ = 48°

2.93 a. major arc
   b. m $\widehat{PQS}$ = m $\widehat{PQ}$ + m $\widehat{QR}$ + m $\widehat{RS}$
       = 48° + 132° + 48°
       = 228°

2.94 a. semicircle
   b. 180°

2.95 Given: m $\widehat{AB}$ = m $\widehat{CD}$
   To Prove: m ∠1 = m ∠2

   1. **STATEMENT**
      $\widehat{AB}$ = $\widehat{CD}$
      REASON
      Given

   2. **STATEMENT**
      m ∠1 = m $\widehat{AB}$, m ∠2 = m $\widehat{CD}$
      REASON
      Central ∠ = arc.

   3. **STATEMENT**
      m ∠1 = m ∠2
      REASON
      Substitution

2.96 Given: m $\widehat{AB}$ = m $\widehat{CD}$
   To Prove: m AB = m CD

   1. **STATEMENT**
      Draw $\overline{OA}$, $\overline{OB}$, $\overline{OC}$, $\overline{OD}$.
      REASON
      Auxiliary lines

   2. **STATEMENT**
      OA = OC, OB = OD
      REASON
      Radii of same ⊙ are =.

   3. **STATEMENT**
      m ∠1 = m ∠2
      REASON
      If ⌢'s =, then central ∠'s =.

   4. **STATEMENT**
      △AOB ≅ △DOC
      REASON
      SAS

   5. **STATEMENT**
      AB = CD
      REASON
      CPCTE

2.97

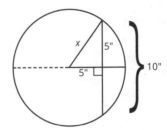

   x = 5√2 in.

2.98

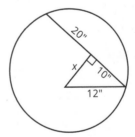

   $x^2 + 10^2 = 12^2$
   $x^2 + 100 = 144$
   $x^2 = 44$
   $\sqrt{x^2} = \sqrt{44}$
   $x = 2\sqrt{11}$ in.

2.99

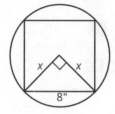

$x^2 + x^2 = 8^2$
$2x^2 = 64$
$x^2 = 32$
$\sqrt{x^2} = \sqrt{32}$
$x = 4\sqrt{2}$ in.

2.100 $AB = 2RB = 2(5) = 10$

2.101 $AR = \frac{1}{2}AB = \frac{1}{2}(12) = 6$

2.102 $(OB)^2 = (OR)^2 + (RB)^2$
$(OB)^2 = 3^2 + 4^2$
$(OB)^2 = 9 + 16$
$(OB)^2 = 25$
$\sqrt{(OB)^2} = \sqrt{25}$
$OB = 5$

2.103 $(OR)^2 + (RB)^2 = (OB)^2$
$(OR)^2 = (OB)^2 - (RB)^2$
$(OR)^2 = 10^2 - 8^2$
$(OR)^2 = 100 - 64$
$(OR)^2 = 36$
$\sqrt{(OR)^2} = \sqrt{36}$
$OR = 6$

2.104 $(OR)^2 + (RB)^2 = (OB)^2$
$(OR)^2 + (AR)^2 = (OB)^2$
$(OR)^2 = (OB)^2 - (AR)^2$
$(OR)^2 = 10^2 - 6^2$
$(OR)^2 = 100 - 36$
$(OR)^2 = 64$
$\sqrt{(OR)^2} = \sqrt{64}$
$OR = 8$

2.105 $(OR)^2 + (RB)^2 = (OB)^2$
$(OR)^2 + \frac{1}{2}(AB)^2 = (OB)^2$
$(OR)^2 + \frac{1}{2}(30)^2 = 17^2$
$(OR)^2 + (15)^2 = 17^2$
$(OR)^2 + 225 = 289$
$(OR)^2 = 64$
$\sqrt{(OR)^2} = \sqrt{64}$
$OR = 8$

2.106 m $\overset{\frown}{AC}$ = m $\overset{\frown}{BC}$ = 20°

2.107 m BAC = 360° – m ∠BOC
= 360° – 30°
= 330°

SELF TEST 2

2.01 yes
2.02 yes
2.03 no
2.04 yes
2.05 yes
2.06

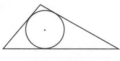

2.07

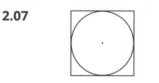

2.08

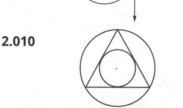

2.09

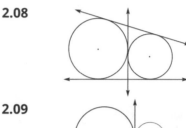

2.010

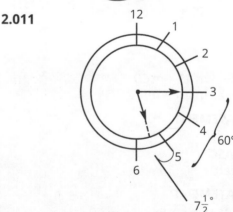

2.011

At 5:15 the hour hand is $\frac{15}{60} = \frac{1}{4}$ of the way
from 5 to 6. The minute hand is on the 3.
$\frac{1}{4}$ of 30° = $7\frac{1}{2}$°
60° of $7\frac{1}{2}$° = $67\frac{1}{2}$°

2.012 $360° \div 12 = 30°$

2.013

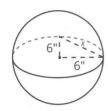

$x = 6\sqrt{2}\,"$

2.014 $\overset{\frown}{AB}$

2.015 $\overline{AB}$

2.016 $m\,\overset{\frown}{DB} = m\,\angle DPB = 60°$

2.017
$$m\,\overset{\frown}{AF} = m\,\overset{\frown}{AD}$$
$$m\,\overset{\frown}{AF} = 180° - m\,\overset{\frown}{DB}$$
$$110° = 180° - m\,\overset{\frown}{DB}$$
$$m\,\overset{\frown}{DB} + 110° = 180°$$
$$m\,\overset{\frown}{DB} = 70°$$

2.018 Since $AC = CD = DB$, these segments are also equal to CP and PD. Triangle CPD is therefore equilateral and $m\,\angle CPD = 60°$.

2.019 t

2.020 $PB = PE + EB$; $PE = EB$
$$PB = 2PE$$
$$= 2(3)$$
$$= 6$$

2.021 **STATEMENT**
$\overline{RS} \perp \overline{TW}$
REASON
Given

2.022 **STATEMENT**
$m\,\overset{\frown}{TR} = m\,\overset{\frown}{RW}$
REASON
Diameter $\perp$ to chord bisects major arc.

2.023 **STATEMENT**
$\overline{TR} = \overline{RW}$
REASON
If $\overset{\frown}{}$'s =, chords =.

2.024 **STATEMENT**
$\triangle TRW$ is isosceles.
REASON
Definition

SECTION 3

3.1
  a. $m\,\overset{\frown}{BA} = 360° - (m\,\overset{\frown}{CDA} + m\,\overset{\frown}{BC})$
          $= 360° - (260° + 30°)$
          $= 360° - 290°$
          $= 70°$

  b. $m\,\overset{\frown}{CD} = 180° - (m\,\overset{\frown}{BA} + m\,\overset{\frown}{BC})$
          $= 180° - (70° + 30°)$
          $= 180° - 100°$
          $= 80°$

  c. $\angle BAD = \frac{1}{2}(m\,\overset{\frown}{BC} + m\,\overset{\frown}{CD})$
            $= \frac{1}{2}(30° + 80°)$
            $= \frac{1}{2}(110°)$
            $= 55°$

  d. $\angle BAC = \frac{1}{2}m\,\overset{\frown}{BC}$
            $= \frac{1}{2}(30°)$
            $= 15°$

  e. $\angle CAD = \frac{1}{2}m\,\overset{\frown}{CD}$
            $= \frac{1}{2}(80°)$
            $= 40°$

3.2
  a. $\angle BAD = \frac{1}{2}m\,\overset{\frown}{BD}$
          $70° = \frac{1}{2}m\,\overset{\frown}{BD}$
         $140° = m\,\overset{\frown}{BD}$

  b. $m\,\overset{\frown}{BA} = 180° - m\,\overset{\frown}{BD}$
          $= 180° - 140°$
          $= 40°$

  c. $\angle CAD = \frac{1}{2}m\,\overset{\frown}{CD}$
            $= \frac{1}{2}(m\,\overset{\frown}{BD} - m\,\overset{\frown}{BC})$
            $= \frac{1}{2}(140° - 50°)$
            $= \frac{1}{2}(90°)$
            $= 45°$

  d. $\angle BAC = \angle BAD - \angle CAD$
          $= 70° - 45°$
          $= 25°$

3.3 a. $\frac{1}{2}SV = \angle U$

$\overset{\frown}{SV} = 2\angle U$
$= 2(70°)$
$= 140°$

$\angle VST = \frac{1}{2}m\overset{\frown}{SV}$
$= \frac{1}{2}(140°)$
$= 70°$

b. $\angle USV = 180° - (\angle USR + \angle VST)$
$= 180° - (50° + 70°)$
$= 180° - 120°$
$= 60°$

$\angle V = 180° - (\angle U + \angle USV)$
$= 180° - (70° + 60°)$
$= 180° - 130°$
$= 50°$

c. $\frac{1}{2}\overset{\frown}{SV} = \angle U$

$\overset{\frown}{SV} = 2\angle U$
$= 2(70°)$
$= 140°$

d. $\frac{1}{2}m\overset{\frown}{US} = \angle V$

$m\overset{\frown}{US} = 2\angle V$
$= 2(50°)$
$= 100°$

e. $\frac{1}{2}m\overset{\frown}{UV} = \angle USV$

$m\overset{\frown}{UV} = 2\angle USV$
$= 2(60°)$
$= 120°$

f. $\angle USV = 180° - (\angle USR + \angle VST)$
$= 180° - (50° + 70°)$
$= 180° - 120°$
$= 60°$

3.4 a. $\frac{1}{2}m\overset{\frown}{SUV} = \angle RSV$

$m\overset{\frown}{SUV} = 2\angle RSV$
$= 2(125°)$
$= 250°$

b. $m\overset{\frown}{SV} = 360° - m\overset{\frown}{SUV}$
$= 360° - 250°$
$= 110°$

c. $\angle TSV = \frac{1}{2}m\overset{\frown}{SV}$

$= \frac{1}{2}(110°)$
$= 55°$

d. $\angle U = \frac{1}{2}m\overset{\frown}{SV}$

$= \frac{1}{2}(110°)$
$= 55°$

3.5 a. 90°

b. $\angle ABD + \angle ADB = 180° - \angle BAD$
$= 180° - 90°$
$= 90°$

3.6 a. $\angle ADB = \frac{1}{2}AB$

$= \frac{1}{2}(120°)$
$= 60°$

b. $m\overset{\frown}{AD} = 180° - m\overset{\frown}{AB}$
$= 180° - 120°$
$= 60°$

c. $\angle ACD = \frac{1}{2}m\overset{\frown}{AD}$

$= \frac{1}{2}(60°)$
$= 30°$

3.7 a. $\angle ABD = 180° - (\angle BAD + \angle ADB)$
$= 180° - (90° + 70°)$
$= 180° - 160°$
$= 20°$

b. $\frac{1}{2}m\overset{\frown}{AB} = \overset{\frown}{ADB}$

$m\overset{\frown}{AB} = 2\angle ADB$
$= 2(70°)$
$= 140°$

c. $\frac{1}{2}m\overset{\frown}{AD} = \angle ABD$

$m\overset{\frown}{AD} = 2\angle ABD$
$= 2(20°)$
$= 40°$

3.8 a. $\frac{1}{2}m\overset{\frown}{DC} = \angle DBC$

$m\overset{\frown}{DC} = 2\angle DBC$
$= 2(40°)$
$= 80°$

b. $m\overset{\frown}{BC} = 180° - m\overset{\frown}{DC}$
$= 180° - 80°$
$= 100°$

c. $\angle ECB = \frac{1}{2}m\overset{\frown}{BC}$

$= \frac{1}{2}(100°)$
$= 50°$

d. $\angle DCF = \frac{1}{2}m\,\widehat{DC}$

$= \frac{1}{2}(80°)$

$= 40°$

e. $\angle BDC = \frac{1}{2}m\,\widehat{BC}$

$= \frac{1}{2}(100°)$

$= 50°$

3.9 a. $\angle Q = \frac{1}{2}m\,\widehat{TS}$

$= \frac{1}{2}(96°)$

$= 48°$

b. $\angle R = \frac{1}{2}m\,\widehat{TS}$

$= \frac{1}{2}(96°)$

$= 48°$

3.10 a. $\angle T = \frac{1}{2}m\,\widehat{QR}$

$= \frac{1}{2}(118°)$

$= 59°$

b. $\angle S = \frac{1}{2}m\,\widehat{QR}$

$= \frac{1}{2}(118°)$

$= 59°$

3.11 a. $\frac{1}{2}m\,\widehat{TS} = \angle Q$

$m\,\widehat{TS} = 2\angle Q$

$= 2(44°)$

$= 88°$

b. $\angle R = \frac{1}{2}m\,\widehat{TS}$

$= \frac{1}{2}(88°)$

$= 44°$

3.12 a. $\frac{1}{2}m\,\widehat{TS} = \angle Q$

$m\,\widehat{TS} = 2\angle Q$

$= 2(47°)$

$= 94°$

b. $\angle R = \frac{1}{2}m\,\widehat{TS}$

$= \frac{1}{2}(94°)$

$= 47°$

3.13 yes

3.14 $m\angle 1 = \frac{1}{2}(120°) = 60°$

3.15 $20° = \frac{1}{2}$ measure of intercepted arc of $\angle 1$

$40° =$ measure of intercepted arc of $\angle 1$

$\angle 1 = 40°$ (central $\angle$ = arc)

3.16 measure of intercepted arc of $\angle 1$

$= 360° - (150° + 130°)$

$= 360° - 280°$

$= 80°$

$\angle 1 = \frac{1}{2}$ measure of intercepted arc

$= \frac{1}{2}(80°)$

$= 40°$

3.17 measure of intercepted arc =

$360° - 274° = 86°$

$m\angle 1 = \frac{1}{2}$ measure of intercepted arc

$= \frac{1}{2}(86°)$

$= 43°$

3.18 $\frac{1}{2}$ measure of intercepted arc = $86°$

measure of intercepted arc

$= 2(86°)$

$= 172°$

measure of intercepted arc of $\angle 1$

measure of intercepted arc

$= 360° - 172°$

$= 188°$

$\angle 1 = \frac{1}{2}$ measure of intercepted arc

$= \frac{1}{2}(188°)$

$= 94°$

3.19 $90°$

3.20 measure of intercepted arc of $\angle 1$

$= 360° - (125° + 125°)$

$= 360° - 250°$

$= 110°$

$\angle 1 = \frac{1}{2}$ measure of intercepted arc

$= \frac{1}{2}(110°)$

$= 55°$

3.21 a. $m\angle 1 = \frac{1}{2}(50° + 30°)$

$= \frac{1}{2}(80°)$

$= 40°$

b. $m \angle 2 = 180° - m \angle 1$
    $= 180° - 40°$
    $= 140°$
c. $m \angle 3 = m \angle 1 = 40°$
d. $m \angle 4 = m \angle 2 = 140°$

3.22 $m \angle 2 = \frac{1}{2}(46° + 42°)$

$= \frac{1}{2}(88°)$

$= 44°$

$m \angle 4 = m \angle 2 = 44°$
$m \angle 1 = 180° - m \angle 2$
$= 180° - 44°$
$= 136°$
$m \angle 3 = m \angle 1 = 136°$

a. 136°
b. 44°
c. 136°
d. 44°

3.23 a. $m \angle 1 = \frac{1}{2}(36° + 40°)$

$= \frac{1}{2}(76°)$

$= 38°$

b. $m \angle 2 = 180° - 38° = 142°$
c. $m \angle 3 = m \angle 1 = 38°$
d. $m \angle 4 = m \angle 2 = 142°$

3.24 a. 78°
b. $m \angle 2 = 180° - m \angle 1$
    $= 180° - 78°$
    $= 102°$
c. $m \angle 3 = m \angle 1 = 78°$
d. $m \angle 4 = m \angle 2 = 102°$
e. $m \widehat{AB} = m \angle 2 = 102°$
f. $m \widehat{BC} = m \angle 3 = 78°$
g. $m \widehat{DC} = m \angle 4 = 102°$

3.25 $m \angle 3 = \frac{1}{2}(80° + 120°)$

$= \frac{1}{2}(200°)$
$= 100°$
$m \angle 4 = m \angle 3 = 100°$
$m \angle 1 = 180° - m \angle 3$
$= 180° - 100°$
$= 80°$
$m \angle 2 = m \angle 1 = 80°$

a. 80°
b. 80°
c. 100°
d. 100°

3.26 $40° = \frac{1}{2}(x + 41°)$

$80° = x + 41°$

$39° = x$

3.27 $89° = \frac{1}{2}(x + 88°)$

$178° = x + 88°$

$x = 90°$

3.28 $137° = \frac{1}{2}(x + 94°)$

$274° = x + 94°$

$x = 180°$

3.29 $50° = \frac{1}{2}(x + x)$

$100° = x + x$

$100° = 2x$

$x = 50°$

3.30 $120° = \frac{1}{2}(x + 2x)$

$240° = 3x$
$x = 80°$

3.31 $180° - 37° = \frac{1}{2}(x + 5 + x - 5)$

$180° - 37° = \frac{1}{2}(2x)$

$143° = \frac{1}{2}(2x)$

$x = 143°$

3.32

$x = \frac{1}{2}y$

$61° = \frac{1}{2}(y + 68°)$

$122° = y + 68°$

$54° = y$

$x = \frac{1}{2}(54°)$

$x = 27°$

3.33

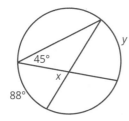

$$x = \frac{1}{2}(88° + y)$$
$$y = 2(45°)$$
$$y = 90°$$
$$x = \frac{1}{2}(88° + 90°)$$
$$x = \frac{1}{2}(178°)$$
$$x = 89°$$

3.34
$$\angle 1 = \frac{1}{2}(100° - 30°)$$
$$\angle 1 = \frac{1}{2}(70°)$$
$$\angle 1 = 35°$$

3.35
$$\angle 1 = \frac{1}{2}(140° - 40°)$$
$$\angle 1 = \frac{1}{2}(100°)$$
$$\angle 1 = 50°$$

3.36
$$\angle 1 = \frac{1}{2}(280° - 60°)$$
$$\angle 1 = \frac{1}{2}(220°)$$
$$\angle 1 = 110°$$

3.37
$$\angle 1 = \frac{1}{2}(300° - 60°)$$
$$\angle 1 = \frac{1}{2}(240°)$$
$$\angle 1 = 120°$$

3.38
$$\angle 1 = \frac{1}{2}(20° - 10°)$$
$$\angle 1 = \frac{1}{2}(10°)$$
$$\angle 1 = 5°$$

3.39
$$28° = \frac{1}{2}(114° - x)$$
$$56° = 114° - x$$
$$x = 58°$$

3.40
$$30° = \frac{1}{2}(x - 40°)$$
$$60° = x - 40°$$
$$x = 100°$$

3.41
$$x = \frac{1}{2}(x + 60° - 20°)$$
$$x = \frac{1}{2}(x + 40°)$$
$$2x = x + 40°$$
$$x = 40°$$

3.42
$$x = \frac{1}{2}[x + 114° - (x + 50°)]$$
$$x = \frac{1}{2}[64°]$$
$$2x = 64°$$
$$x = 32°$$

3.43
$$70° = \frac{1}{2}[(360° - x) - x]$$
$$70° = \frac{1}{2}[360° - 2x]$$
$$140° = 360° - 2x$$
$$2x = 220°$$
$$x = 110°$$

3.44
$$90° = \frac{1}{2}[x - (360° - x)]$$
$$90° = \frac{1}{2}[2x - 360°]$$
$$180° = 2x - 360°$$
$$2x = 540°$$
$$x = 270°$$

3.45
$$m\,\widehat{ED} = 180° - (m\,\widehat{BA} + m\,\widehat{AE})$$
$$= 180° - (68° + 53°)$$
$$= 180° - 121°$$
$$= 59°$$

$$m\,\angle 1 = \frac{1}{2}(m\,\widehat{BA} + m\,\widehat{ED})$$
$$= \frac{1}{2}(68° + 59°)$$
$$= \frac{1}{2}(127°)$$
$$= 63\frac{1}{2}°$$

3.46
$$m\,\widehat{CD} = 180° - (m\,\widehat{BC})$$
$$= 180° - 72°$$
$$= 108°$$

$$m\,\angle 2 = \frac{1}{2}(m\,\widehat{BA} + m\,\widehat{CB} + m\,\widehat{CD})$$
$$= \frac{1}{2}(68° + 72° + 108°)$$
$$= \frac{1}{2}(248°)$$
$$= 124°$$

3.47 $m \angle 3 = \frac{1}{2}m\overset{\frown}{ED}$

$\quad\quad\quad = \frac{1}{2}(59°)$

$\quad\quad\quad = 29\frac{1}{2}°$

3.48 $m \angle 4 = \frac{1}{2}(m\overset{\frown}{CB} + m\overset{\frown}{CD})$

$\quad\quad\quad = \frac{1}{2}(72° + 108°)$

$\quad\quad\quad = \frac{1}{2}(180°)$

$\quad\quad\quad = 90°$

3.49 $m \angle 5 = \frac{1}{2}m\overset{\frown}{CD}$

$\quad\quad\quad = \frac{1}{2}(108°)$

$\quad\quad\quad = 54°$

3.50 $m \angle 6 = \frac{1}{2}(m\overset{\frown}{AE} + m\overset{\frown}{BCD})$

$\quad\quad\quad = \frac{1}{2}(53° + 180°)$

$\quad\quad\quad = \frac{1}{2}(233°)$

$\quad\quad\quad = 116\frac{1}{2}°$

3.51 $m \angle 7 = m\overset{\frown}{BA} + m\overset{\frown}{AE}$

$\quad\quad\quad = 68° + 53°$

$\quad\quad\quad = 121°$

3.52 $90°$

3.53 $2 \cdot x = 3 \cdot 6$

$\quad\quad 2x = 18$

$\quad\quad x = 9$

3.54 $12 \cdot x = 9 \cdot 4$

$\quad\quad 12x = 36$

$\quad\quad x = 3$

3.55 $\frac{8}{2} = \frac{x}{2}$

$\quad\quad x^2 = 16$

$\quad\quad \sqrt{x^2} = \sqrt{16}$

$\quad\quad x = 4$

3.56 $\frac{x}{6} = \frac{6}{3}$

$\quad\quad 3x = 36$

$\quad\quad x = 12$

3.57 $2 \cdot x = 3 \cdot 4$

$\quad\quad 2x = 12$

$\quad\quad x = 6$

3.58 $\frac{x + 2}{6} = \frac{6}{2}$

$\quad\quad 2x + 4 = 36$

$\quad\quad 2x = 32$

$\quad\quad x = 16$

3.59 $4(x + 4) = 3(8)$

$\quad\quad 4x + 16 = 24$

$\quad\quad 4x = 8$

$\quad\quad x = 2$

3.60 $cx = ab$

$\quad\quad x = \frac{ab}{c}$

3.61 $AM \cdot MB = CM \cdot MD$

$\quad\quad 7 \cdot 6 = 8 \cdot MD$

$\quad\quad 8MD = 42$

$\quad\quad MD = \frac{42}{8} = \frac{21}{4} = 5\frac{1}{4}$

$\quad\quad CD = CM + MD$

$\quad\quad CD = 8 + 5\frac{1}{4}$

$\quad\quad CD = 13\frac{1}{4}$

3.62 $AM \cdot MB = CM \cdot DM$

$\quad\quad AM(AB - AM) = 8 \cdot 6$

$\quad\quad AM(16 - AM) = 48$

$\quad\quad 16AM - (AM)^2 = 48$

$\quad\quad (AM)^2 - 16AM + 48 = 0$

$\quad\quad (AM - 12)(AM - 4) = 0$

$\quad\quad AM - 12 = 0 \text{ or } AM - 4 = 0$

$\quad\quad AM = 12 \quad\quad AM = 4$

3.63 $AM \cdot MB = CM \cdot MD$

$\quad\quad AM(AB - AM) = CM(CD - CM)$

$\quad\quad 8(16 - 8) = CM(20 - CM)$

$\quad\quad 64 = 20CM - (CM)^2$

$\quad\quad (CM)^2 - 20CM + 64 = 0$

$\quad\quad (CM - 16)(CM - 4) = 0$

$\quad\quad CM - 16 = 0 \text{ or } CM - 4 = 0$

$\quad\quad CM = 16 \quad\quad CM = 4$

3.64 $AM \cdot MB = CM \cdot MD$

$\quad\quad AM(AB - AM) = (CD - MD)MD$

$\quad\quad AM(12 - AM) = (12 - 3)3$

$\quad\quad 12AM - (AM)^2 = 27$

$\quad\quad (AM)^2 - 12AM + 27 = 0$

$\quad\quad (AM - 9)(AM - 3) = 0$

$\quad\quad AM - 9 = 0 \text{ or } AM - 3 = 0$

$\quad\quad AM = 9 \quad\quad AM = 3$

3.65 $\frac{PB}{PA} = \frac{PA}{PE}$

$\quad\quad \frac{BE + PE}{PA} = \frac{PA}{PE}$

$\quad\quad \frac{BE + 4}{6} = \frac{6}{4}$

$\quad\quad 4(BE + 4) = 36$

$\quad\quad 4BE + 16 = 36$

$\quad\quad 4BE = 20$

$\quad\quad BE = 5$

3.66

$$\frac{PC}{PA} = \frac{PA}{PD}$$

$$\frac{DC + PD}{PA} = \frac{PA}{PD}$$

$$\frac{7\sqrt{2} + 5\sqrt{2}}{PA} = \frac{PA}{5\sqrt{2}}$$

$$\frac{12\sqrt{2}}{PA} = \frac{PA}{5\sqrt{2}}$$

$$(PA)^2 = 120$$

$$\sqrt{(PA)^2} = \sqrt{120}$$

$$PA = 2\sqrt{30}$$

3.67

$$\frac{BP}{PA} = \frac{PA}{EP}$$

$$\frac{BP}{PA} = \frac{PA}{BP - BE}$$

$$\frac{BP}{10} = \frac{10}{BP - 21}$$

$$BP(BP - 21) = 10(10)$$

$$(BP)^2 - 21BP = 100$$

$$(BP)^2 - 21BP - 100 = 0$$

$$(BP - 25)(BP + 4) = 0$$

$$BP - 25 = 0 \ \text{ or } \ BP + 4 = 0$$

$$BP = 25 \ \text{ or } \ BP = -4;$$

$$\text{not acceptable}$$

$$\therefore BP = 25$$

3.68

$$PC \cdot PD = PB \cdot PE$$

$$6 \cdot 4 = (x + 5) \cdot x$$

$$24 = x^2 + 5x$$

$$x^2 + 5x - 24 = 0$$

$$(x + 8)(x - 3) = 0$$

$$x + 8 = 0$$

$$x = -8; \text{ not acceptable}$$

$$\text{or } x - 3 = 0$$

$$x = 3$$

$$\therefore x = 3$$

3.69 1. **STATEMENT**
$PA = PB$
REASON
Given

2. **STATEMENT**
$\dfrac{PA}{PC} = \dfrac{PB}{PD}$
REASON
Two secant segments theorem

3. **STATEMENT**
$\dfrac{PA}{PC} = \dfrac{PA}{PD}$
REASON
Substitution

4. **STATEMENT**
$PA \cdot PC = PA \cdot PD$
REASON
POP

5. **STATEMENT**
$PC = PD$
REASON
Division property of equality

3.70 1. **STATEMENT**
$\overline{AB}$ is diameter, $\overline{BC}$ is tangent to circle O.
REASON
Given

2. **STATEMENT**
$\angle A = \angle A$
REASON
Reflexive

3. **STATEMENT**
$\angle CBA$ is rt. $\angle$
REASON
Radius $\perp$ to tangent

4. **STATEMENT**
$\angle BXA = 90°$
REASON
Inscribed in semicircle

5. **STATEMENT**
$\angle CBA = \angle BXA$
REASON
All rt. $\angle$'s =.

6. **STATEMENT**
$\triangle AXB \cong \triangle ABC$
REASON
AA

SELF TEST 3

3.01   inscribed

3.02   tangent

3.03   90°

3.04 $\frac{1}{2}(\overset{\frown}{XPQ} - \overset{\frown}{XQ})$

3.05   equal

3.06   central ∠'s

3.07   90°

3.08   half the sum of the intercepted arcs

3.09   half the difference of the intercepted arcs

3.010   bisects

3.011 $\overline{BT}$, $\overline{BU}$, or $\overline{BD}$

3.012 $\overline{RS}$

3.013 $\overleftrightarrow{CD}$

3.014   ∠DBU

3.015   no

3.016 $\frac{1}{2}(\overset{\frown}{BG} + \overset{\frown}{CD})$

3.017 $\frac{1}{2}(\overset{\frown}{CD} - \overset{\frown}{GE})$

3.018 $\frac{1}{2}(m\overset{\frown}{CD} + m\overset{\frown}{BG}) = ∠DFC$

        $\frac{1}{2}(55° + m\overset{\frown}{BG}) = 40°$

          $55° + m\overset{\frown}{BG} = 80°$

             $m\overset{\frown}{BG} = 25°$

3.019 $\frac{1}{2}(m\overset{\frown}{CD} - m\overset{\frown}{GE}) = m∠A$

        $\frac{1}{2}(55° - m\overset{\frown}{GE}) = 15°$

          $55° - m\overset{\frown}{GE} = 30°$

             $m\overset{\frown}{GE} = 25°$

3.020   right

3.021 $2 \cdot HD = 3 \cdot 7$

        $2HD = 21$

        $HD = \frac{21}{2} = 10\frac{1}{2}$

3.022 $\frac{12}{x} = \frac{x}{3}$

        $x^2 = 36$

        $\sqrt{x^2} = \sqrt{36}$

        $x = 6$

3.023 $x \cdot 10 = 5 \cdot 8$

        $10x = 40$

        $x = 4$

3.024 $\frac{16}{8} = \frac{8}{x}$

        $16x = 64$

        $x = 4$

3.025 $(5 + 3)3 = (x + 2)2$

        $8(3) = (x + 2)2$

        $24 = 2x + 4$

        $20 = 2x$

        $x = 10$

LIFEPAC TEST

1. r

2. s

3. $\perp$

4. J

5. 3

6. If chords are =, then arcs are =.

7. If arcs are =, then chords are =.

8. Diameter $\perp$ to chord bisects the chord.

9. $A = \frac{1}{2}m\overset{\frown}{BCD}$

$m\overset{\frown}{BCD} = 360° - m\overset{\frown}{BD}$

$\phantom{m\overset{\frown}{BCD}} = 360° - 150°$

$\phantom{m\overset{\frown}{BCD}} = 210°$

$\angle A = \frac{1}{2}(210°)$

$ = 105°$

10. $m\angle C = \frac{1}{2}m\overset{\frown}{BD}$

$m\angle BDR = \frac{1}{2}m\overset{\frown}{BD}$

$m\angle BDR = m\angle C = 63°$

11. $m\overset{\frown}{DC} = 360° - m\,DAC$

$\frac{1}{2}m\overset{\frown}{DAC} = m\angle RDC$

$\frac{1}{2}m\overset{\frown}{DAC} = 120°$

$m\overset{\frown}{DAC} = 2(120°)$

$m\overset{\frown}{DAC} = 240°$

$m\overset{\frown}{DC} = 360° - 240° = 120°$

12. $\angle 1 = \frac{1}{2}(m\overset{\frown}{VU} - m\overset{\frown}{ST})$

$ = \frac{1}{2}(80° - 40°)$

$ = \frac{1}{2}(40°)$

$ = 20°$

13. $m\angle 2 = \frac{1}{2}(m\overset{\frown}{UV} + m\overset{\frown}{ST})$

$ = \frac{1}{2}(70° + 30°)$

$ = \frac{1}{2}(100°)$

$ = 50°$

14. $m\angle 3 = \frac{1}{2}(m\overset{\frown}{VB} - m\overset{\frown}{BS})$

$ = \frac{1}{2}(60° - 30°)$

$ = \frac{1}{2}(30°)$

$ = 15°$

15. $\frac{1}{2}(m\overset{\frown}{UV} - m\overset{\frown}{ST}) = m\angle 1$

$\frac{1}{2}(m\overset{\frown}{UV} - 20°) = 30°$

$m\overset{\frown}{UV} - 20° = 60°$

$m\overset{\frown}{UV} = 80°$

16. $40°$

17. $\overset{\frown}{AC}$

18. $m\overset{\frown}{BC} = 180° - (m\angle 1 + m\angle 3)$

$\phantom{m\overset{\frown}{BC}} = 180° - (20° + 20°)$

$\phantom{m\overset{\frown}{BC}} = 180° - 40°$

$\phantom{m\overset{\frown}{BC}} = 140°$

19. $m\overset{\frown}{ABC} = 180° - m\angle 3$

$\phantom{m\overset{\frown}{ABC}} = 180° - 30°$

$\phantom{m\overset{\frown}{ABC}} = 150°$

20. $5 \cdot x = 10 \cdot 4$

$5x = 40$

$x = 8$

21. $\dfrac{8+4}{x} = \dfrac{x}{4}$

$\dfrac{12}{x} = \dfrac{x}{4}$

$x^2 = 48$

$\sqrt{x^2} = \sqrt{48}$

$x = 4\sqrt{3}$

22. $(5 + 4)4 = (x + 3)3$

$(9)4 = (x + 3)3$

$36 = 3x + 9$

$27 = 3x$

$9 = x$

23. $x \cdot x = 2 \cdot 6$

$x^2 = 12$

$\sqrt{x^2} = \sqrt{12}$

$x = 2\sqrt{3}$

24.

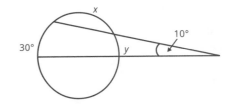

$10° = \frac{1}{2}(30° - y)$

$20° = 30° - y$

$y = 10°$

$x = 180° - (30° - 10°)$

$ = 180° - 40°$

$ = 140°$

25. $\frac{1}{2}$ measure of intercepted arc = 98°

measure of intercepted arc = 2(98°) = 196°

measure of intercepted arc of

$x = 360° - 196° = 164°$

$\angle x = \frac{1}{2}(164°) = 82°$

ALTERNATE LIFEPAC TEST

1. $\overline{OA}$ or $\overline{OB}$ or $\overline{OD}$
2. $\overleftrightarrow{AC}$
3. $\overline{AB}$
4. $\overrightarrow{BD}$
5. $\angle ABD$ or $\angle ODB$
6. $\angle DOB$ or $\angle DOA$
7. 2
8. 2
9. S
10. S
11. $\overset{\frown}{RAS}$ is a semicircle; therefore, m $\overset{\frown}{RAS}$ = 180°.
12. The measure of a minor arc equals the measure of the central angle;
    m $\overset{\frown}{AR}$ = m $\angle 1$ = 50°.
13. The measure of a minor arc equals the measure of the central angle;
    m $\angle 2$ = m $\overset{\frown}{RB}$ = 48°.
14. m $\angle 1$ = 180° - m $\angle AOS$
    m $\angle AOS$ = m $\overset{\frown}{AS}$
    m $\angle 1$ = 180° - m $\overset{\frown}{AS}$
    m $\angle 1$ = 180° - 126°
    m $\angle 1$ = 54°
15. m $\overset{\frown}{ASB}$ = m $\overset{\frown}{AS}$ + m $\overset{\frown}{SB}$
    m $\overset{\frown}{AS}$ = 180° - m $\overset{\frown}{AR}$
    m $\overset{\frown}{AR}$ = m $\angle 1$ = 47°
    m $\overset{\frown}{AS}$ = 180° - 47°
    m $\overset{\frown}{AS}$ = 133°
    Since m $\overset{\frown}{AR}$ = m $\overset{\frown}{RB}$, m $\overset{\frown}{SB}$ = m $\overset{\frown}{AS}$.
    m $\overset{\frown}{ASB}$ = 133° + 133°
    m $\overset{\frown}{ASB}$ = 266°
16. Since m $\overset{\frown}{BC}$ = m $\overset{\frown}{DE}$, BC = DE; BC = 7.
17. DE = BC
    m $\overset{\frown}{DE}$ = m $\overset{\frown}{BC}$
    m $\overset{\frown}{DE}$ = 70°
18. Since BC = DE, AX = AY = 5.
19. Since AX = AY, BC = DE.
    $BX = \frac{1}{2}BC$
    $BX = \frac{1}{2}DE = \frac{1}{2}(4) = 2$

20. m $\overset{\frown}{AB}$ = $\frac{1}{2}$m $\overset{\frown}{BD}$
    m $\overset{\frown}{AB}$ = $\frac{1}{2}$(100°)
    m $\overset{\frown}{AB}$ = 50°
21. m $\overset{\frown}{AD}$ = m $\overset{\frown}{AB}$
    m $\overset{\frown}{BC}$ = 180° - m $\overset{\frown}{AB}$
    m $\overset{\frown}{BC}$ = 180° - m $\overset{\frown}{AD}$
    m $\overset{\frown}{BC}$ = 180° - 40°
    m $\overset{\frown}{BC}$ = 140°
22. Draw auxiliary line PD to form rt. $\triangle PXD$.
    $XD = \frac{1}{2}BD$
    $XD = \frac{1}{2}(16)$ $XD = 8$
    $PD = \sqrt{6^2 + 8^2}$
    $PD = \sqrt{36 + 64}$
    $PD = \sqrt{100}$ $PD = 10$
23. Use Theorem 6-11.
    $x = \frac{1}{2}(360° - 250°)$
    $x = \frac{1}{2}(110°)$
    $x = 55°$
24. $20 = \frac{1}{2}(x + 10)$
    $40 = x + 10$
    $40 - 10 = x$
    $30 = x$
    $x = 30°$
25. $(6 + 4)(4) = (8)(x)$
    $(10)(4) = 8x$
    $40 = 8x$
    $\frac{40}{8} = \frac{8x}{8}$
    $5 = x$
26. The hour hand is $\frac{28}{60}$, or $\frac{7}{15}$, of the way from 1 to 2: $\frac{7}{15}$ of 30° = $\frac{7}{15} \times \frac{\cancel{30}}{1}$ = 14°. The minute hand is $\frac{3}{5}$ of the way from 5 to 6: $\frac{3}{5}$ of 30° = $\frac{3}{5} \times \frac{\cancel{30}}{1}$ = 18°. The total arc is 16° + 90° + 18° = 124°. The angle formed by the hands of the clock at 1:28 is 124°.

1:28

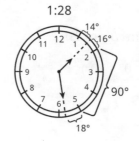

MATH 1006

ALTERNATE LIFEPAC TEST

NAME _____

DATE _____

SCORE _____

Refer to the figure to name the following parts (each answer, 3 points).

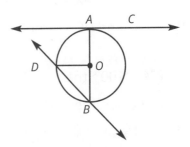

Given: point *O* is center

1. a radius _____

2. a tangent _____

3. a diameter _____

4. a secant _____

5. an inscribed angle _____

6. a central angle _____

Refer to the figure to complete the following items (each answer, 3 points).

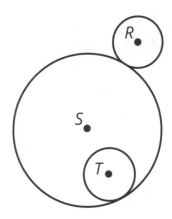

7. The number of common external tangents that can be drawn common to circle *S* and circle *R* is _____ .

8. The number of common internal tangents that can be drawn common to circle *T* and circle *R* is _____ .

9. Circle *T* is internally tangent to circle _____ .

10. Circle *R* is externally tangent to circle _____ .

Refer to the figures to complete the following items (each answer, 3 points).

Given: *RS* diameter

11. m $\overset{\frown}{RAS}$ = _____

12. If m ∠1 = 50°, then m $\overset{\frown}{AR}$ = _____ .

13. If m $\overset{\frown}{RB}$ = 48°, then m ∠2 = _____ .

14. If m $\overset{\frown}{AS}$ = 126°, then m ∠1 = _____ .

15. If m $\overset{\frown}{AR}$ = m $\overset{\frown}{RB}$ and m ∠1 = 47°, then m $\overset{\frown}{ASB}$ = _____ .

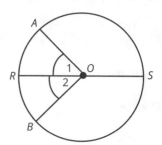

16. If *DE* = 7 and m $\overset{\frown}{BC}$ = m $\overset{\frown}{DE}$, then *BC* = _____ .

17. If m $\overset{\frown}{BC}$ = 70° and *DE* = *BC*, then m $\overset{\frown}{DE}$ = _____ .

18. If *BC* = *DE* and *AX* = 5, then *AY* = _____ .

19. If *AX* = *AY* and *DE* = 4, then *BX* = _____ .

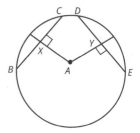

20. If m $\overset{\frown}{BD}$ = 100°, then m $\overset{\frown}{AB}$ = _____ .

21. If m $\overset{\frown}{AD}$ = 40°, then m $\overset{\frown}{BC}$ = _____ .

22. If *BD* = 16 and *PX* = 6, then *PD* = _____ .

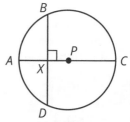

Find *x* **in the given figures** (each answer, 3 points).

23. *x* = _____

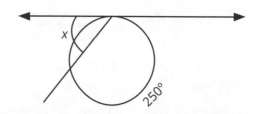

24. *x* = _____

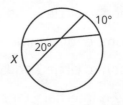

25. *x* = _____

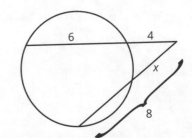

Work the following problem (3 points).

26. Find the angle formed by the hands of a clock.

_____

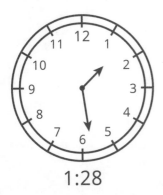

1:28

MATH 1007

Unit 7: Construction and Locus

TEACHER NOTES

MATERIALS NEEDED FOR LIFEPAC	
Required	Suggested
• compasses and straightedges	(None)

ADDITIONAL LEARNING ACTIVITIES

Section 1: Basic Construction

1. Write the equation $\frac{a}{b} = \frac{c}{x}$ on the chalkboard. Then write a proportion such as $\frac{4}{8} = \frac{7}{x}$ on the chalkboard. Let the class tell what they think the length of x will be in inches. Now let a student come to the chalkboard to draw the fourth proportional x (the LIFEPAC explains how to make this construction). Have the student copy a 4-inch segment for a, an 8-inch segment for b, and a 7-inch segment for c. After the fourth proportional x has been found, let the same student measure the length of x with a yardstick; the length should be 14 inches.

2. This activity is recommended for the more advanced student. On a sheet of paper construct a circle with the given segment as radius.

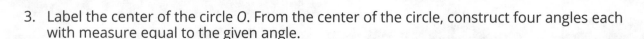

3. Label the center of the circle O. From the center of the circle, construct four angles each with measure equal to the given angle.

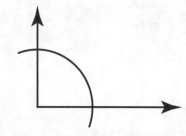

4. Label the end points of the angles on the circle A, B, C, and D. Now bisect $\angle AOB$, $\angle BOC$, $\angle COD$, and $\angle AOD$. Label the end points on the circle J, K, L, and M. Next construct the perpendicular bisectors of $\overline{OJ}$, $\overline{OK}$, $\overline{OL}$, and $\overline{OM}$; extend the bisectors to the circle. Label the points at which the bisectors intersect each other W, X, Y, and Z. Last, construct tangents to the circle at point A, point B, point C, and point D.

Section 2: Figure Construction

1. Let one student choose a triangle, median of a triangle, or altitude of a triangle to be constructed. If necessary, he also constructs any lengths or angles to be used for the construction and labels any drawings. Then let a second student construct and label the triangle, median, or altitude as specified.

   Example: First student: Says to construct a median of a triangle.
                                       Then he constructs and labels the triangle.

   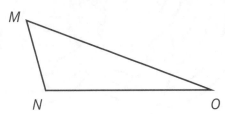

   Second student: Constructs and labels the median.

   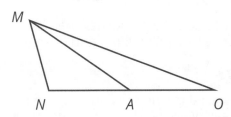

   One of the medians is $\overline{MA}$.

2. Based on your knowledge of the number of degrees in a circle and polygon construction, construct a regular nonagon (9-sided figure); a regular decagon (10-sided figure); a regular dodecagon (12-sided figure). Construct each polygon with each side equal to r.

   ————————————————— r

Section 3: Locus

1. Discuss with your class how the Archimedean spiral is formed as a locus of points moving around a fixed point, or pole. The points increase in distance from the pole in arithmetic sequence.

2. Have the students construct a donut by using thirty-six positions of a circle as it rolls around a base circle of the same size. Note: drawing is schematic only.

3. Have the students construct a cardioid by drawing a base circle and a number of other circles that are centered on the base circle and pass through a fixed point on that circle. Note: drawing is schematic only.

4. Have one student think of and sketch a locus. Then have another student describe the locus. Let the students take turns sketching and describing the loci.

Administer the LIFEPAC Test.

The test is to be administered in one session. Give no help except with directions.
Evaluate the tests and review areas where the students have done poorly.
Review the pages and activities that stress the concepts tested.
If necessary, administer the Alternate LIFEPAC Test

ANSWER KEYS

SECTION 1

1.1 through 1.10

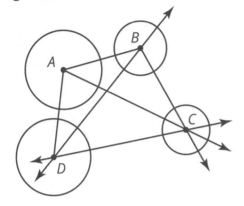

1.11 through 1.13

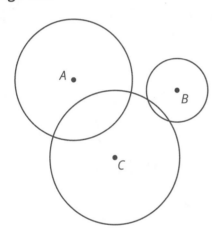

1.14 through 1.16

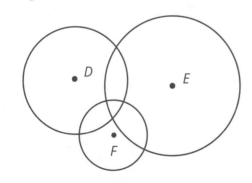

1.17

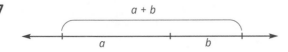

1.18

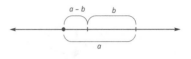

1.19

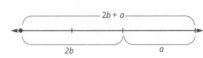

1.20

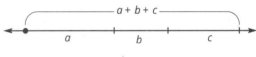

1.21

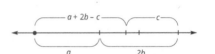

1.22

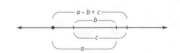

1.23

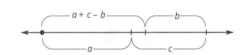

1.24

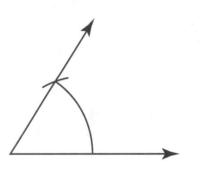

1.25

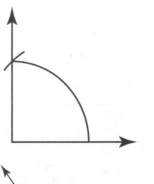

1.26

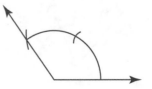

1.27

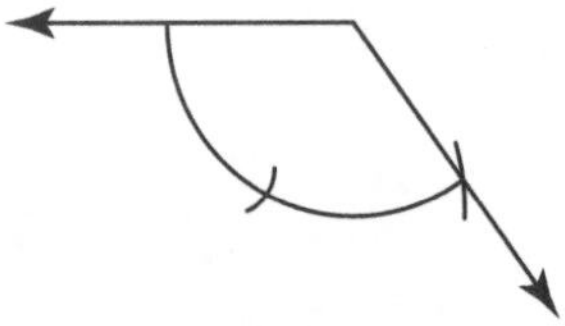

1.28

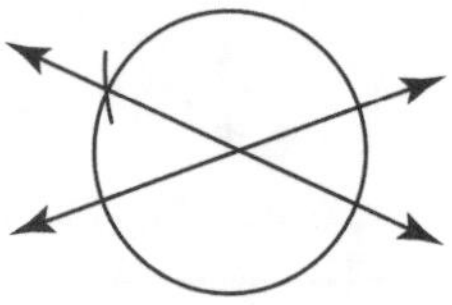

1.29

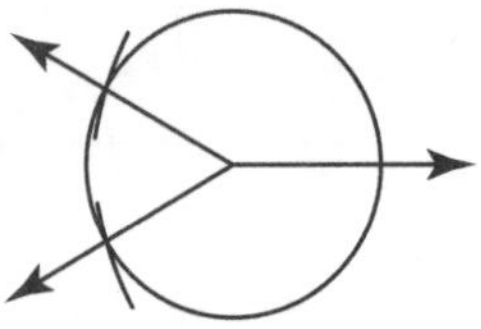

1.30

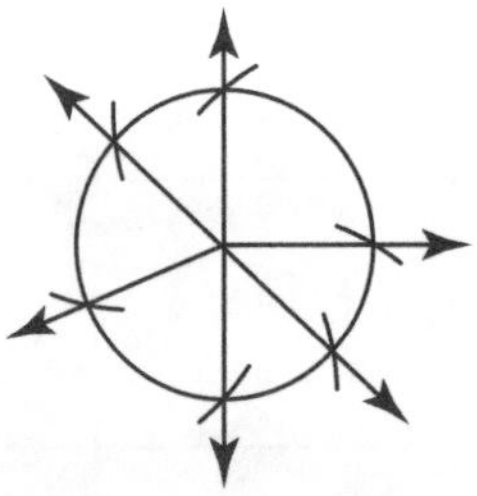

1.31

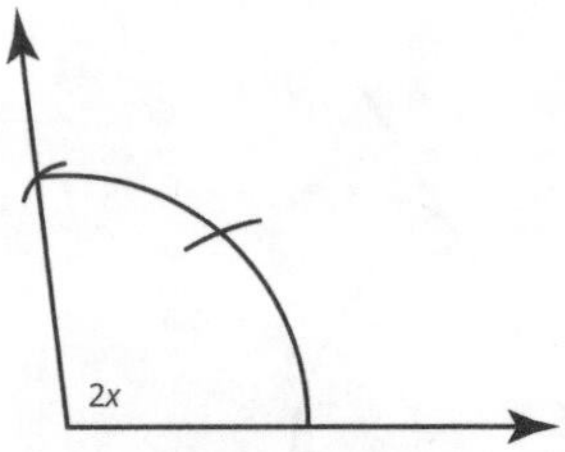

2x

1.32

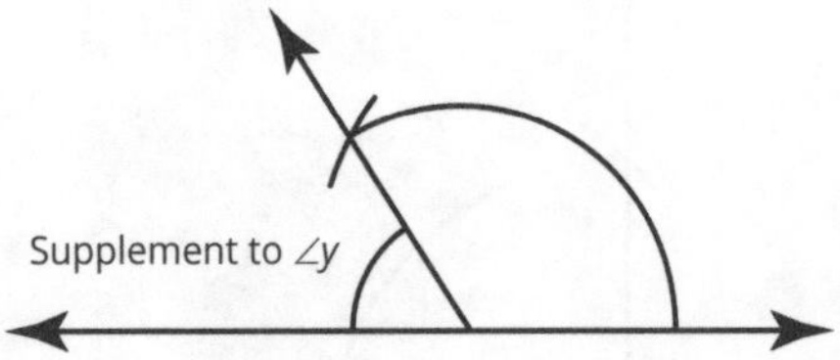

Supplement to ∠y

1.33

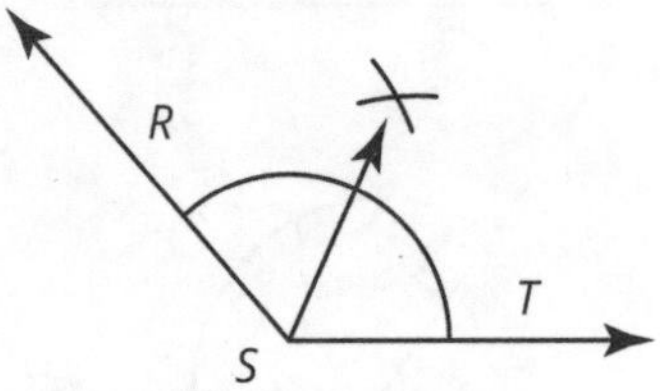

R

T

S

1.34

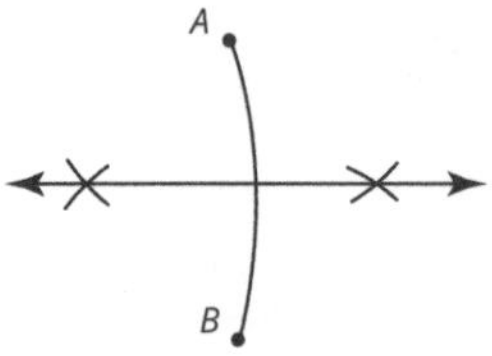

A

B

1.35

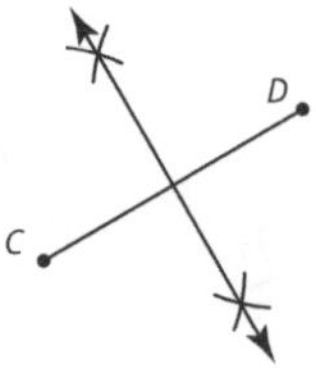

D

C

1.36

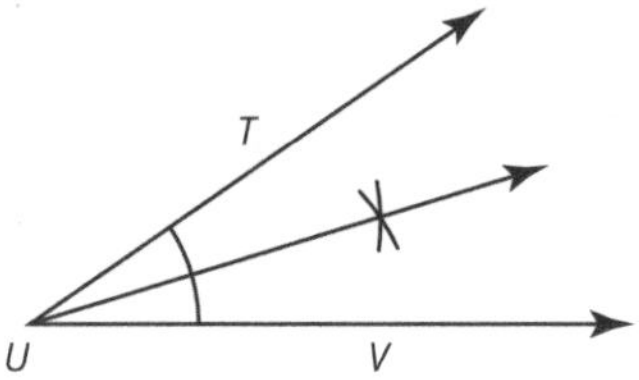

T

U   V

1.37

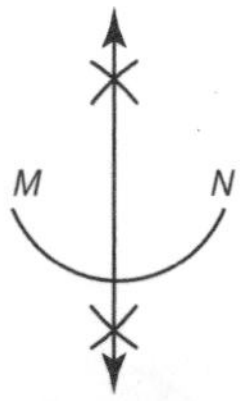

M   N

1.38

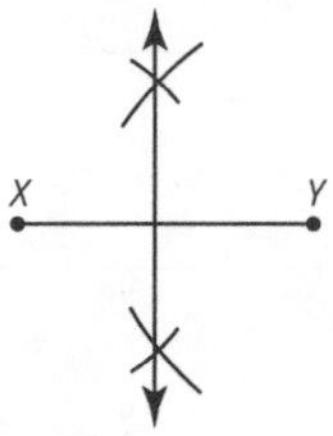

X   Y

1.39

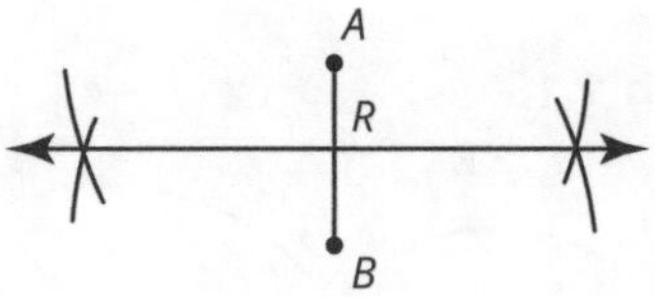

A

R

B

1.40

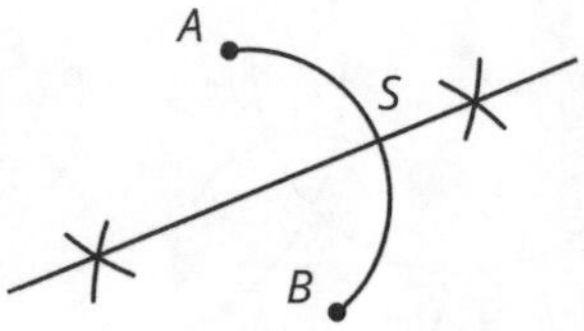

A

S

B

1.41

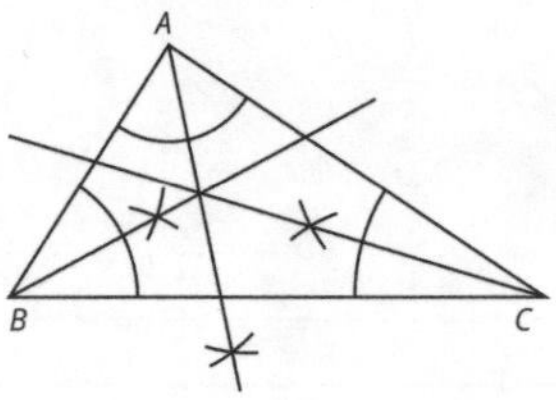

A

B   C

1.42 The point of intersection is the center of a circle that contains the arc.

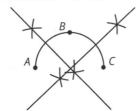

1.43

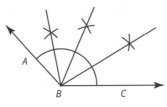

1.44

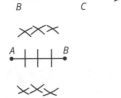

1.45

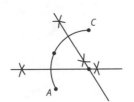

1.46

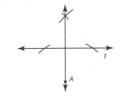

1.47

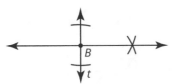

1.48

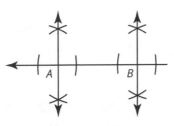

1.49

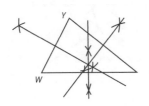

1.50

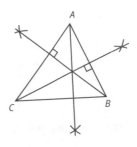

Yes, the perpendiculars intersect in one point.

1.51

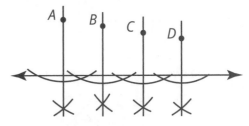

The lines are all parallel.

1.52

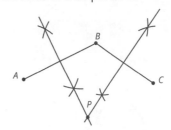

PA, *PB*, and *PC* are equal.

1.53

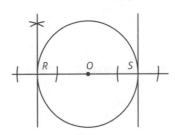

1.54

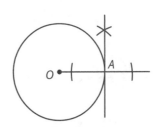

1.55

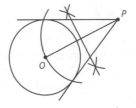

1.56

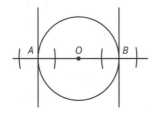

The two tangents are parallel.

1.57

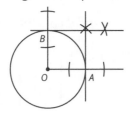

The two tangents are perpendicular.

1.58

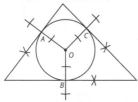

The sides of the triangle are tangents to the circle.

1.59

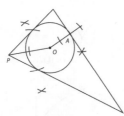

The circle is inscribed in the triangle.

1.60

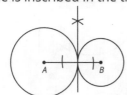

1.61

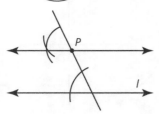

1.62

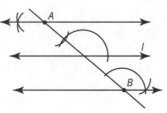

The lines constructed are parallel.

1.63

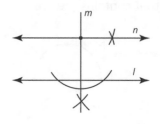

m and *n* are perpendicular.

1.64

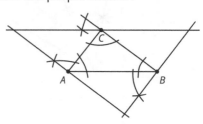

The two triangles are similar.

1.65   Example:

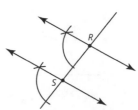

1.66

1.67

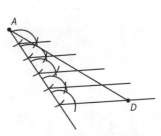

1.68

1.69

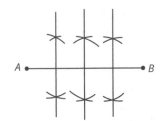

1.70

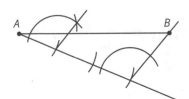

1.71

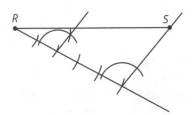

1.72

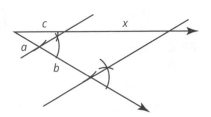

1.73

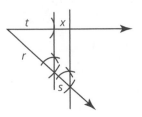

1.74

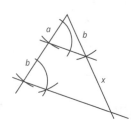

1.75

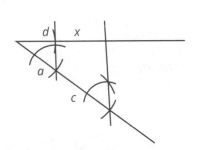

1.76

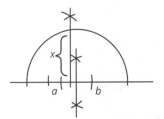

1.77

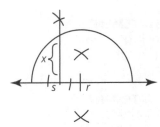

1.78

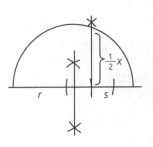

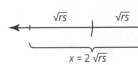

1.79

1. **STATEMENT**
   $\overline{AB}$
   REASON
   Given

2. **STATEMENT**
   $AX = BX = AY = BY$
   REASON
   Same radii

3. **STATEMENT**
   $XY = XY$
   REASON
   Reflexive

4. **STATEMENT**
   $\triangle XAY \cong \triangle XBY$
   REASON
   SSS

5. **STATEMENT**
   $\angle 1 = \angle 2$
   REASON
   CPCTE

6. **STATEMENT**
   $XM = XM$
   REASON
   Reflexive

7. **STATEMENT**
   $\triangle AXM \cong \triangle BXM$
   REASON
   SAS

8. **STATEMENT**
   $AM = MB$
   REASON
   CPCTE

9. **STATEMENT**
   M is midpoint of $\overline{AB}$
   REASON
   Definition of midpoint

10. **STATEMENT**
    $\overleftrightarrow{XY}$ bisects $\overline{AB}$
    REASON
    Definition of bisector

1.80

1. **STATEMENT**
   $\angle ABC$
   REASON
   Given

2. **STATEMENT**
   $BX = BY, XD = YD$
   REASON
   Same radii

3. **STATEMENT**
   $BD = BD$
   REASON
   Reflexive

4. **STATEMENT**
   $\triangle BXD \cong \triangle BYD$
   REASON
   SSS

5. **STATEMENT**
   $\angle 1 = \angle 2$
   REASON
   CPCTE

6. **STATEMENT**
   $\overrightarrow{BD}$ bisects $\angle ABC$
   REASON
   Definition of $\angle$ bisector

1.81

1. **STATEMENT**
   $\overset{\frown}{AB}$
   REASON
   Given

2. **STATEMENT**
   $BX = BY = AX = AY$
   REASON
   Same radii

3. **STATEMENT**
   $XY = XY$
   REASON
   Reflexive

4. **STATEMENT**
   $\triangle AXY \cong \triangle BXY$
   REASON
   SSS

5. **STATEMENT**
   $\angle 1 = \angle 2$
   REASON
   CPCTE

6. **STATEMENT**
   $XP = XP$
   REASON
   Reflexive

7. **STATEMENT**
$\triangle AXP \cong \triangle BXP$
REASON
SAS

8. **STATEMENT**
$AP = PB$
REASON
CPCTE

9. **STATEMENT**
$\overarc{AP} = \overarc{PB}$
REASON
If chords are =, then arcs are =.

10. **STATEMENT**
$\overleftrightarrow{XY}$ bisects $\overarc{AB}$
REASON
Definition of a bisector

1.82 1. **STATEMENT**
Circle O; point A
REASON
Given

2. **STATEMENT**
$\angle OXA$ is right $\angle$.
REASON
Angle inscribed in semicircle is a right $\angle$.

3. **STATEMENT**
$\overline{OX} \perp \overline{AX}$
REASON
If right $\angle$'s are formed, lines are $\perp$.

4. **STATEMENT**
$\overleftrightarrow{AX}$ is tangent to circle O
REASON
Line $\perp$ to radius at its outer end point is tangent to the circle.

1.83 1. **STATEMENT**
line m, point P not on m
REASON
Given

2. **STATEMENT**
$\angle 1 = \angle 2$
REASON
By Construction 2

3. **STATEMENT**
$m \mid\mid n$
REASON
If corresponding $\angle$'s =, then lines $\mid\mid$.

1.84 1. **STATEMENT**
$\overline{AB}$
REASON
Given

2. **STATEMENT**
$AW = WX = XY$
REASON
Same radii

3. **STATEMENT**
$\angle W = \angle X = \angle Y$
REASON
By Construction 2

4. **STATEMENT**
$\overline{DW} \mid\mid \overline{EX} \mid\mid \overline{BY}$
REASON
If corresponding $\angle$'s =, then lines $\mid\mid$.

5. **STATEMENT**
$\dfrac{AD}{AW} = \dfrac{DE}{WX} = \dfrac{EB}{XY}$
REASON
Lines $\mid\mid$ to side of $\triangle$ divide other sides proportionally.

6. **STATEMENT**
$AD = DE = EB$
REASON
Division property of equality

167

SELF TEST 1

1.01

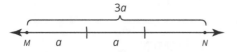

1.02

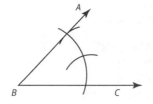

1.03

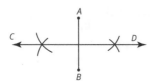

1.04

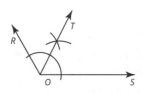

1.05

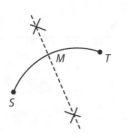

1.06

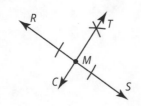

1.07

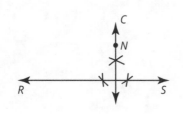

1.08

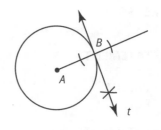

1.09

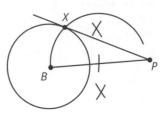

1.010

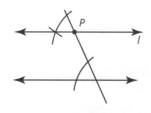

1.011

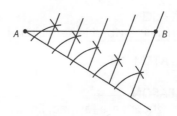

1.012

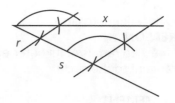

1.013

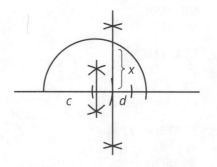

SECTION 2

2.1

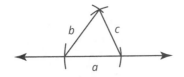

2.2

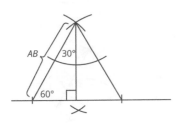

2.3

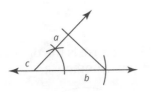

2.4

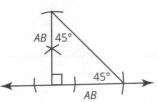

2.5

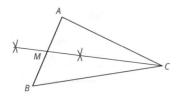

2.6

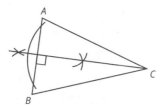

2.7

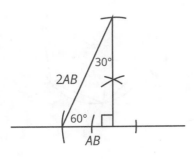

2.8

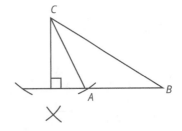

2.9

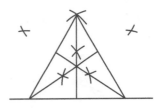

2.10

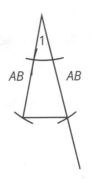

2.11

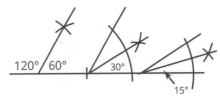

2.12

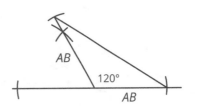

2.13 The altitudes intersect at the right-angle vertex.

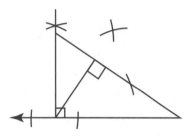

2.14 The altitudes intersect in the interior of the triangle.

2.15 The altitudes intersect in the exterior of the triangle.

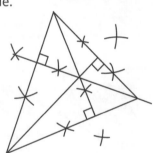

2.16

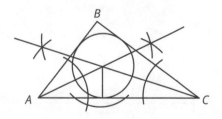

2.17

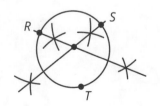

2.18

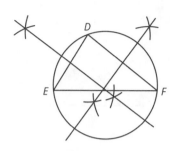

2.19

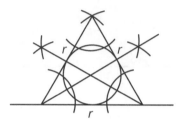

2.20 a. The hypotenuse is the diameter.
b. Bisect the hypotenuse

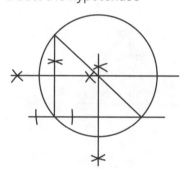

2.21

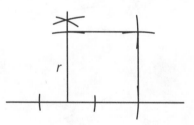

2.22

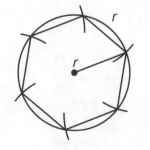

2.23

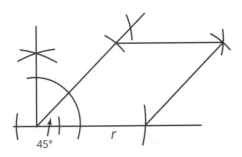

2.24

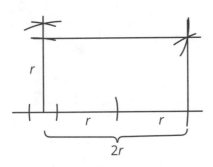

2.25

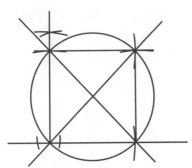

2.26

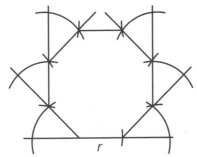

2.27 a. Six equilateral triangles are formed.
b. Join six equilateral triangles.

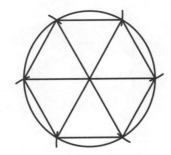

2.28 Two squares are formed.

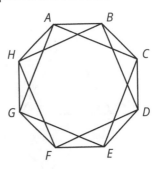

2.29 1. **STATEMENT**
Side = a
REASON
Given

2. **STATEMENT**
$AB = BC = CD = DE = EF = FA = A$
REASON
Same radii

3. **STATEMENT**
$\triangle AOB$, $\triangle BOC$, $\triangle COD$, and so on are equilateral.
REASON
All sides are equal to a.

4. **STATEMENT**
$\angle 1 = \angle 2 = \angle 3 \ldots = \angle 12$
REASON
All $\angle$'s of equilateral $\triangle$ are =.

5. **STATEMENT**
$\angle 2 + \angle 3 = \angle 4 + \angle 5 = \angle 6 + \angle 7 = \angle 8 + \angle 9 = \angle 10 + \angle 11 = \angle 12 + \angle 1$
REASON
Addition property of equality

6. **STATEMENT**
$\angle A = \angle B = \angle C = \angle D = \angle E = \angle F$
REASON
$\angle$ addition and substitution

7. **STATEMENT**
Polygon $ABCDEF$ is a regular hexagon.
REASON
Definition of regular hexagon

SELF TEST 2

2.01

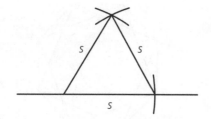

2.02

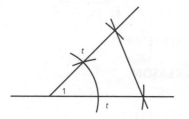

2.03

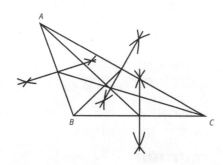

2.04

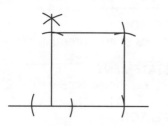

2.05

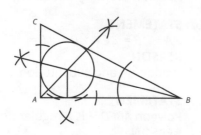

2.06

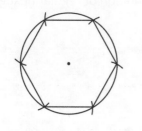

2.07

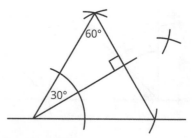

2.08 $\overline{CE}$ is altitude to $\overline{DE}$
$\overline{DE}$ is altitude to $\overline{CE}$

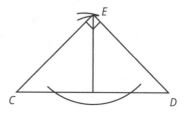

2.09

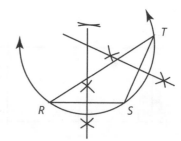

2.010

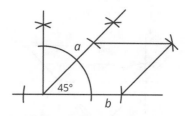

2.011

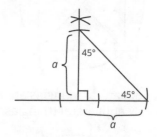

2.012

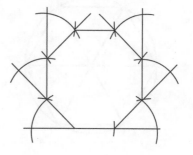

SECTION 3

3.1 A circle with center at *P* and radius of 2".

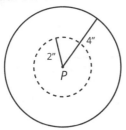

3.6 A circle concentric with the given circles with radius of 6".

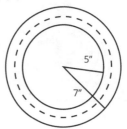

3.2 A pair of parallel lines 12" apart, one on each side of *t*.

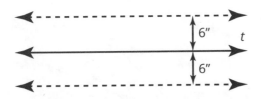

3.7 Two perpendicular lines that bisect the vertical angles formed.

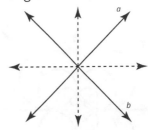

3.3 A line parallel to the given lines and midway between them.

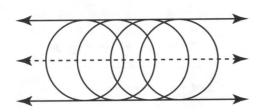

3.8 A circle with radius of 2" and center at *P*.

3.4 A ray that is the bisector of the given angle.

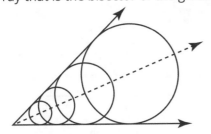

3.9 A ray that is the bisector of the angle.

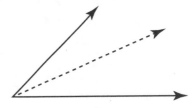

3.5 A cylinder with radius of 3".

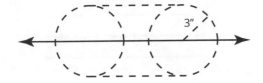

3.10 Two parallel planes 6" apart, both parallel to *R*.

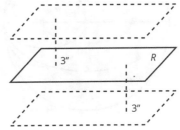

3.11 A line that is the perpendicular bisector of $\overline{RS}$.

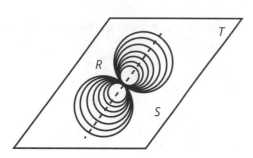

3.12 Two perpendicular lines that are the bisectors of the vertical angles formed.

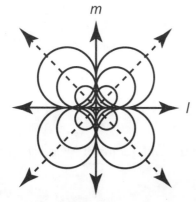

3.13 Two concentric circles with radii 7" and 3".

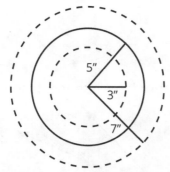

3.14 A sphere concentric with the larger sphere and having a radius of 4.

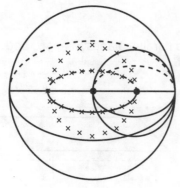

3.15

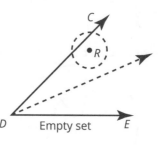

Empty set

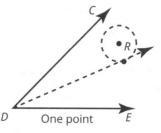

One point

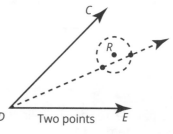

Two points

3.16

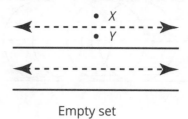

Empty set

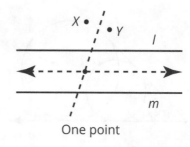

One point

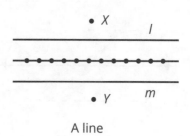

A line

3.17

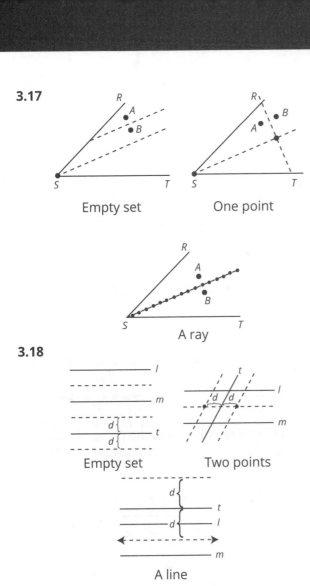

Empty set   One point

A ray

3.18

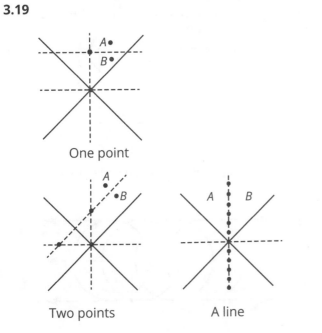

Empty set   Two points

A line

3.19

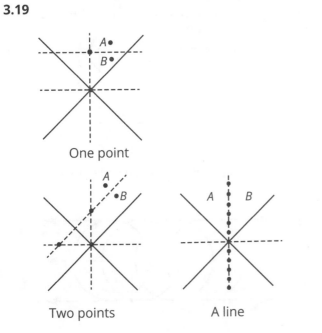

One point

Two points   A line

3.20

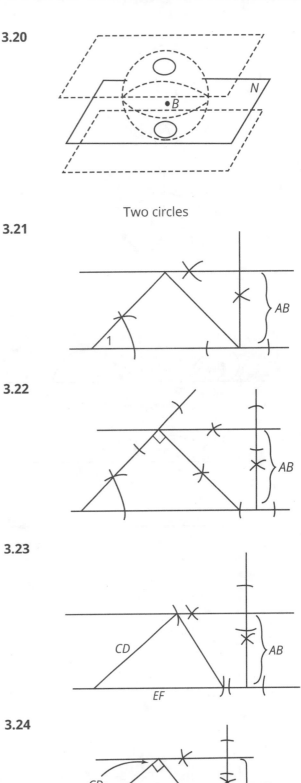

Two circles

3.21

3.22

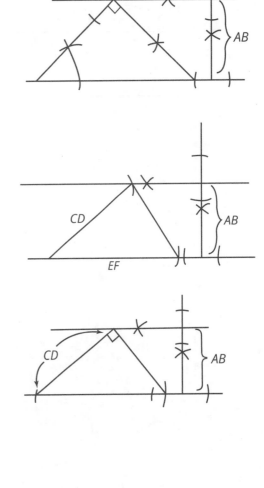

3.23

3.24

3.25

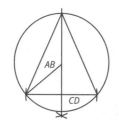

3.26

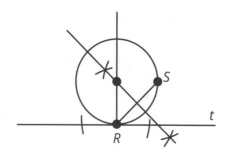

3.27 a.

b.

c.

SELF TEST 3

3.01 A plane parallel to the floor and 1 foot above it.

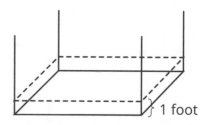

3.02 Two parallel lines 12" apart, both parallel to *t*.

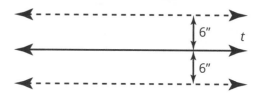

3.03 A line perpendicular to the plane of the square, passing through the intersection of the diagonals.

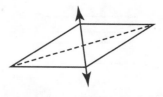

3.04 A plane parallel to and midway between the two given planes.

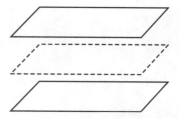

3.05 A line parallel to and midway between the given lines.

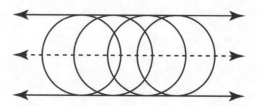

3.06   Empty set, One point, One line
3.07   Empty set, One point, One line
3.08   Empty set, One point, Two points
3.09   Empty set, One point, A circle
3.010 Empty set, One point, Two points, Three points, Four points
3.011 Empty set, One point, A circle

3.012

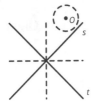

Empty set

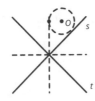

One point

Two points

Three points

Four points

3.013

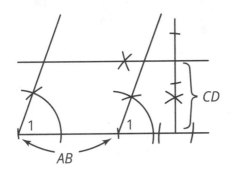

3.014

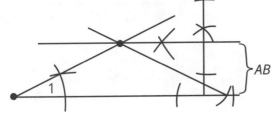

3.015

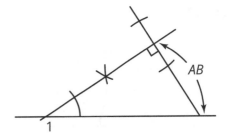

LIFEPAC TEST

1.

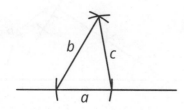

2.

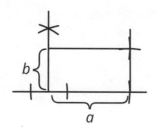

3.

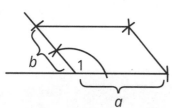

4.

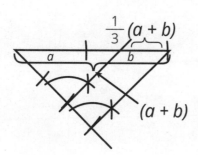

5.

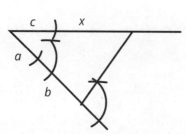

6.

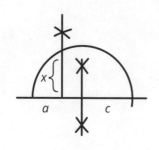

7.

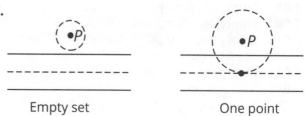

Empty set   One point

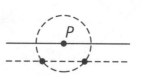

Two poiints

8.

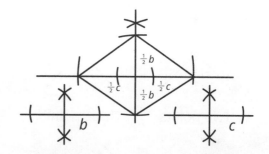

9. A part of a plane 4 ft. by 8 ft. and 3 inches above the table

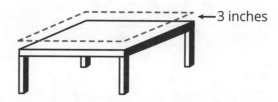

←—3 inches

10.

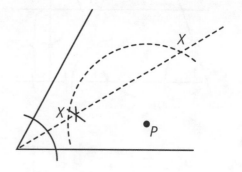

ALTERNATE LIFEPAC TEST

1.

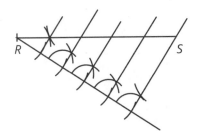

2.

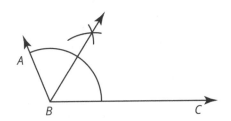

3.

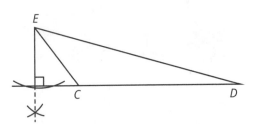

4.

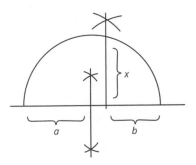

5.

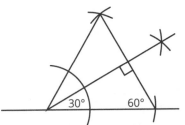

6.

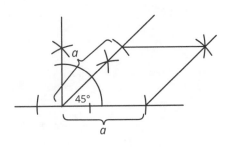

7.

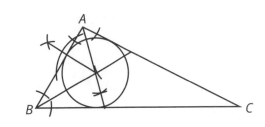

8.

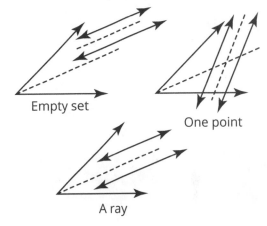

Empty set

One point

A ray

9.

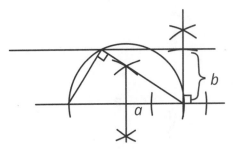

10.

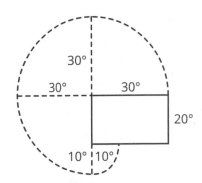

The locus is the interior of three-quarters of a circle with a 30-foot radius, plus one-quarter of a circle with a 10-foot radius.

MATH 1007

ALTERNATE LIFEPAC TEST

NAME _____

DATE _____

SCORE _____

Complete the following items. Use only straightedge and compass for constructions and leave all construction arcs on your paper (each numbered item, 5 points).

1. Divide *RS* into five equal parts.

2. Bisect ∠*ABC*.

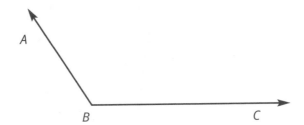

3. Construct the altitude to *CD*.

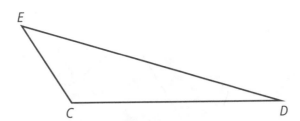

4. Construct x so that $x = \sqrt{ab}$

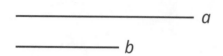

5. Construct a 30°-60°-90° triangle.

6. Construct a rhombus with a 45° angle and a side equal to a.

7. Inscribe a circle in triangle *ABC*.

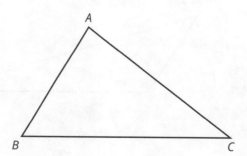

8. What is the locus of points in a plane equidistant from the side's of an angle and equidistant from two parallel lines? Show all solutions.

9. Construct a right triangle with hypotenuse equal to *a* and altitude to the hypotenuse equal to *b*.

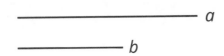

10. A barn has dimensions of 20 by 30 feet. A cow is tied to an outside corner of the barn by a rope 30 feet long. What is the locus of points where the cow may graze? Make a sketch and describe.

MATH 1008

Unit 8: Area and Volume

TEACHER NOTES

MATERIALS NEEDED FOR LIFEPAC	
Required	Suggested
• protractors, compasses and straightedges	(None)

ADDITIONAL LEARNING ACTIVITIES

Section 1: Polygons

1. Discuss these questions with your class.

    a. How do the areas of an equilateral triangle, a square, a regular pentagon, a regular hexagon, and a regular octagon compare if each one has the same length side? Use a convenient length such as 6 inches to find the answer.

    b. If you double the length of the side of an equilateral triangle, how does the area of the smaller triangle compare with the area of the larger triangle?

    c. If you double the length of the side of a square, how does the area of the smaller square compare with the area of the larger square?

    d. What do you notice about the area comparisons in the preceding questions (b) and (c)?

2. People who get lost in a desert invariably do so because instead of walking in a straight line they walk in a large circle and eventually come back to their starting point without realizing it. The reason a person walks in a large circle without realizing it is that a person's legs are never exactly the same length, and so the steps he takes with his left foot and right foot are slightly different. An exaggerated diagram is shown following this activity.

    The radius of the circle in which a person walks is a function of the difference between the lengths of his steps and approximates $r = \dfrac{24}{d}$, where r is the radius of the circle in feet and d is the difference between the lengths of steps in inches. Suppose the steps a person takes with his left foot are $\dfrac{1}{16}''$ longer than the steps he takes with his right foot. Have the class compute the radius of the circle the person would walk if he were blindfolded.

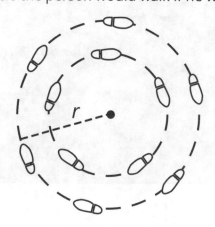

3. Have the class copy the dodecagon shown following this activity. Then have them draw 4 line segments in the dodecagon as shown. Note that the dodecagon is now divided into six parts. Point out to the class that the resulting figure has line symmetry and that one of the six parts seems to be an equilateral triangle. Have the class cut the six pieces apart with scissors and try to rearrange them to form a square (it can be done!).

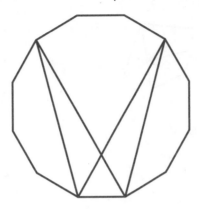

Section 2: Circles

1. Ask a biology teacher at your school to explain to the class how biologists use π to compute bacterial growth.

2. Invite an actuary (a person who estimates risks, rates, premiums, and other factors for insurance companies) to come and explain to the class how π is used to compute probabilities.

3. Let one student at a time work on this activity. Write the division problem $7\overline{)22.00}$ at the top of a long sheet of paper. The fraction $\frac{22}{7}$ is an approximation for π. Let each student take turns dividing the problem. Emphasize that each student should be as accurate as possible and should check his work carefully since the work of each student depends on the previous work. Each student may want to check the problem before he continues working on it to be sure the answers are correct.

4. Research the history of pi; use concordances, encyclopedias, books, online resources, and magazine articles.

Section 3: Solids

1. Compare the lateral area of a cube with side equal to 1 to the lateral area of a square-based pyramid with sides of base equal to 1 and slant height equal to 1. Then compare the total area of the same cube (side equal to 1) to the lateral area of the same square-based pyramid (sides of base equal to 1 and slant height equal to 1).

2. Ask the class if, based on their comparisons of the lateral areas and total areas of the cube and square-based pyramid, they think the volume of the cube compared to the volume of the pyramid will have the same ratio as the previous comparisons. Then have the class find the volume of the cube (side equal to 1) and the volume of the pyramid (sides of base equal to 1 and slant height equal to 1). Ask the class why the ratio of the volume of the cube to the volume of the pyramid is not the same ratio as the ratio of the lateral areas and the ratio of the total area.

Administer the LIFEPAC Test.

ANSWER KEYS

SECTION 1

1.1 Examples:

1.2 a. $3 + 5 + 8 + 2 = 18$
     b. $3 + 3 + 3 + 3 + 3 + 3 = 18$
     c. $2 + 2 + 2 + 2 + 2 + 2 + 2 + 2 = 16$
     d. $2 + 5 + 3 + 7 + 9 + 6 = 32$

1.3 20 square inches

1.4 c., e., and f.

1.5 no

1.6 yes

1.7 They are =. Two $\cong \triangle$'s are formed.
     P18 says their areas are =.

1.8 yes

1.9 yes

1.10 no

1.11 $12(8) = 96$ sq. in.

1.12 $7^2 = 49$ sq. ft.

1.13 a. $\frac{1}{2}(2) = 1$ sq. ft.
      b. $6(24) = 144$ sq. in.

1.14 $16 \div 8 = 2$ cm

1.15 $\sqrt{25} = 5$ ft.

1.16 $12(12) = 144$ sq. in.

1.17 $A = bh$

$$8\frac{3}{4} = 3\frac{1}{2}h$$

$$8\frac{3}{4} \div 3\frac{1}{2} = h$$

$$\frac{35}{4}\left(\frac{2}{7}\right) = h$$

$$\frac{5}{2} = h$$

$$h = 2\frac{1}{2} \text{ ft.}$$

1.18 $A = 15(20) = 300$ sq. ft.
$$\frac{300}{9} = 33\frac{1}{3} \text{ sq. yds.}$$

1.19 $2(36)(15) = 1,080$ sq. ft.
     $1,080 \div 100 = 10.8$ shingling squares
     $10.8(70) = \$756$

1.20 $6(300) = 1,800$ sq. ft.
     $1,800 \div 400 = 4.5$ gallons

1.21 a. $18(4) = 72$ sq. cm
     b. $18(2) + 18(2) = 36 + 36 = 72$ sq. cm
     c. $4(2) + 4(2) = 8 + 8 = 16$ sq. cm

1.22

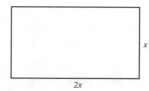

$$2(26)(3) = \qquad 156$$
$$2(30)(3) = \qquad \underline{+\ 180}$$
$$\qquad\qquad 336 \text{ sq. ft. or}$$

$$26(36) = \qquad 936$$
$$20(30) = \qquad \underline{-\ 600}$$
$$\qquad\qquad 336 \text{ sq. ft.}$$

1.23

$$2x(x) = 50$$
$$2x^2 = 50$$
$$x^2 = 25$$
$$\sqrt{x^2} = \sqrt{25}$$
$$x = 5 \text{ yds.}$$
$$2x = 2(5) = 10 \text{ yds.}$$

1.24 $(2)(2)(3) = 12$ sq. ft.
$$12 \div 9 = 1\frac{1}{3} \text{ sq. yds.}$$

1.25 $20(10) = \qquad 200$
     $30(40) = \qquad 1,200$
     $15(20) = \quad \underline{+\quad 300}$
     $\qquad\qquad\quad 1,700$ sq. ft.
     $150(100) = 15,000$ sq. ft.

     $15,000$
     $\underline{-\ 1,700}$
     $13,300$ sq. ft. of grass

1.26 $3\frac{1}{2}\left(\frac{3}{4}\right) = \frac{7}{2}\left(\frac{3}{4}\right) = \frac{21}{8} = 2\frac{5}{8}$ sq. ft.

1.27 $8(4) = 32$ sq. in.

1.28 $1\frac{1}{2}\left(\frac{1}{2}\right) = \frac{3}{2}\left(\frac{1}{2}\right) = \frac{3}{4}$ sq. ft.

1.29 x yards = $3x$ feet
$3x(y) = 3xy$ sq. ft.

For Problems 1.30 through 1.33 refer to the following figure where $\overline{AD}$ is the hypotenuse of $\triangle ADX$.

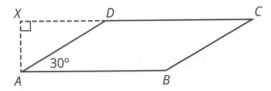

1.30 $A = bh$
$h = AX$
$AX = \frac{1}{2}(AD)$
$= \frac{1}{2}(6)$
$= 3$ in.
$A = 10(3) = 30$ sq. in.

1.31 $6(3\sqrt{3}) = 18\sqrt{3}$ sq. ft.

1.32 $A = bh$
$h = AX$
$AX = \frac{1}{2}(AD)$
$= \frac{1}{2}(4\sqrt{3})$
$= 2\sqrt{3}$ in.
$A = 8(2\sqrt{3}) = 16\sqrt{3}$ sq. in.

1.33 $4\sqrt{2}(3) = 12\sqrt{2}$ sq. ft.

1.34

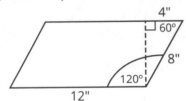

$12(4\sqrt{3}) = 48\sqrt{3}$ sq. in.

1.35

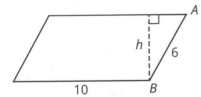

$A = bh$
$30\sqrt{2} = 10h$
$3\sqrt{2} = h$

$\therefore \angle A = 45°$
$\angle B = 180° - 45° = 135°$

1.36   a. $A = bh$
$A = \frac{b}{3}(3h)$
divided by 3

b. $A = bh$
$A = (2b)\frac{h}{2}$
multiply by 2

1.37   The diagonals of a rhombus divide it into 4 congruent right triangles. The base of one triangle equals $\frac{1}{2}d_1$ of the rhombus and its height equals $\frac{1}{2}d_2$. Therefore, the area of one of the triangles equals $\frac{1}{2}(\frac{1}{2}d_1)(\frac{1}{2}d_2)$.

The area of the rhombus = $4(\frac{1}{2})(\frac{1}{2}d_1)(\frac{1}{2}d_2)$
$= \frac{4}{8}d_1d_2$
$= \frac{1}{2}d_1d_2$

1.38 $A = \frac{1}{2}bh$
$A = \frac{1}{2}(4)(6)$
$= 12$ sq. in.

1.39 $A = \frac{1}{2}bh$
$10 = \frac{1}{2}(b)(5)$
$20 = 5b$
$\frac{20}{5} = b$
4 in. $= b$

1.40 $A = \frac{1}{2}bh$
$12 = \frac{1}{2}(5)h$
$24 = 5h$
$\frac{24}{5}$ ft. $= h$

1.41 $A = \frac{1}{2}bh$
$= \frac{1}{2}(2\sqrt{3})(3\sqrt{3})$
$= \frac{1}{2}(18)$
$= 9$ sq. in.

1.42 $A = \frac{1}{2}bh$

$= \frac{1}{2}(6)(4)$

$= 12$ sq. in.

1.43 $c^2 = a^2 + b^2$

$13^2 = 5^2 + b^2$

$169 = 25 + b^2$

$144 = b^2$

$\sqrt{144} = \sqrt{b^2}$

$12 = b$

$A = \frac{1}{2}bh$

$= \frac{1}{2}(12)(5)$

$= 30$ sq. ft.

1.44 $c^2 = a^2 + b^2$

$6^2 = a^2 + 2^2$

$36 = a^2 + 4$

$32 = a^2$

$\sqrt{32} = \sqrt{a^2}$

$4\sqrt{2} = a$

$A = \frac{1}{2}bh$

$= \frac{1}{2}(4\sqrt{2})(2)$

$= 4\sqrt{2}$ sq. in.

1.45 $c^2 = a^2 + b^2$

$4^2 = (2\sqrt{3})^2 + b^2$

$16 = 12 + b^2$

$4 = b^2$

$\sqrt{4} = \sqrt{b^2}$

$2 = b$

$A = \frac{1}{2}bh$

$= \frac{1}{2}(2\sqrt{3})(2)$

$= 2\sqrt{3}$ sq. ft.

1.46 $A = \frac{1}{2}bh$

$= \frac{1}{2}(5\sqrt{2})(4\sqrt{2})$

$= 20$ sq. cm

1.47 a. $p = 3s$

$= 3(6)$

$= 18$ in.

b. $A = \frac{1}{4}s^2\sqrt{3}$

$= \frac{1}{4}(6)^2(\sqrt{3})$

$= \frac{1}{4}(36)(\sqrt{3})$

$= 9\sqrt{3}$ sq. in.

1.48 a. $p = 3s$

$= 3(5)$

$= 15$ in.

b. $A = \frac{1}{4}s^2\sqrt{3}$

$= \frac{1}{4}(5)^2(\sqrt{3})$

$= \frac{1}{4}(25)(\sqrt{3})$

$= \frac{25}{4}\sqrt{3}$ sq. in.

1.49 a. $p = 3s$

$12 = 3s$

4 ft. $= s$

b. $A = \frac{1}{4}s^2\sqrt{3}$

$= \frac{1}{4}(4)^2(\sqrt{3})$

$= \frac{1}{4}(16)(\sqrt{3})$

$= 4\sqrt{3}$ sq. ft.

1.50 a. $A = \frac{1}{4}s^2\sqrt{3}$

$9\sqrt{3} = \frac{1}{4}s^2\sqrt{3}$

$36\sqrt{3} = s^2\sqrt{3}$

$36 = s^2$

$\sqrt{36} = \sqrt{s^2}$

6 ft. $= s$

b. $p = 3s$

$= 3(6)$

$= 18$ ft.

1.51 a. $p = 3s$

$30 = 3s$

10 ft. $= s$

b. $A = \frac{1}{4}s^2\sqrt{3}$

$= \frac{1}{4}(10)^2(\sqrt{3})$

$= \frac{1}{4}(100)(\sqrt{3})$

$= 25\sqrt{3}$ sq. ft.

1.52

$A = \frac{1}{2}d_1d_2$

$= \frac{1}{2}(9)(12)$

$= 54$ sq. ft.

1.53

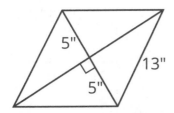

$$13^2 = 5^2 + (\frac{d}{2})^2$$
$$169 = 25 + (\frac{d}{2})^2$$
$$144 = (\frac{d}{2})^2$$
$$\sqrt{144} = \sqrt{(\,)\frac{d}{2}}$$
$$12 = \frac{d}{2}$$
$$24 = d$$
$$A = \frac{1}{2}d_1 d_2$$
$$= \frac{1}{2}(10)(24)$$
$$= 120 \text{ sq. in.}$$

1.54

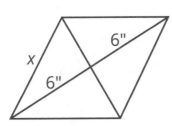

$$x^2 = 6^2 + (\frac{x}{2})^2$$
$$x^2 = 36 + \frac{x^2}{4}$$
$$\frac{3x^2}{4} = 36$$
$$x^2 = 36(\frac{4}{3})$$
$$x^2 = 48$$
$$\sqrt{x^2} = \sqrt{48}$$
$$x = 4\sqrt{3}$$
$$A = \frac{1}{2}d_1 d_2$$
$$= \frac{1}{2}(12)(4\sqrt{3})$$
$$= 24\sqrt{3} \text{ sq. in.}$$

1.55
$$A = \frac{1}{2}h(b_1 + b_2)$$
$$= \frac{1}{2}(4)(10 + 6)$$
$$= 2(16)$$
$$= 32$$

1.56
$$A = \frac{1}{2}h(b_1 + b_2)$$
$$18 = \frac{1}{2}(2)(6 + b_2)$$
$$18 = 6 + b_2$$
$$12 = b_2$$

1.57
$$A = \frac{1}{2}h(b_1 + b_2)$$
$$12 = \frac{1}{2}(3)(b_1 + 5)$$
$$24 = 3(b_1 + 5)$$
$$24 = 3b_1 + 15$$
$$9 = 3b_1$$
$$\frac{9}{3} = b_1$$
$$3 = b_1$$

1.58
$$A = \frac{1}{2}h(b_1 + b_2)$$
$$24 = \frac{1}{2}(h)(5 + 3)$$
$$24 = \frac{1}{2}(h)(8)$$
$$48 = 8h$$
$$6 = h$$

1.59
$$A = \frac{1}{2}h(b_1 + b_2)$$
$$= \frac{1}{2}(1)(\frac{1}{2} + \frac{1}{4})$$
$$= \frac{1}{2}(\frac{3}{4})$$
$$= \frac{3}{8}$$

1.60
$$A = \frac{1}{2}h(b_1 + b_2)$$
$$4\sqrt{6} = \frac{1}{2}(h)(5\sqrt{2} + 3\sqrt{2})$$
$$4\sqrt{6} = \frac{1}{2}(h)(8\sqrt{2})$$
$$4\sqrt{6} = 4\sqrt{2}h$$
$$\frac{4\sqrt{6}}{4\sqrt{2}} = h$$
$$\sqrt{3} = h$$

1.61

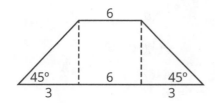

$$A = \frac{1}{2}h(b_1 + b_2)$$

$$= \frac{1}{2}(h)(12 + 6)$$

$$= \frac{1}{2}(3)(18)$$

$$= 27$$

1.62

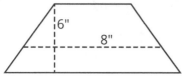

$$A = \frac{1}{2}h(b_1 + b_2)$$

$$m = \frac{1}{2}(b_1 + b_2)$$

$$A = hm$$

$$= (6)(8)$$

$$= 48 \text{ sq. in.}$$

1.63

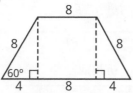

$$A = \frac{1}{2}h(b_1 + b_2)$$

$$= \frac{1}{2}(4\sqrt{3})(16 + 8)$$

$$= \frac{1}{2}(4\sqrt{3})(24)$$

$$= 48\sqrt{3}$$

1.64

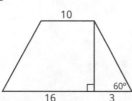

$$A = \frac{1}{2}h(b_1 + b_2)$$

$$= \frac{1}{2}(3\sqrt{3})[(16 + 3) + 10]$$

$$= \frac{1}{2}(3\sqrt{3})(29)$$

$$= \frac{87\sqrt{3}}{2}$$

1.65

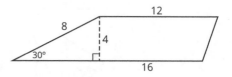

$$A = \frac{1}{2}h(b_1 + b_2)$$

$$= \frac{1}{2}(4)(16 + 12)$$

$$= \frac{1}{2}(4)(28)$$

$$= 56$$

1.66

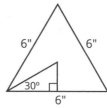

$$A = \frac{1}{2}ap$$

$$= \frac{1}{2}(\sqrt{3})(18)$$

$$= 9\sqrt{3} \text{ sq. in.}$$

1.67

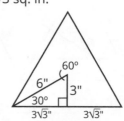

$$A = \frac{1}{2}ap$$

$$= \frac{1}{2}(3)(18\sqrt{3})$$

$$= 27\sqrt{3} \text{ sq. in.}$$

1.68

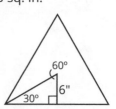

$$A = \frac{1}{2}ap$$

$$= \frac{1}{2}(6)(36\sqrt{3})$$

$$= 108\sqrt{3} \text{ sq. in.}$$

1.69

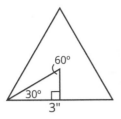

$A = \frac{1}{2}ap$

$\quad = \frac{1}{2}(\frac{1}{2}\sqrt{3})(9)$

$\quad = \frac{9}{4}\sqrt{3}$ sq. in.

1.70

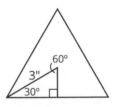

$A = \frac{1}{2}ap$

$\quad = \frac{1}{2}(\frac{3}{2})9\sqrt{3}$

$\quad = \frac{27}{4}\sqrt{3}$ sq. in.

1.71

$A = \frac{1}{2}ap$

$\quad = \frac{1}{2}(2\sqrt{3})(24)$

$\quad = 24\sqrt{3}$ sq. in.

1.72

$p = 48"$
$s = 8"$

$A = \frac{1}{2}ap$

$\quad = \frac{1}{2}(4\sqrt{3})(48)$

$\quad = 96\sqrt{3}$ sq. in.

1.73

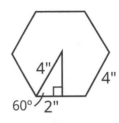

$A = \frac{1}{2}ap$

$\quad = \frac{1}{2}(2\sqrt{3})(24)$

$\quad = 24\sqrt{3}$

1.74

$A = \frac{1}{2}ap$

$\quad = \frac{1}{2}(3\sqrt{3})(36)$

$\quad = 54\sqrt{3}$ sq. in.

1.75 $p = 8(10) = 80$

$A = \frac{1}{2}ap$

$\quad = \frac{1}{2}(K)(80)$

$\quad = 40K$

1.76

$p = 36$
$s = 12$

$A = \frac{1}{4}s^2\sqrt{3}$

$\quad = \frac{1}{4}(12)^2(\sqrt{3})$

$\quad = \frac{1}{4}(144)(\sqrt{3})$

$\quad = 36\sqrt{3}$

$A = 36\sqrt{3}$

A hexagon is 6 equilateral triangles.

$$A = 6(\frac{1}{4}s^2\sqrt{3})$$

$$36\sqrt{3} = \frac{3s^2\sqrt{3}}{2}$$

$$72\sqrt{3} = 3s^2\sqrt{3}$$

$$24 = s^2$$

$$\sqrt{24} = \sqrt{s^2}$$

$$2\sqrt{6} \text{ in.} = s$$

1.77

$$\frac{A}{A'} = (\frac{s}{s'})^2$$

$$\frac{50}{100} = (\frac{s}{s'})^2$$

$$\frac{1}{2} = (\frac{s}{s'})^2$$

$$\sqrt{\frac{1}{2}} = \sqrt{(\frac{s}{s'})^2}$$

$$\sqrt{\frac{1}{2}} = \frac{s}{s'}$$

$$\frac{s}{s'} = \frac{\sqrt{2}}{2}$$

1.78

$$\frac{A}{A'} = (\frac{s}{s'})^2$$

$$\frac{90}{A'} = (\frac{15}{9})^2$$

$$\frac{90}{A'} = (\frac{5}{3})^2$$

$$\frac{90}{A'} = \frac{25}{9}$$

$$25A' = 810$$

$$A' = 32.4 \text{ sq. in.}$$

1.79

$$\frac{A}{A'} = (\frac{s}{s'})^2$$

$$\frac{196}{A'} = (\frac{4}{8})^2$$

$$\frac{196}{A'} = (\frac{1}{2})^2$$

$$\frac{196}{A'} = \frac{1}{4}$$

$$A' = 784 \text{ sq. in.}$$

1.80

$$\frac{A}{A'} = (\frac{s}{s'})^2$$

$$\frac{1}{9} = (\frac{3}{s'})^2$$

$$\sqrt{\frac{1}{9}} = \sqrt{(\frac{3}{s'})^2}$$

$$\frac{1}{3} = \frac{3}{s'} \qquad s' = 9$$

$$\frac{1}{9} = (\frac{4}{s'})^2$$

$$\sqrt{\frac{1}{9}} = \sqrt{(\frac{4}{s'})^2}$$

$$\frac{1}{3} = \frac{4}{s'} \qquad s' = 12$$

$$\frac{1}{9} = (\frac{5}{s'})^2$$

$$\sqrt{\frac{1}{9}} = \sqrt{(\frac{5}{s'})^2}$$

$$\frac{1}{3} = \frac{5}{s'} \qquad s' = 15$$

$$\frac{1}{9} = (\frac{6}{s'})^2$$

$$\sqrt{\frac{1}{9}} = \sqrt{(\frac{6}{s'})^2}$$

$$\frac{1}{3} = \frac{6}{s'} \qquad s' = 18$$

1.81

$$\frac{A}{A'} = (\frac{s}{s'})^2$$

$$\frac{36}{64} = (\frac{s}{s'})^2$$

$$\sqrt{\frac{36}{64}} = \sqrt{(\frac{s}{s'})^2}$$

$$\frac{6}{8} = \frac{s}{s'}$$

$$\frac{s}{s'} = \frac{3}{4}$$

1.82

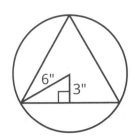

$A_I = \frac{1}{4}(6\sqrt{3})^2(\sqrt{3})$

$\quad = \frac{1}{4}(108)(\sqrt{3})$

$\quad = 27\sqrt{3}$ sq. in.

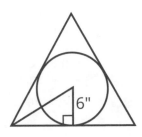

$A_C = \frac{1}{4}(12\sqrt{3})^2(\sqrt{3})$

$\quad = \frac{1}{4}(432)(\sqrt{3})$

$\quad = 108\sqrt{3}$ sq. in.

$\frac{A_I}{A_C} = \frac{27\sqrt{3}}{108\sqrt{3}} = \frac{1}{4}$ or 1:4.

1.83 $\frac{A}{A'} = (\frac{s}{s'})^2$

$\quad = (\frac{2}{4})^2 = \frac{4}{16} = \frac{1}{4}$ or 1:4.

1.84 $\frac{A}{A'} = (\frac{s}{s'})^2$

$\quad = (\frac{2}{3})^2 = \frac{4}{9}$ or 4:9.

1.85 $\frac{A}{A'} = (\frac{s}{s'})^2$

$\quad = (\frac{3}{5})^2 = \frac{9}{25}$ or 9:25.

SELF TEST 1

1.01 e
1.02 e
1.03 b
1.04 g or e or c
1.05 f or e
1.06 c
1.07 a
1.08 d or a
1.09 $A = \frac{1}{2}ap$

$\quad A = \frac{1}{2}(k)(15)$

$\quad A = \frac{15}{2}k$

1.010

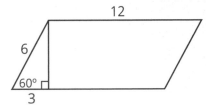

$A = \frac{1}{2}ap$

$A = \frac{1}{2}(4\sqrt{3})(48)$

$A = 96\sqrt{3}$ sq. in.

1.011 $A = \frac{1}{2}bh$

$\quad A = \frac{1}{2}(10)(16)$

$\quad A = 80$ sq. in.

1.012

$A = bh$
$A = 12(3\sqrt{3})$
$A = 36\sqrt{3}$

1.013 $A = \frac{1}{2}h(b_1 + b_2)$

$\quad A = \frac{1}{2}(10)(8 + 16)$

$\quad A = \frac{1}{2}(10)(24)$

$\quad A = 120$

1.014 $A = \frac{1}{4}s^2\sqrt{3}$

$A = \frac{1}{4}(6)^2(\sqrt{3})$

$A = \frac{1}{4}(36)(\sqrt{3})$

$A = 9\sqrt{3}$ sq. in.

1.015 $\frac{A}{A'} = (\frac{8}{10})^2 = (\frac{4}{5})^2 = \frac{16}{25}$ or 16:25

1.016

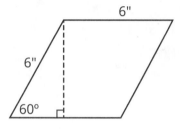

$A = bh$
$A = 6(3\sqrt{3})$
$A = 18\sqrt{3}$ sq. in.

1.017

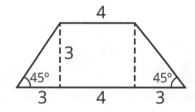

$A = \frac{1}{2}h(b_1 + b_2)$

$A = \frac{1}{2}(3)(10 + 4)$

$A = \frac{1}{2}(3)(14)$

$A = 21$

1.018 $A = bh$
$A = 3.5(1.7)$
$A = 5.95$ cm^2

1.019 $A = \frac{1}{2}bh$

$A = \frac{1}{2}(16)(8)$
$A = 64$ sq. in.

1.020 $A = s^2$
$A = (3.2)^2$
$A = 10.24$ sq. in.

1.021 $A = bh$
$A = 10(6)$
$A = 60$

1.022

A_{walls}	$= bh$
A	$= (24 + 20 + 24 + 20)(10)$
A	$= (88)(10)$
A	$= 880$ sq. ft.
$A_{\triangle's}$	$= 2(\frac{1}{2}bh)$
A	$= 2[\frac{1}{2}(20)(5)]$
A	$= 100$ sq. ft.

Total area = 880 + 100 = 980 sq. ft.

Two costs = 980
$\times$ 2
1,960 sq. ft. to cover

1,960 ÷ 350 = 5.6 gal. ≐ 6 gal.

SECTION 2

2.1 $C = 2\pi r$
   $= 2\pi(5)$
   $= 10\pi$ in.

2.2 $C = 2\pi r$
   $= 2\pi(7)$
   $= 14\pi$ ft.

2.3 $C = 2\pi r$
   $= 2\pi(3\frac{1}{2})$
   $= 7\pi$ cm

2.4 $C = 2\pi r$
   $= 2\pi(3\frac{1}{4})$
   $= \frac{13}{2}\pi$ in.

2.5 $C = 2\pi r$
   $= 2\pi(\frac{x}{2})$
   $= \pi x$ mi.

2.6 $C = 2\pi r$
   $= 2\pi(36)$
   $= 72\pi$ in.

2.7 $C = 2\pi r$
   $= 2(3.14)(4)$
   $= 25.12 \doteq 25$ in.

2.8 $C = 2\pi r$
   $= 2(3.14)(6)$
   $= 37.68 \doteq 38$ ft.

2.9 $C = 2\pi r$
   $= 2(3.14)(5.1)$
   $= 32.028 \doteq 32.0$ cm

2.10 $C = 2\pi r$
   $= 2(3.14)(4.6)$
   $= 28.888 \doteq 28.9$ in.

2.11 $C = 2\pi r$
   $= 2(3.14)(3.21)$
   $= 20.1588 \doteq 20.16$ ft.

2.12 $C = 2\pi r$
   $= 2(3.14)(6.53)$
   $= 41.0084 \doteq 41.01$ cm

2.13 $C = 2\pi r$
   $12\pi = 2\pi r$
   $\frac{12\pi}{2\pi} = r$
   6 in. $= r$

2.14 $C = 2\pi r$
   $15\pi = 2\pi r$
   $\frac{15\pi}{2\pi} = r$
   $\frac{15}{2}$ ft. $= r$

2.15 $C = 2\pi r$
   $6\sqrt{2}\pi = 2\pi r$
   $\frac{6\sqrt{2}\pi}{2\pi} = r$
   $3\sqrt{2}$ in. $= r$

2.16 $C = 2\pi r$
   $5\sqrt{3}\pi = 2\pi r$
   $\frac{5\sqrt{3}\pi}{2\pi} = r$
   $\frac{5}{2}\sqrt{3}$ cm $= r$

2.17 $C = 2\pi r$
   $8t\pi = 2\pi r$
   $\frac{8t\pi}{2\pi} = r$
   $4t$ ft. $= r$

2.18 $C = 2\pi r$
   $\pi = 2\pi r$
   $\frac{\pi}{2\pi} = r$
   $\frac{1}{2}$ yd. $= r$

2.19

   $C = 2\pi r$
   $= 2\pi(10)$
   $= 20\pi$
   $20\pi(10) = 200\pi$ inches

2.20 $66 \div 6 = 11$ ft. per revolution
   $C = 2\pi r$
   $11 = 2(\frac{22}{7})r$
   $77 = 2(22)r$
   $77 = 44r$
   $\frac{77}{44} = r$
   $\frac{7}{4}$ ft. $= r$

2.21
$$C_c = 2\pi r$$
$$= 2\pi(\frac{1}{2})(\sqrt{2})$$
$$= \sqrt{2}\pi$$

$$C_I = 2\pi r$$
$$= 2\pi(\frac{1}{2})$$
$$= \pi$$

$$\frac{C_c}{C_I} = \frac{\sqrt{2}\pi}{\pi}$$
$$= \frac{\sqrt{2}}{1} \text{ or } \sqrt{2}:1$$

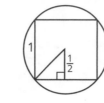

2.22

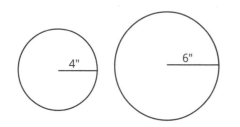

$$C_1 = 2\pi r$$
$$C_1 = 2\pi(4)$$
$$C_1 = 8\pi$$

$$C_2 = 2\pi r$$
$$C_2 = 2\pi(6)$$
$$C_2 = 12\pi$$

$$C_3 = C_1 + C_2 = 20\pi$$
$$C_3 = 2\pi r$$
$$20\pi = 2\pi r$$
$$10 \text{ in.} = r$$

2.23
$$C_1 = 2\pi r$$
$$= 2\pi(5)$$
$$= 10\pi \text{ in.}$$

$$C_2 = 2\pi r$$
$$= 2\pi(\frac{11}{2})$$
$$= 11\pi \text{ in.}$$

$$C_2 - C_1 = 11\pi - 10\pi$$
$$= \pi$$
$$= 3.14 \text{ in.}$$

2.24
$$C_1 = 2\pi r$$
$$= 2\pi(40)$$
$$= 2(3.14)(40)$$
$$= 80(3.14)$$
$$= 251.2 \text{ ft.}$$
$$\frac{\times \quad 10}{= 2,512 \text{ ft.}}$$

2.24 cont'd
$$C_2 = 2\pi r$$
$$= 2\pi(41)$$
$$= 2(3.14)(41)$$
$$= 82(3.14)$$
$$= 257.48 \text{ ft.}$$
$$\frac{\times \quad 10}{= 2,574.8 \text{ ft.}}$$
$$\frac{- 2,512 \quad \text{ft.}}{= \quad 62.8 \text{ ft. farther}}$$

2.25
$$A = \pi r^2$$
$$= 3.14(6)^2$$
$$= 3.14(36)$$
$$= 113.04$$

2.26
$$A = \pi r^2$$
$$= 3.14(4)^2$$
$$= 3.14(16)$$
$$= 50.24$$

2.27
$$A = \pi r^2$$
$$= 3.14(2)^2$$
$$= 3.14(4)$$
$$= 12.56$$

2.28
$$A = \pi r^2$$
$$= 3.14(5)^2$$
$$= 3.14(25)$$
$$= 78.5$$

2.29
$$A = \pi r^2$$
$$= 3.14(6)^2$$
$$= 3.14(36)$$
$$= 113.04$$

2.30
$$A = \pi r^2$$
$$= 3.14(6.5)^2$$
$$= 3.14(42.25)$$
$$= 132.665$$

2.31
$$C = 2\pi r$$
$$8\pi = 2\pi r$$
$$4 = r$$
$$A = \pi r^2$$
$$= \pi(4)^2$$
$$= 16\pi$$

2.32
$$C = 2\pi r$$
$$3\pi = 2\pi r$$
$$\frac{3\pi}{2\pi} = r$$
$$\frac{3}{2} = r$$
$$A = \pi r^2$$
$$= \pi(\frac{3}{2})^2$$
$$= \frac{9}{4}\pi$$

2.33 $C = 2\pi r$
$4\sqrt{3}\pi = 2\pi r$
$\dfrac{4\sqrt{3}\pi}{2\pi} = r$
$2\sqrt{3} = r$

$A = \pi r^2$
$= \pi(2\sqrt{3})^2$
$= 12\pi$

2.34 $A = \pi r^2$
$36\pi = \pi r^2$
$36 = r^2$
$\sqrt{36} = \sqrt{r^2}$
$r = 6$

$C = 2\pi r$
$= 2\pi(6)$
$= 12\pi$

2.35

$A = \pi r^2$
$= \pi(6\sqrt{3})^2$
$= 108\pi$

2.36

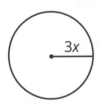

$A = \pi r^2$
$27\pi = \pi(3x)^2$
$27\pi = 9x^2\pi$
$\dfrac{27\pi}{9\pi} = x^2$
$3 = x^2$
$\sqrt{3} = x$

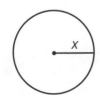

$x = \sqrt{3}$
$A = \pi r^2$
$= \pi(\sqrt{3})^2$
$= 3\pi$

2.37

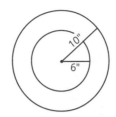

$A_L = \pi r^2$
$= \pi(10)^2$
$= 100\pi$
$A_S = \pi r^2$
$= \pi(6)^2$
$= 36\pi$
$A_L - A_S = 100\pi - 36\pi$
$= 64\pi$

2.38

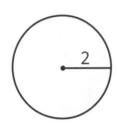

$A = \pi r^2$
$= \pi(2)^2$
$= 4\pi$

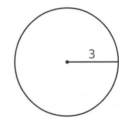

$A = \pi r^2$
$= \pi(3)^2$
$= 9\pi$

$A = 4\pi + 9\pi = 13\pi$
$A = \pi r^2$
$13\pi = \pi r^2$
$\dfrac{13\pi}{\pi} = r^2$
$13 = r^2$
$\sqrt{13} = \sqrt{r^2}$
$\sqrt{13} = r$

2.39

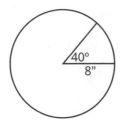

length of arc = $\frac{40°}{360°}(2\pi)(8)$

$= \frac{1}{9}(16\pi)$

$= \frac{16}{9}\pi$ in.

2.40

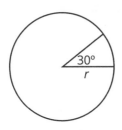

length of arc = $\frac{m}{360°}(2\pi r)$

$2\pi = \frac{30°}{360°}(2\pi r)$

$2\pi = \frac{1}{12}(2\pi r)$

$2\pi = \frac{1}{6}\pi r$

$\frac{2\pi(6)}{\pi} = r$

12 in. $= r$

2.41

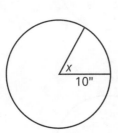

length of arc = $\frac{m}{360°}(2\pi r)$

$4\pi = \frac{x}{360°}(2\pi)(10)$

$4\pi = \frac{x}{360°}(20\pi)$

$4\pi = \frac{\pi}{18}x$

$4\pi(\frac{18}{\pi}) = x$

$x = 72°$

2.42

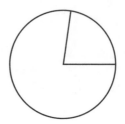

length of arc = $\frac{m}{360°}(2\pi r)$

length of arc = $\frac{80°}{360°}(2\pi)(26)$

$= \frac{2}{9}(52\pi)$

$= \frac{104}{9}\pi$ in.

2.43

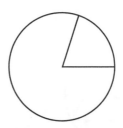

length of arc = $\frac{m}{360°}(2\pi r)$

$12\pi = \frac{x}{360°}(2\pi)(10)$

$12\pi = \frac{x}{360°}(20\pi)$

$12\pi = \frac{\pi x}{18}$

$12\pi(\frac{18}{\pi}) = x$

$216° = x$

2.44   a. $\frac{1}{360}$

b. $\frac{30}{360} = \frac{1}{12}$

c. $\frac{45}{360} = \frac{1}{8}$

d. $\frac{60}{360} = \frac{1}{6}$

e. $\frac{90}{360} = \frac{1}{4}$

2.45

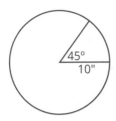

$$\text{area of sector} = \frac{m}{360°}(\pi r^2)$$

$$A = \frac{45°}{360°}(\pi)(10)^2$$

$$= \frac{45°}{360°}(100\pi)$$

$$= \frac{1}{8}(100\pi)$$

$$= \frac{25}{2}\pi \text{ sq. in.}$$

2.46

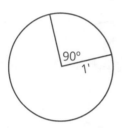

$$\text{area of sector} = \frac{m}{360°}(\pi r^2)$$

$$A = \frac{90°}{360°}(\pi)(1)^2$$

$$= \frac{1}{4}\pi \text{ sq. ft.}$$

2.47

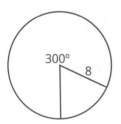

$$\text{area of sector} = \frac{m}{360°}(\pi r^2)$$

$$A = \frac{300°}{360°}(\pi)(8)^2$$

$$= \frac{5}{6}(64\pi)$$

$$= \frac{160}{3}\pi$$

2.48

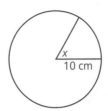

$$\text{area of sector} = \frac{m}{360°}(\pi r^2)$$

$$40\pi = \frac{x}{360°}(\pi)(10)^2$$

$$40\pi = \frac{x}{360°}(100\pi)$$

$$40\pi(\frac{360}{\pi}) = 100x$$

$$14,400 = 100x$$

$$\frac{14,400}{100} = x$$

$$144° = x$$

2.49

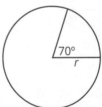

$$\text{area of sector} = \frac{m}{360°}(\pi r^2)$$

$$7\pi = \frac{70°}{360°}(\pi r^2)$$

$$7(360) = 70r^2$$

$$360 = \frac{70r^2}{7}$$

$$360 = 10r^2$$

$$\frac{360}{10} = r^2$$

$$36 = r^2$$

$$\sqrt{36} = \sqrt{r^2}$$

$$6 \text{ ft.} = r$$

2.50

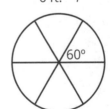

$$\text{area of sector} = \frac{m}{360°}(\pi r^2)$$

$$A = \frac{60°}{360°}(\pi)(5)^2$$

$$= \frac{1}{6}(25\pi)$$

$$= \frac{25}{6}\pi \text{ inches}$$

2.51

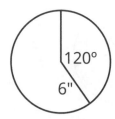

area of sector = $\frac{m}{360°}(\pi r^2)$

$$A = \frac{120°}{360°}(\pi)(6)^2$$

$$= \frac{1}{3}(36\pi)$$

$$= 12\pi \text{ sq. in.}$$

2.52

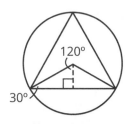

area of sector = $\frac{m}{360°}(\pi r^2)$

$$A = \frac{120°}{360°}(\pi)(2)^2$$

$$= \frac{1}{3}(4\pi)$$

$$= \frac{4}{3}\pi$$

2.53

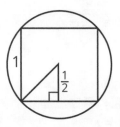

area of sector = $\frac{m}{360°}(\pi r^2)$

$$A = \frac{90°}{360°}(\pi)(3)^2$$

$$= \frac{1}{4}(9\pi)$$

$$= \frac{9}{4}\pi$$

2.54

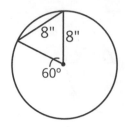

area of segment = area of sector – area of triangle

$$A = \frac{60°}{360°}(\pi)(8)^2 - \frac{1}{2}(8)(4\sqrt{3})$$

$$= \frac{1}{6}(64\pi) - 4(4\sqrt{3})$$

$$= \frac{64\pi}{6} - 16\sqrt{3}$$

$$= (\frac{32}{3}\pi - 16\sqrt{3}) \text{ sq. in.}$$

2.55

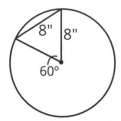

area of larger segment = area of circle – area of smaller segment

$$A = (8)^2(\pi) - (\frac{32}{3}\pi - 16\sqrt{3})$$

$$= 64\pi - \frac{32}{3}\pi + 16\sqrt{3}$$

$$= (\frac{160}{3}\pi + 16\sqrt{3}) \text{ sq. in.}$$

2.56

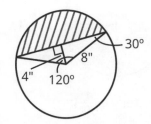

area of segment = area of sector – area of triangle

$$A = \frac{120°}{360°}(\pi)(8)^2 - \frac{1}{2}(8\sqrt{3})(4)$$

$$= \frac{1}{3}(64\pi) - (4\sqrt{3})(4)$$

$$= (\frac{64}{3}\pi - 16\sqrt{3}) \text{ sq. in.}$$

2.57

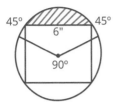

area of segment = area of sector – area of triangle

$A = \dfrac{90°}{360°}(\pi)(3\sqrt{2})^2 - \dfrac{1}{2}(3\sqrt{2})(3\sqrt{2})$

$\quad = \dfrac{1}{4}(18\pi) - \dfrac{1}{2}(18)$

$\quad = (\dfrac{9}{2}\pi - 9)$ sq. in.

2.58

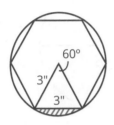

area of segment = area of sector – area of triangle

$A = \dfrac{60°}{360°}(\pi)(3)^2 - \dfrac{1}{4}(3)^2(\sqrt{3})$

$\quad = \dfrac{1}{6}(9\pi) - \dfrac{1}{4}(9\sqrt{3})$

$\quad = \dfrac{9}{6}\pi - \dfrac{9}{4}\sqrt{3}$

$\quad = (\dfrac{3}{2}\pi - \dfrac{9}{4}\sqrt{3})$ sq. in.

2.59

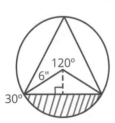

area of segment = area of sector – area of triangle

$A = \dfrac{120°}{360°}(\pi)(6)^2 - \dfrac{1}{2}(6\sqrt{3})(3)$

$\quad = \dfrac{1}{3}(36\pi) - (3\sqrt{3})(3)$

$\quad = (12\pi - 9\sqrt{3})$ sq. in.

2.60 $A = A_{triangle} - 3A_{sectors}$

$\quad = \dfrac{1}{4}(6)^2(\sqrt{3}) - 3(\dfrac{60°}{360°})(\pi)(3)^2$

$\quad = \dfrac{1}{4}(36)(\sqrt{3}) - 3(\dfrac{1}{6})(\pi)(9)$

$\quad = 9\sqrt{3} - \dfrac{1}{2}(9\pi)$

$\quad = 9\sqrt{3} - \dfrac{9}{2}\pi$

2.61 $A = A_{square} - A_{sector}$

$\quad = 6^2 - \dfrac{90°}{360°}(\pi)(6)^2$

$\quad = 36 - \dfrac{1}{4}(\pi)(36)$

$\quad = 36 - \dfrac{36}{4}\pi$

$\quad = 36 - 9\pi$

2.62

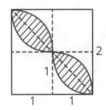

$A = 4$ times area of a segment

$\quad = 4(\text{area of sector} - \text{area of triangle})$

$\quad = 4[\dfrac{90°}{360°}(\pi)(1)^2 - \dfrac{1}{2}(1)(1)]$

$\quad = 4[\dfrac{1}{4}(\pi)(1) - \dfrac{1}{2}]$

$\quad = 4[\dfrac{\pi}{4} - \dfrac{1}{2}]$

$\quad = \pi - 2$

2.63

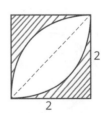

$A = A_{square} - 2 \text{ segments}$

$\quad = A_{square} - (\text{area of sector} - \text{area of triangle})$

$\quad = 2^2 - 2[\dfrac{90°}{360°}(\pi)(2)^2 - \dfrac{1}{2}(2)(2)]$

$\quad = 2^2 - 2[\dfrac{1}{4}(\pi)(4) - 1(2)]$

$\quad = 4 - 2(\pi - 2)$

$\quad = 4 - 2\pi + 4$

$\quad = 8 - 2\pi$

2.64

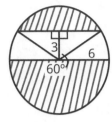

$A = \dfrac{1}{2}$ area of $\odot$ + area of segment

$= \dfrac{1}{2}$ area of $\odot$ + area of sector – area of $\triangle$

$= \dfrac{1}{2}(\pi)(6)^2 + \dfrac{120°}{360°}(\pi)(6)^2 - \dfrac{1}{2}(6\sqrt{3})(3)$

$= \dfrac{1}{2}(\pi)(36) + \dfrac{1}{3}\pi(36) - 3\sqrt{3}(3)$

$= 18\pi + 12\pi - 9\sqrt{3}$

$= 30\pi - 9\sqrt{3}$

2.65

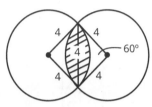

$A = 2$(area of segment)
$ = 2$(area of sector – area of triangle)

$= 2[\dfrac{60°}{360°}(\pi)(4)^2 - \dfrac{1}{4}(4)^2(\sqrt{3})]$

$= 2[\dfrac{1}{6}\pi(16) - \dfrac{1}{4}(16\sqrt{3})]$

$= 2(\dfrac{16}{6}\pi - 4\sqrt{3})$

$= 2(\dfrac{8}{3}\pi - 4\sqrt{3})$

$= \dfrac{16}{3}\pi - 8\sqrt{3}$

2.66

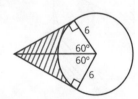

$A = 2$(area of rt. $\triangle$ – area of sector)

$= 2[\dfrac{1}{2}(6\sqrt{3})(6)] - \dfrac{120°}{360°}\pi(6)^2$

$= 2[3\sqrt{3}(6)] - \dfrac{1}{3}\pi(36)$

$= 2(18\sqrt{3}) - 12\pi$

$= 36\sqrt{3} - 12\pi$

SELF TEST 2

2.01

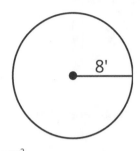

$A = \pi r^2$
$A = 3.14(8)^2$
$A = 3.14(64)$
$A = 200.96$ sq. ft.

2.02

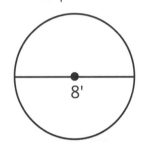

$C = 2\pi r$
$C = 2\pi(4)$
$C = 8\pi$ ft.

2.03

$A_{rectangle} = 2(11)$
$A \phantom{_{rectangle}} = 22$
$A_{circle} = \pi r^2$
$\phantom{A_{circle}} 22 = \pi r^2$
$\phantom{A_{circle}} 22 = \dfrac{22}{7}r^2$
$22(\dfrac{7}{22}) = r^2$
$ 7 = r^2$
$ \sqrt{7} = \sqrt{r^2}$
$ r = \sqrt{7}$ ft.

2.04

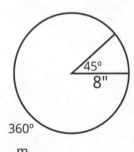

$360°$

$A = \dfrac{m}{360°}\pi r^2$

$A = \dfrac{45°}{360°}\pi(8)^2$

$A = \dfrac{1}{8}\pi(64)$

$A = 8\pi$ sq. in.

2.05 length of arc $= \frac{m}{360°}(2\pi r)$

$= \frac{45°}{360°}(2\pi)(8)$

$= \frac{1}{8}(2\pi)(8)$

$= 2\pi$ in.

2.06

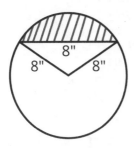

area of segment = area of sector – area of triangle

$A = \frac{60°}{360°}\pi(8)^2 - \frac{1}{4}(8)^2(\sqrt{3})$

$= \frac{1}{6}\pi(64) - \frac{1}{4}(64)(\sqrt{3})$

$= (\frac{32}{3}\pi - 16\sqrt{3})$ sq. in.

2.07

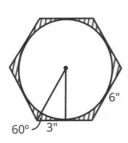

$A = A_{hex.} - A_{\odot}$

$A_{hex.} = \frac{1}{2}ap$

$= \frac{1}{2}(3\sqrt{3})(36)$

$= 54\sqrt{3}$

$A_{\odot} = \pi r^2$

$= \pi(3\sqrt{3})^2$

$= 27\pi$

$A = (54\sqrt{3} - 27\pi)$ sq. in.

2.08 $A = 2$(area of sector)

$= 2[\frac{60°}{360°}\pi(4)^2]$

$= 2[\frac{1}{6}\pi(16)]$

$= 2(\frac{16}{6}\pi)$

$= \frac{16}{3}\pi$

2.09 $A = A_{large\,\odot} - A_{small\,\odot}$

$= \pi(6)^2 - \pi(3)^2$

$= 36\pi - 9\pi$

$= 27\pi$

2.010

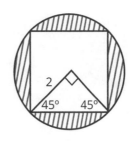

$A = A_{\odot} - A_{square}$

$= \pi(2)^2 - (2\sqrt{2})^2$

$= 4\pi - 8$

2.011

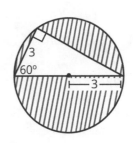

$A = A_{\odot} - A_{\triangle}$

$= \pi(3)^2 - \frac{1}{2}(3)(3\sqrt{3})$

$= 9\pi - \frac{9}{2}\sqrt{3}$

2.012 $A = 2$(area of triangle)

$A = 2(\frac{1}{2})(4)(4)$

$A = 16$

2.013 b

2.014 e

2.015 c

2.016 d

2.017 a

2.018 g

2.019 f

2.020 h or b

SECTION 3

3.1 a. *L.A.* = *ph*
             = 10(5)
             = 50 sq. ft.
     b. *T.A.* = *ph* + 2*B*
             = 50 + 2(6)
             = 50 + 12
             = 62 sq. ft.
     c.   *V* = *Bh*
             = 6(5)
             = 30 cu. ft.

3.2 a. *L.A.* = *ph*
             = 9(6)
             = 54 sq. in.
     b. *T.A.* = *ph* + 2*B*
             $= 54 + 2(\frac{1}{4})(3)^2(\sqrt{3})$

             $= 54 + 2(\frac{1}{4})(9\sqrt{3})$

             $= 54 + (\frac{9}{2}\sqrt{3})$ sq. in.
     c.   *V* = *Bh*
             $= (\frac{9}{4}\sqrt{3})(6)$

             $= \frac{27}{2}\sqrt{3}$ cu. in.

3.3 a. *L.A.* = *ph*
             = 20(6)
             = 120 sq. in.
     b. *T.A.* = *ph* + 2*B*
             $= 120 + 2(\frac{1}{2})(k)(20)$
             = (120 + 20*k*) sq. in.
     c.   *V* = *Bh*
             $= (\frac{1}{2})(k)(20)(6)$
             = 60*k* cu. in.

3.4 a. $c^2 = a^2 + b^2$
             $c^2 = 4^2 + 6^2$
             $c^2 = 16 + 36$
             $c^2 = 52$
             $\sqrt{c^2} = \sqrt{52}$
             $c = 2\sqrt{13}$
         L.A. = *ph*
             $= (10 + 2\sqrt{13})(8)$
             $= (80 + 16\sqrt{13})$ sq. ft.
     b. *T.A.* = *L.A.* + 2*B*
             $= 80 + 16\sqrt{13} + 2(\frac{1}{2})(4)(6)$
             $= 80 + 16\sqrt{13} + 24$
             $= (104 + 16\sqrt{13})$ sq. ft.
     c.   *V* = *Bh*
             = 12(8)
             = 96 cu. ft.

3.5 a. *L.A.* = *ph*
             = 48(12)
             = 576 sq. in.
     b. *T.A.* = *ph* + 2*B*
             $= 576 + 2(12)^2$
             = 576 + 2(144)
             = 576 + 288
             = 864 sq. in.
     c.   *V* = *Bh*
             = 144(12)
             = 1,728 cu. in.

3.6

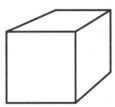

         T.A. = 96
         A_{face} = 96 ÷ 6
                 = 16 sq. in.
         $A = s^2$
         $16 = s^2$
         $\sqrt{16} = \sqrt{s^2}$
             4 = *s*
         V = *Bh*
             = 16(4)
             = 64 cu. in.

3.7

3" 4" 12"

         $4^2 + 3^2 = s^2$
         $16 + 9 = s^2$
             $25 = s^2$
         $\sqrt{25} = \sqrt{s^2}$
             s = 5

     a.   *V* = *Bh*
             = (24)(12)
             = 288 cu. in.
     b. *L.A.* = *ph*
             = 20(12)
             = 240 sq. in.

3.8

V = 300 cu. in.
h = 6 in.
$V = Bh$
$300 = B(6)$
$\frac{300}{6} = B$
50 sq. in. = B

3.9

$L.A.$ = 88 sq. ft.
h = 16 ft.
$L.A. = ph$
$88 = p(16)$
$\frac{88}{16} = p$
5.5 ft. = p

3.10

$V_{wall} = Bh$
$= 20(1)(6)$
$= 120$ cu. ft.
$\times\ 1{,}728$
$207{,}360$ cu. in.
$\times\ \ 10\%$
$20{,}736$ cu. in. of mortar
$207{,}360$
$-\ 20{,}736$
$186{,}624$ cu. in. of wall

$V_{one\ brick} = Bh$
$= 8(4)(2)$
$= 64$ cu. in.

$186{,}624 \div 64 = 2{,}916$ bricks

3.11   a. $L.A. = \frac{1}{2}pl$
$l = \sqrt{1^2 + 3^2}$
$= \sqrt{1 + 9}$
$= \sqrt{10}$
$L.A. = \frac{1}{2}(8)(\sqrt{10})$
$= 4\sqrt{10}$

b. $T.A. = \frac{1}{2}pl + B$
$= 4\sqrt{10} + 2^2$
$= 4\sqrt{10} + 4$

c. $V = \frac{1}{3}Bh$
$= \frac{1}{3}(4)(3)$
$= 4$

3.12   a. $L.A. = \frac{1}{2}pl$

$L.A. = \frac{1}{2}(24)(6)$
$= 72$

b.

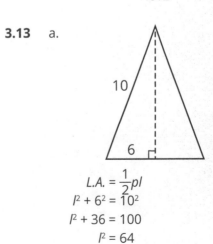

$T.A. = \frac{1}{2}pl + B$
$= 72 + \frac{1}{2}(2\sqrt{3})(24)$
$= 72 + 24\sqrt{3}$

c.

$V = \frac{1}{3}Bh$
$h^2 + (2\sqrt{3})^2 = 6^2$
$h^2 + 12 = 36$
$h^2 = 24$
$\sqrt{h^2} = \sqrt{24}$
$h = 2\sqrt{6}$

$V = \frac{1}{3}(24\sqrt{3})(2\sqrt{6})$
$= 16\sqrt{18}$
$= 48\sqrt{2}$

3.13   a.

$L.A. = \frac{1}{2}pl$
$l^2 + 6^2 = 10^2$
$l^2 + 36 = 100$
$l^2 = 64$

$\sqrt{l^2} = \sqrt{64}$

$l = 8$

$L.A. = \frac{1}{2}(36)(8)$

$\quad = 144$

b. $T.A. = \frac{1}{2}pl + B$

$\quad = 144 + \frac{1}{4}(12)^2(\sqrt{3})$

$\quad = 144 + \frac{1}{4}(144)(\sqrt{3})$

$\quad = 144 + 36\sqrt{3}$

c.

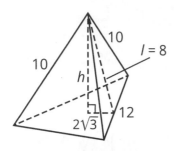

$V = \frac{1}{3}Bh$

$h^2 + (2\sqrt{3})^2 = 8^2$

$h^2 + 12 = 64$

$h^2 = 52$

$\sqrt{h^2} = \sqrt{52}$

$h = 2\sqrt{13}$

$V = \frac{1}{3}(36\sqrt{3})(2\sqrt{13})$

$\quad = 24\sqrt{39}$

3.14 a.

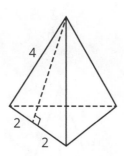

$L.A. = \frac{1}{2}pl$

$l^2 + 2^2 = 4^2$

$l^2 + 4 = 16$

$l^2 = 12$

$\sqrt{l^2} = \sqrt{12}$

$l = 2\sqrt{3}$

$L.A. = \frac{1}{2}(12)(2\sqrt{3})$

$\quad = 12\sqrt{3}$

b. $T.A. = \frac{1}{2}pl + B$

$\quad = 12\sqrt{3} + \frac{1}{4}(4)^2(\sqrt{3})$

$\quad = 12\sqrt{3} + \frac{1}{4}(16\sqrt{3})$

$\quad = 12\sqrt{3} + 4\sqrt{3}$

$\quad = 16\sqrt{3}$

c.

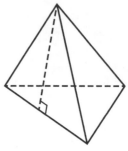

$V = \frac{1}{3}Bh$

$h^2 + (\frac{2\sqrt{3}}{3})^2 = (2\sqrt{3})^2$

$h^2 + \frac{12}{9} = 12$

$h^2 + \frac{4}{3} = 12$

$h^2 = \frac{32}{3}$

$\sqrt{h^2} = \sqrt{}$

$h = \frac{\sqrt{32}}{\sqrt{3}}$

$h = \frac{4\sqrt{2}}{\sqrt{3}} \cdot \frac{\sqrt{3}}{\sqrt{3}}$

$h = \frac{4\sqrt{6}}{3}$

$V = \frac{1}{3}(4\sqrt{3})(\frac{4\sqrt{6}}{3})$

$\quad = \frac{16\sqrt{18}}{9}$

$\quad = \frac{16(3\sqrt{2})}{9}$

$\quad = \frac{16}{3}\sqrt{2}$

3.15 a.

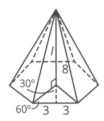

$$L.A. = \frac{1}{2}pl$$
$$l = \sqrt{8^2 + (3\sqrt{3})^2}$$
$$= \sqrt{64 + 27}$$
$$= \sqrt{91}$$
$$L.A. = \frac{1}{2}(36)(\sqrt{91})$$
$$= 18\sqrt{91}$$

b. $T.A. = \frac{1}{2}pl + B$
$$= 18\sqrt{91} + \frac{1}{2}(3\sqrt{3})36$$
$$= 18\sqrt{91} + 54\sqrt{3}$$

c. $V = \frac{1}{3}Bh$
$$= \frac{1}{3}(54\sqrt{3})(8)$$
$$= 144\sqrt{3}$$

3.16 $V = \frac{1}{3}Bh$
$$= \frac{1}{3}(24\sqrt{3})(6\sqrt{3})$$
$$= 48\sqrt{9}$$
$$= 144$$

3.17 $V = \frac{1}{3}Bh$
$$32 = \frac{1}{3}(16)h$$
$$96 = 16h$$
$$\frac{96}{16} = h$$
$$6 \text{ in.} = h$$

3.18

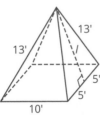

$$L.A. = \frac{1}{2}pl$$
$$l^2 + 5^2 = 13^2$$
$$l^2 + 25 = 169$$
$$l^2 = 144$$
$$\sqrt{l^2} = \sqrt{144}$$
$$l = 12$$

$$L.A. = \frac{1}{2}(40)(12)$$
$$= 240$$

$$T.A. = \frac{1}{2}pl + B$$
$$= 240 + 100$$
$$= 340 \text{ sq. ft.}$$

3.19

$$V = \frac{1}{3}Bh$$
$$l^2 + 3^2 = 10^2$$
$$l^2 + 9 = 100$$
$$l^2 = 91$$
$$\sqrt{l^2} = \sqrt{91}$$
$$l = \sqrt{91}$$

$$h^2 + 3^2 = l^2$$
$$h^2 + 3^2 = (\sqrt{91})^2$$
$$h^2 + 9 = 91$$
$$h^2 = 82$$
$$\sqrt{h^2} = \sqrt{82}$$
$$h = \sqrt{82}$$

$$V = \frac{1}{3}Bh$$
$$= \frac{1}{3}(36)(\sqrt{82})$$
$$= 12\sqrt{82} \text{ cu. ft.}$$

3.20

$$V = \frac{1}{3}Bh$$
$$l^2 + (\frac{3}{2})^2 = 3^2$$
$$l^2 + \frac{9}{4} = 9$$
$$l^2 = \frac{27}{4}$$
$$\sqrt{l^2} = \sqrt{\frac{27}{4}}$$
$$l = \frac{3\sqrt{3}}{2}$$

$$h^2 + (\frac{\sqrt{3}}{2})^2 = l^2$$

$$h^2 + (\frac{\sqrt{3}}{2})^2 = (\frac{3\sqrt{3}}{2})^2$$

$$h^2 + \frac{3}{4} = \frac{27}{4}$$

$$h^2 = \frac{24}{4}$$

$$h^2 = 6$$

$$\sqrt{h^2} = \sqrt{6}$$

$$h = \sqrt{6}$$

$$V = \frac{1}{3}(\frac{1}{4})(3)^2(\sqrt{3})(\sqrt{6})$$

$$= \frac{1}{3}(\frac{1}{4})(9)(\sqrt{3})(\sqrt{6})$$

$$= \frac{3}{4}\sqrt{18}$$

$$= \frac{9\sqrt{2}}{4} \text{ cu. in.}$$

3.21 a. $L.A. = 2\pi rh$
$= 2\pi(4)(5)$
$= 40\pi$

b. $T.A. = 2\pi rh + 2\pi r^2$
$= 40\pi + 2\pi(4)^2$
$= 40\pi + 2\pi(16)$
$= 40\pi + 32\pi$
$= 72\pi$

c. $V = \pi r^2 h$
$= \pi(4)^2(5)$
$= \pi(16)(5)$
$= 80\pi$

3.22 a. $L.A. = 2\pi rh$
$= 2\pi(2)(4)$
$= 16\pi$

b. $T.A. = 2\pi rh + 2\pi r^2$
$= 16\pi + 2\pi(2)^2$
$= 16\pi + 2\pi(4)$
$= 16\pi + 8\pi$
$= 24\pi$

c. $V = \pi r^2 h$
$= \pi(2)^2(4)$
$= \pi(4)(4)$
$= 16\pi$

3.23 a. $L.A. = 2\pi rh$
$= 2\pi(2)(3)$
$= 12\pi$

b. $T.A. = 2\pi rh + 2\pi r^2$
$= 12\pi + 2\pi(2)^2$
$= 12\pi + 2\pi(4)$
$= 12\pi + 8\pi$
$= 20\pi$

c. $V = \pi r^2 h$
$= \pi(2)^2(3)$
$= \pi(4)(3)$
$= 12\pi$

3.24 a. $L.A. = 2\pi rh$
$= 2\pi(1)(1)$
$= 2\pi$

b. $T.A. = 2\pi rh + 2\pi r^2$
$= 2\pi + 2\pi(1)^2$
$= 2\pi + 2\pi$
$= 4\pi$

c. $V = \pi r^2 h$
$= \pi(1)^2(1)$
$= \pi$

3.25 a. $L.A. = 2\pi rh$
$= 2\pi(6)(20)$
$= 240\pi$

b. $T.A. = 2\pi rh + 2\pi r^2$
$= 240\pi + 2\pi(6)^2$
$= 240\pi + 2\pi(36)$
$= 240\pi + 72\pi$
$= 312\pi$

c. $V = \pi r^2 h$
$= \pi(6)^2(20)$
$= \pi(36)(20)$
$= 720\pi$

3.26 $C = 2\pi r$
$16\pi = 2\pi r$
$\frac{16\pi}{2\pi} = r$
$8 = r$
$V = \pi r^2 h$
$= \pi(8)^2(6)$
$= \pi(64)(6)$
$= 384\pi \text{ cu. in.}$

3.27 $L.A. = 2\pi rh$
$70\pi = 2\pi(5)h$
$70\pi = 10\pi h$
$\frac{70\pi}{10\pi} = h$
$7 \text{ in.} = h$

3.28

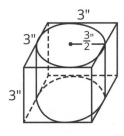

$$V = \pi r^2 h$$

$$= \pi(\tfrac{3}{2})^2(3)$$

$$= \pi(\tfrac{9}{4})(3)$$

$$= \tfrac{27}{4}\pi \text{ cu. in.}$$

3.29
$$V = \pi r^2 h$$
$$320\pi = \pi r^2(5)$$
$$\frac{320\pi}{5\pi} = r^2$$
$$64 = r^2$$
$$\sqrt{64} = \sqrt{r^2}$$
$$8 \text{ in.} = r$$

3.30
$$V_T = \pi r^2 h$$
$$= \pi(3)^2(2)$$
$$= \pi(9)(2)$$
$$= 18\pi \text{ cu. in.}$$

$$V_S = \pi r^2 h$$
$$= \pi(2)^2(3)$$
$$= \pi(4)(3)$$
$$= 12\pi \text{ cu. in.}$$

The tuna can contains more food.

3.31 a. $h^2 + r^2 = l^2$
$$5^2 + 3^2 = l^2$$
$$25 + 9 = l^2$$
$$34 = l^2$$
$$\sqrt{34} = \sqrt{l^2}$$
$$l = \sqrt{34}$$

b. $L.A. = \pi r l$
$$= \pi(3)(\sqrt{34})$$
$$= 3\sqrt{34}\pi$$

c. $T.A. = \pi r l + \pi r^2$
$$= 3\sqrt{34}\pi + \pi(3)^2$$
$$= 3\sqrt{34}\pi + 9\pi$$

d. $V = \tfrac{1}{3}\pi r^2 h$
$$= \tfrac{1}{3}\pi(3)^2(5)$$
$$= \tfrac{1}{3}\pi(9)(5)$$
$$= 15\pi$$

3.32 a. $h^2 + r^2 = l^2$
$$h^2 + 6^2 = 10^2$$
$$h^2 + 36 = 100$$
$$h^2 = 64$$
$$\sqrt{h^2} = \sqrt{64}$$
$$h = 8$$

b. $L.A. = \pi r l$
$$= \pi(6)(10)$$
$$= 60\pi$$

c. $T.A. = \pi r l + \pi r^2$
$$= 60\pi + \pi(6)^2$$
$$= 60\pi + 36\pi$$
$$= 96\pi$$

d. $V = \tfrac{1}{3}\pi r^2 h$
$$= \tfrac{1}{3}\pi(6)^2(8)$$
$$= \tfrac{1}{3}\pi(36)(8)$$
$$= 96\pi$$

3.33 a. $L.A. = \pi r l$
$$12\pi = \pi(2)l$$
$$\frac{12\pi}{2\pi} = l$$
$$6 = l$$

b. $h^2 + r^2 = l^2$
$$h^2 + 2^2 = 6^2$$
$$h^2 + 4 = 36$$
$$h^2 = 32$$
$$\sqrt{h^2} = \sqrt{32}$$
$$h = 4\sqrt{2}$$

c. $T.A. = \pi r l + \pi r^2$
$$= \pi(2)(6) + \pi(2)^2$$
$$= 12\pi + 4\pi$$
$$= 16\pi$$

d. $V = \tfrac{1}{3}\pi r^2 h$
$$= \tfrac{1}{3}\pi(2)^2(4\sqrt{2})$$
$$= \tfrac{1}{3}\pi(4)(4\sqrt{2})$$
$$= \tfrac{16}{3}\sqrt{2}\pi$$

3.34 Note: must find *b* before *a* can be determined

b.
$$V = \tfrac{1}{3}\pi r^2 h$$
$$100\pi = \tfrac{1}{3}\pi(5)^2 h$$
$$100\pi = \tfrac{1}{3}\pi 25 h$$
$$\frac{100\pi}{\pi}\left(\tfrac{3}{25}\right) = h$$
$$12 = h$$

a. $h^2 + r^2 = l^2$
    $12^2 + 5^2 = l^2$
    $144 + 25 = l^2$
    $169 = l^2$
    $\sqrt{169} = \sqrt{l^2}$
    $13 = l$

c. $L.A. = \pi r h$
    $= \pi(5)(13)$
    $= 65\pi$

d. $T.A. = \pi r l + \pi r^2$
    $= 65\pi + \pi(5)^2$
    $= 65\pi + 25\pi$
    $= 90\pi$

3.35 a. $L.A. = \pi r l$
    $8\pi = \pi r(4)$
    $\dfrac{8\pi}{4\pi} = r$
    $2 = r$

b. $h^2 + r^2 = l^2$
    $h^2 + 2^2 = 4^2$
    $h^2 + 4 = 16$
    $h^2 = 12$
    $\sqrt{h^2} = \sqrt{12}$
    $h = 2\sqrt{3}$

c. $T.A. = \pi r l + \pi r^2$
    $= 8\pi + \pi(2)^2$
    $= 8\pi + 4\pi$
    $= 12\pi$

d. $V = \dfrac{1}{3}\pi r^2 h$
    $= \dfrac{1}{3}\pi(2)^2(2\sqrt{3})$
    $= \dfrac{1}{3}\pi(4)(2\sqrt{3})$
    $= \dfrac{8}{3}\sqrt{3}\pi$

3.36 $T.A. = \pi r l + \pi r^2$
    $24\pi = \pi(3)l + \pi(3)^2$
    $24\pi = 3\pi l + 9\pi$
    $15\pi = 3\pi l$
    $\dfrac{15\pi}{3\pi} = l$
    $5" = l$
    $h^2 + r^2 = l^2$
    $h^2 + 3^2 = 5^2$
    $h^2 + 9 = 25$
    $h^2 = 16$
    $\sqrt{h^2} = \sqrt{16}$
    $h = 4"$
    $V = \dfrac{1}{3}\pi r^2 h$

$= \dfrac{1}{3}\pi(3)^2(4)$

$= \dfrac{1}{3}\pi(9)(4)$

$= 12\pi$

3.37

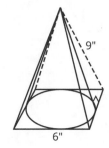

9"

6"

$h^2 + r^2 = l^2$
$h^2 + 3^2 = 9^2$
$h^2 + 9 = 81$
$h^2 = 72$
$\sqrt{h^2} = \sqrt{72}$
$h = 6\sqrt{2}$
$V = \dfrac{1}{3}\pi r^2 h$
$= \dfrac{1}{3}\pi(3)^2(6\sqrt{2})$
$= \dfrac{1}{3}\pi(9)(6\sqrt{2})$
$= 18\sqrt{2}\pi$

3.38 $V_{cube} = Bh$
    $= 4(2)$
    $= 8$ cu. in.
    $V_{cone} = \dfrac{1}{3}\pi r^2 h$
    $8 = \dfrac{1}{3}\pi(3)^2 h$
    $8 = \dfrac{1}{3}\pi(9)h$
    $8 = 3\pi h$
    $h = \dfrac{8}{3\pi}$ in.

3.39 $V = \dfrac{1}{3}\pi r^2 h$
    $= \dfrac{1}{3}\pi(5)^2(12)$
    $= \dfrac{1}{3}\pi(25)(12)$
    $= 100\pi$ cu. ft.

3.40 $L.A. = \pi r l$
    $h^2 + r^2 = l^2$
    $12^2 + 5^2 = l^2$
    $144 + 25 = l^2$
    $169 = l^2$
    $\sqrt{169} = \sqrt{l^2}$
    $l = 13$

L.A. = 3.14(5)(13)

    = 204.1 sq. ft.

204.1 ÷ 15 ≐ 13.6

Fourteen skins are needed.

3.41 $S = 4\pi r^2$

       $= 4\pi(4)^2$

       $= 4\pi(16)$

       $= 64\pi$ sq. in.

    $V = \frac{4}{3}\pi r^3$

      $= \frac{4}{3}\pi(4)^3$

      $= \frac{4}{3}\pi(64)$

      $= \frac{256}{3}\pi$ cu. in.

3.42   a.

    $S_1 = 4\pi(2r)^2$

       $= 4\pi(4r^2)$

       $= 16\pi r^2$

    $\frac{s}{s_1} = \frac{4\pi r^2}{16\pi r^2} = \frac{1}{4}$

   b. $V = \frac{4}{3}\pi r^3$

    $V_1 = \frac{4}{3}\pi(2r)^3$

      $= \frac{4}{3}\pi 8r^3$

    $\frac{v}{v_1} = \frac{\frac{4}{3}\pi r^2}{\frac{4}{3}\pi 8r^3} = \frac{1}{8}$

3.43

    $V = \frac{4}{3}\pi r^3$

      $= \frac{4}{3}(\frac{22}{7})(7)$

      $= \frac{4}{3}(\frac{22}{7})(\frac{343}{1})$

      $= 1{,}437\frac{1}{3}$ cu. ft.

3.44 $S = 4\pi r^2$

      $= 4\pi(2)^2$

      $= 4\pi(4)$

      $= 16\pi$ sq. in.

3.45   a. $V = \frac{4}{3}\pi r^3$

    $288\pi = \frac{4}{3}\pi r^3$

  $288\pi(\frac{3}{4\pi}) = r^3$

    $216 = r^3$

   $\sqrt[3]{216} = \sqrt[3]{r^3}$

      $r = 6''$

   b. $V = \frac{4}{3}\pi r^3$

    $144\pi = \frac{4}{3}\pi r^3$

  $144\pi(\frac{3}{4\pi}) = r^3$

    $108 = r^3$

   $\sqrt[3]{108} = \sqrt[3]{r^3}$

      $r = \sqrt[3]{108}''$

3.46 $S = 4\pi r^2$

    $16\pi = 4\pi r^2$

    $\frac{16\pi}{4\pi} = r^2$

     $4 = r^2$

   $\sqrt{4} = \sqrt{r^2}$

    $r = 2$ in.

    $V = \frac{4}{3}\pi r^3$

     $= \frac{4}{3}\pi(2)^3$

     $= \frac{4}{3}\pi(8)$

     $= \frac{32}{3}\pi$ cu. in.

3.47 $V = \frac{4}{3}\pi r^3$

    $288\pi = \frac{4}{3}\pi r^3$

  $288\pi(\frac{3}{4\pi}) = r^3$

    $216 = r^3$

   $\sqrt[3]{216} = \sqrt[3]{r^3}$

      $r = 6$

  $S = 4\pi r^2$

    $= 4\pi(6)^2$

    $= 4\pi(36)$

    $= 144\pi$

3.48

$$V_1 = \frac{4}{3}\pi r^3$$

$$= \frac{4}{3}\pi(6)^3$$

$$= \frac{4}{3}\pi(216)$$

$$= 288\pi$$

$$V_2 = \frac{4}{3}\pi r^3$$

$$= \frac{4}{3}\pi(5)^3$$

$$= \frac{4}{3}\pi(125)$$

$$= \frac{500}{3}\pi$$

$$V_1 - V_2 = \frac{864}{3}\pi - \frac{500}{3}\pi = \frac{364}{3}\pi \text{ cu. in.}$$

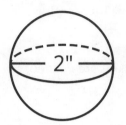

$$V = \frac{4}{3}\pi r^3$$

$$= \frac{4}{3}\pi(1)^3$$

$$= \frac{4}{3}\pi$$

The cone is $\frac{1}{3}\pi$ larger than the scoop of ice cream; therefore, the cone will not overflow.

3.49

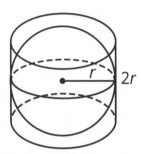

$$S_{sphere} = 4\pi r^2$$

$$L.A._{cylinder} = 2\pi rh$$

$$= 2\pi r(2r)$$

$$= 4\pi r^2$$

3.50

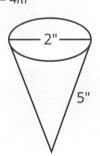

$$V = \frac{1}{3}Bh$$

$$= \frac{1}{3}\pi r^2 h$$

$$= \frac{1}{3}\pi(1)^2(5)$$

$$= \frac{5}{3}\pi$$

SELF TEST 3

3.01 e
3.02 c
3.03 a
3.04 b
3.05 d
3.06 b
3.07 e
3.08 c
3.09 d
3.010 a
3.011 g
3.012 f
3.013 h or b
3.014 a. $L.A. = ph$
  $= 16(6)$
  $= 96$ sq. ft.
  b. $T.A. = ph + 2B$
  $= 96 + 2(15)$
  $= 96 + 30$
  $= 126$ sq. ft.
  c. $V = Bh$
  $= 15(6)$
  $= 90$ cu. ft.

3.015 a.

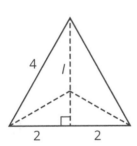

$L.A. = \frac{1}{2}pl$
$l^2 + 2^2 = 4^2$
$l^2 + 4 = 16$
$l^2 = 12$
$\sqrt{l^2} = \sqrt{12}$
$l = 2\sqrt{3}$
$L.A. = \frac{1}{2}(12)(2\sqrt{3})$
  $= 6(2\sqrt{3})$
  $= 12\sqrt{3}$

b. $T.A. = \frac{1}{2}pl + B$
  $= 12\sqrt{3} + \frac{1}{4}(4)^2(\sqrt{3})$
  $= 12\sqrt{3} + \frac{1}{4}(16)(\sqrt{3})$
  $= 12\sqrt{3} + 4\sqrt{3}$
  $= 16\sqrt{3}$

3.015 cont'd

c.

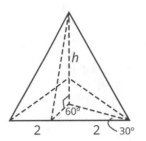

$V = \frac{1}{3}Bh$
$h^2 + (\frac{2\sqrt{3}}{3})^2 = (2\sqrt{3})^2$
$h^2 + \frac{12}{9} = 12$
$h^2 + \frac{4}{3} = 12$
$h^2 = \frac{32}{3}$
$\sqrt{h^2} = \sqrt{\frac{32}{3}}$
$h = \frac{\sqrt{32}}{\sqrt{3}} = \frac{4\sqrt{2}}{\sqrt{3}} \cdot \frac{\sqrt{3}}{\sqrt{3}} = \frac{4\sqrt{6}}{3}$
$V = \frac{1}{3}(4\sqrt{3})(\frac{4\sqrt{6}}{3})$
  $= \frac{16\sqrt{18}}{9}$
  $= \frac{16(3\sqrt{2})}{9}$
  $= \frac{16\sqrt{2}}{3}$

3.016 a. $L.A. = \pi rl$
  $l = \sqrt{6^2 + 8^2}$
  $= \sqrt{36 + 64}$
  $= \sqrt{100}$
  $= 10$
  $L.A. = \pi(6)(10)$
  $= 60\pi$ sq. in.
  b. $T.A. = \pi rl + \pi r^2$
  $= 60\pi + \pi(6)^2$
  $= 60\pi + 36\pi$
  $= 96\pi$ sq. ft.
  c. $V = \frac{1}{3}\pi r^2 h$
  $= \frac{1}{3}\pi(6)^2(8)$
  $= \frac{1}{3}\pi(36)(8)$
  $= 96\pi$ cu. in.

3.017 a. *L.A.* = 2π*rh*
          = 2π(3)(10)
          = 60π sq. in.

   b. *T.A.* = 2π*rh* + 2π*r*^{2}
          = 60π + 2π(3)^2
          = 60π + 2π(9)
          = 60π + 18π
          = 78π sq. in.

   c. *V* = π*r*^{2}*h*
          = π(3)^2(10)
          = π(9)(10)
          = 90π cu. in.

3.018 *S* = 4π*r*^{2}
          = 4π(8)^2
          = 4π(64)
          = 256π sq. in.

   $V = \frac{4}{3}\pi r^3$

   $= \frac{4}{3}\pi(8)^3$

   $= \frac{4}{3}\pi(512)$

   $= \frac{2,048}{3}\pi$ cu. in.

LIFEPAC TEST

1. $A = lw$
$= 4(2)$
$= 8$

2. $L.A. = ph$
$= 12(3)$
$= 36$

3. $T.A. = L.A. + 2B$
$= 36 + 2(8)$
$= 36 + 16$
$= 52$

4. $V = Bh$
$= 8(3)$
$= 24$

5. $l = \sqrt{5^2 + 12^2}$
$= \sqrt{25 + 144}$
$= \sqrt{169}$
$= 13$

6. $L.A. = \frac{1}{2}pl$
$= \frac{1}{2}(40)(13)$
$= 260$

7. $T.A. = L.A. + B$
$= 260 + 100$
$= 360$

8. $V = \frac{1}{3}Bh$
$= \frac{1}{3}(100)(12)$
$= 400$

9. $L.A. = 2\pi rh$
$= 2\pi(4)(6)$
$= 48\pi$

10. $T.A. = L.A. + 2B$
$= 48\pi + 2\pi r^2$
$= 48\pi + 2\pi(4)^2$
$= 48\pi + 2\pi(16)$
$= 48\pi + 32\pi$
$= 80\pi$

11. $V = \pi r^2 h$
$= \pi(4)^2(6)$
$= \pi(16)(6)$
$= 96\pi$

12. $l = \sqrt{5^2 + 11^2}$
$= \sqrt{25 + 121}$
$= \sqrt{146}$

13. $L.A. = \pi rl$
$= \pi(5)(\sqrt{146})$
$= 5\sqrt{146}\pi$

14. $T.A. = L.A. + B$
$= 5\sqrt{146}\pi + \pi r^2$
$= 5\sqrt{146}\pi + \pi(5)^2$
$= 5\sqrt{146}\pi + 25\pi$

15. $V = \frac{1}{3}\pi r^2 h$
$= \frac{1}{3}\pi(5)^2(11)$
$= \frac{1}{3}\pi(25)(11)$
$= \frac{275}{3}r$

16. $S = 4\pi r^2$
$= 4\pi(3)^2$
$= 4\pi(9)$
$= 36\pi$

17. $V = \frac{4}{3}\pi r^3$
$= \frac{4}{3}\pi(3)^3$
$= \frac{4}{3}\pi(27)$
$= 36\pi$

18. $A = \pi r^2$
$= \pi(6)^2$
$= 36\pi$

19. $A_O - AXB = \frac{AB}{360°}\pi r^2$
$= \frac{60°}{360°}\pi(6)^2$
$= \frac{1}{6}\pi(36)$
$= 6\pi$

20. $A_{AXB} = A_{sector} - A_\triangle$
$= 6\pi - \frac{s^2}{4}\sqrt{3}$
$= 6\pi - \frac{6^2}{4}\sqrt{3}$
$= 6\pi - \frac{36}{4}\sqrt{3}$
$= 6\pi - 9\sqrt{3}$

21. $C = 2\pi r$
$= 2\pi(6)$
$= 12\pi$

22. Apothem is long leg of 30°-60°-90° $\triangle$.
$a = 4\sqrt{3}$.

23. Radius is same length as side of hexagon.
$r = 8$.

24. central $\angle = \frac{360°}{m} = \frac{360°}{6} = 60°$

25. $A = \frac{1}{2}ap$
$= \frac{1}{2}(4\sqrt{3})(48)$
$= 2\sqrt{3}(48)$
$= 96\sqrt{3}$

ALTERNATE LIFEPAC TEST

1. $A = bh$
    $A = 3(6)$
    $A = 18$ sq. in.

2. $A = s^2$
    $A = 4^2$
    $A = 4(4)$
    $A = 16$ sq. in.

3.

    $h = 3$
    $A = bh$
    $A = 8(3)$
    $A = 24$

4. $P = 4s$
    $6 = 4s$
    $\dfrac{6}{4} = \dfrac{4s}{4}$
    $s = \dfrac{3}{2}$
    $A = s^2$
    $A = (\dfrac{3}{2})^2$
    $A = \dfrac{3}{2}(\dfrac{3}{2})$
    $A = \dfrac{9}{4}$ sq. ft. or $2\dfrac{1}{4}$ sq. ft.

5. $A = \dfrac{1}{2}(b_1 + b_2)$
    $A = \dfrac{1}{2}(4)(6 + 8)$
    $A = 2(14)$
    $A = 28$ sq. in.

6. $P = 5(6)$
    $P = 30$
    $A = \dfrac{1}{2}ap$
    $A = \dfrac{1}{2}(K)(30)$
    $A = 15K$

7. $P = 6s$
    $24 = 6s$
    $\dfrac{24}{6} = \dfrac{6s}{6}$
    $s = 4$

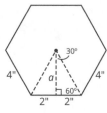

$a = 2\sqrt{3}$
$A = \dfrac{1}{2}ap$
$A = \dfrac{1}{2}(2\sqrt{3})(24)$
$A = 24\sqrt{3}$ sq. in.

8. $A = \dfrac{1}{4}s^2\sqrt{3}$
    $A = \dfrac{1}{4}(6)^2(\sqrt{3})$
    $A = \dfrac{1}{4}(36)(\sqrt{3})$
    $A = 9\sqrt{3}$ sq. in.

9. $C = 2\pi r$
    $C = 2\pi(4)$
    $C = 8\pi$ in.

10. $A = \pi r^2$
    $A = \pi(4)^2$
    $A = \pi(4)(4)$
    $A = 16\pi$ sq. in.

11. $A = \dfrac{m\frown}{360}(\pi r^2)$
    $A = \dfrac{90}{360}(\pi)(4)^2$
    $A = \dfrac{1}{4}\dfrac{\cancel{90}}{\cancel{360}}(\pi)(4)(4)$
    $A = \dfrac{1}{\cancel{4}}(\pi)(\cancel{16})^4$
    $A = 4\pi$ sq. in.

12.

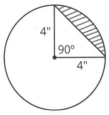

Area of sector = $\dfrac{90}{360}(\pi)(4)^2$

$\qquad = \dfrac{1}{4}\dfrac{\cancel{90}}{\cancel{360}}(\pi)(4)(4)$

$\qquad = \dfrac{1}{\cancel{4}}(\pi)(\cancel{16}^4)$

$\qquad = 4\pi$

Area of triangle = $\dfrac{1}{2}bh$

$\qquad = \dfrac{1}{2}(4)(4)$

$\qquad = \dfrac{1}{2}(16)$

$\qquad = 8$

Area of segment = $(4\pi - 8)$ sq. in.

13. $V = bh$
$V = (6 \cdot 4)(2)$
$V = (24)(2)$
$V = 48$ cu. in.

14. $T.A. = ph + 2B$
$p = 2(6) + 2(4)$
$p = 12 + 8$
$p = 20$

$h = 2$

$B = 6(4)$
$B = 24$

$T.A. = 20(2) + 2(24)$
$T.A. = 40 + 48$
$T.A. = 88$ sq. in.

15. $S = 4\pi r^2$
$S = 4\pi(3)^2$
$S = 4\pi(3)(3)$
$S = 4\pi(9)$
$S = 36\pi$ sq. in.

16. $V = \dfrac{4}{3}\pi r^3$

$V = \dfrac{4}{3}\pi(3)^3$

$V = \dfrac{4}{3}\pi(3)(3)(3)$

$V = \dfrac{4}{3}\pi(\cancel{27}^9)$
$\quad\ \ _1$

$V = 36\pi$ cu. in.

17. $C = \pi d$
$C = \pi(8)$
$C = 8\pi$ in.

18. $A = \pi r^2$

$r = \dfrac{1}{2}(8)$

$r = 4$
$A = \pi(4)^2$
$A = \pi(4)(4)$
$A = 16\pi$ sq. in.

19. $V = \pi r^2 h$

$r = \dfrac{1}{2}(8)$

$r = 4$
$V = \pi(4)^2(4)$
$V = \pi(4)(4)(4)$
$V = 64\pi$ cu. in.

20.

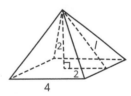

Use the Pythagorean Theorem.
$l = \sqrt{2^2 + 2^2}$
$l = \sqrt{4 + 4}$
$l = \sqrt{8}$
$l = \sqrt{4 \cdot 2} = \sqrt{4} \cdot \sqrt{2}$
$l = 2\sqrt{2}$

21. $A = s^2$
$A = 4^2$
$A = (4)(4)$
$A = 16$

22. $V = \frac{1}{3}Bh$

    $V = \frac{1}{3}(4 \cdot 4)(2)$

    $V = \frac{1}{3}(16)(2)$

    $V = \frac{1}{3}(32)$

    $V = \frac{32}{3}$ or $10\frac{2}{3}$

23. Use the Pythagorean Theorem.

    $l = \sqrt{3^2 + 4^2}$

    $l = \sqrt{9 + 16}$

    $l = \sqrt{25}$

    $l = 5$

24. $L.A. = \pi rl$

    $L.A. = \pi(3)(5)$

    $L.A. = 15\pi$

25. $V = \frac{1}{3}\pi r^2 h$

    $V = \frac{1}{3}\pi(3)^2(4)$

    $V = \frac{1}{3}\pi(3)(3)(4)$

    $V = \frac{1}{3}\pi(\overset{3}{9})(4)$

    $V = 12\pi$

MATH 1008

ALTERNATE LIFEPAC TEST

NAME _____

DATE _____

SCORE _____

Find the area of each of these quadrilaterals (each answer, 4 points).

1. A rectangle with length 3" and width 6". _____

2. A square with side 4 inches long. _____

3. A parallelogram with sides 8 and 6, and with an angle measure of 30°. _____

4. A square with perimeter 6 feet. _____

5. A trapezoid with bases 6" and 8" having a height of 4". _____

Find the area of each of these regular polygons (each answer, 4 points).

6. A pentagon with sides of 6 and apothem of K. _____

7. A hexagon with perimeter of 24". _____

8. A triangle with side equal to 6". _____

Find the following measures for a circle with radius equal to 4" and with a central angle equal to 90° (each answer, 4 points).

9. Circumference _____

10. Area _____

11. Area of smaller sector _____

12. Area of smaller segment _____

Find the following measures for these figures (each answer, 4 points).

13. Volume _____

14. Total area _____

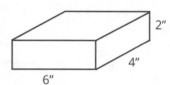

15. Surface area _____

16. Volume _____

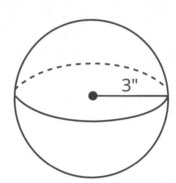

17. Circumference of base _____

18. Area of base _____

19. Volume _____

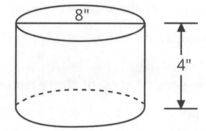

20. Slant height _____

21. Area of base _____

22. Volume _____

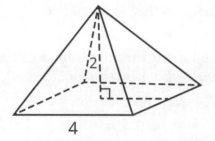

23. Slant height _____

24. Lateral area _____

25. Volume _____

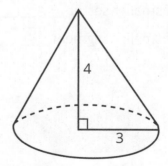

MATH 1009

Unit 9: Coordinate Geometry

TEACHER NOTES

MATERIALS NEEDED FOR LIFEPAC	
Required	Suggested
• protractors and straightedges	(None)

ADDITIONAL LEARNING ACTIVITIES

Section 1: Ordered Pairs

1. Discuss these questions with your class.

   What kind(s) of symmetry does a prism have? a pyramid? a cylinder? a cone? a sphere?

2. Let the students play "Battleship," a game that involves finding coordinates to "sink" the other player's battleships. The commercial game may be used or you may wish to make your own.

   To make a "Battleship" game board, acquire a small piece of plywood or other suitable material, (no larger than a foot square). Cut the plywood in half (for two sides of the game board for two players). Mark off $\frac{1}{4}$" lengths along each of the sides of both boards. Connect the lines to form $\frac{1}{4}$-" squares. At the intersection of each of the lines, drill a small hole. Paint a light-colored line down the middle of each board and across the middle of each board to represent the x- and y-axes. With a stencil or freehand, paint a small letter x at the top of each vertical line and paint a small letter y to the right of each horizontal line. Varnish the game boards and let dry. Acquire or make 12 or 14 small pegs ($\frac{1}{4}$" in diameter by 1" high), 6 or 7 for each player. On the top of each of two of the pegs, paint the letter A; the letter B; the letter C; the letter D; the letter E; the letter F; and the letter G. Each player plays with one set of pegs labeled A through G (or A through F).

   To play, each player must not see the other player's board (a partition may be placed between the game boards and the boards hinged together, or the students may sit not facing each other). Each player chooses six (or seven) holes on his game board in which to place his pegs. The first player names a point (any point) by a coordinate, such as (2, -4), on the second player's board. If the second player has a peg in the position named, he must remove it. If he does not have a peg there, he names a point on the first player's board. If the first player has a peg in the position named, he must remove it. If he does not have a peg there, he names another point on the second player's board. The play continues until one of the players has lost all his pegs.

Section 2: Distance

1. Water pressure in the ocean is a function of depth. Have the students copy the following table and plot a graph demonstrating the relationship.

Depth (in miles)	1	2	3	4	5
Pressure (in tons/sq. in.)	1.5	2.3	3.45	4.6	5.75

Section 3: Lines

1. The number of chirps that a cricket makes in a minute is a function of the surrounding temperature. The formula is $t = \frac{n}{4} + 40$, where t represents the temperature in °F and n is the number of cricket chirps in one minute. Have the students copy the following table and use the formula to find the missing numbers. Then have them graph the result.

n	40	60	80	100	120	140
t	50	___	___	___	___	75

2. Mark Twain once made a strange prediction about the future of the Mississippi River. The river is constantly changing course from wide bends to more direct paths, resulting in "cutoffs." As a result, the length of the Mississippi becomes shorter and shorter. Twain passed on these observations: "The Mississippi between Cairo and New Orleans was 1,215 miles long 176 years ago. It was 1,180 after the cutoff of 1722 … its length is only 973 miles at present (1875)." Have students plot these points on a graph. They will note that the points seem to lie along a straight line. If the students extend the line until it intersects the time axis, the line appears that sometime about the year 2600 not much of a river will be left. What is wrong with this reasoning?

3. On a sheet of graph paper, mark an origin (0, 0). Then draw the following points, curves, and lines with a compass and straightedge.

    Points: (3, 7), (7, 7), and (5, 5)

    Curves: the lower three-fourths of the circle whose equation is $(x - 5)^2 + (y - 5)^2 = 25$; end points are (1, 8) and (9, 8)

    the upper half of the circle with center (3, 7), $r = \frac{1}{2}$

    the upper half of the circle with center (7, 7), $r = \frac{1}{2}$

    the lower half of the circle whose equation is $(x - 5)^2 + (y - 4)^2 = \frac{25}{4}$; end points are on the line $y = 4$ (draw only the half-circle)

    the curve with center (3, 3) and whose end points are on the lines $x = 2$ and $x = 3$ (draw only the curve) the curve with center (7, 3) and whose end points are on the lines $x = 7$ and $x = 8$ (draw only the curve)

the left half of the circle with center (0, 6), $r = 1$

the right half of the circle with center (10, 6), $r = 1$

the left half of the circle with center (0, 6), $r = \frac{1}{3}$

the right half of the circle with center (10, 6), $r = \frac{1}{3}$

Lines: $y = 8$; end points are (-2, 8) and (12, 8)

$y = 10$; end points are (-2, 10) and (2, 10)

$m = 0$; end points are (8, 10) and (12, 10)

line || to $y = 8$; end points are (2, 12) and (8, 12)

line has no slope; equation is $x = 2$; end points are (2, 10) and (2, 12)

line has no slope; equation is $x = 8$; end points are (8, 10) and (8, 12)

line ⊥ to $y = 8$; end points are (-2, 8) and (-2, 10)

line ⊥ to $y = 10$; end points are (12, 8) and (12, 10)

What figure did you draw?

Section 4: Proofs by Coordinate Methods

1. Prove that the opposite sides of a square are equal. Prove that the opposite sides of a rhombus are equal. Prove that the opposite sides of a parallelogram are equal. Are the proofs the same? Why or why not?

2. Prove that the diagonals of a square are equal. Prove that the diagonals of a rectangle are equal. Prove that the diagonals of a rhombus are equal. Are the proofs the same? Why or why not?

Administer the LIFEPAC Test.

The test is to be administered in one session. Give no help except with directions.
Evaluate the tests and review areas where the students have done poorly.
Review the pages and activities that stress the concepts tested.
If necessary, administer the Alternate LIFEPAC Test

ANSWER KEYS

SECTION 1

1.1

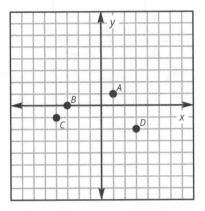

1.2

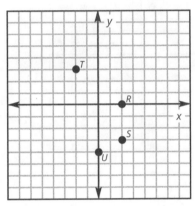

1.3   Triangle

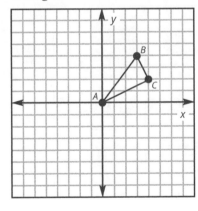

1.4   Rectangle

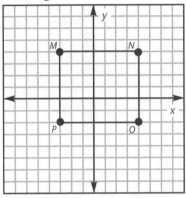

1.5   Trapezoid

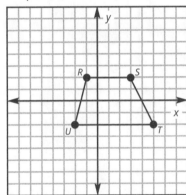

1.6   Square

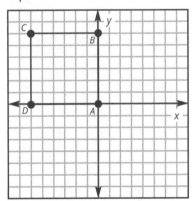

1.7

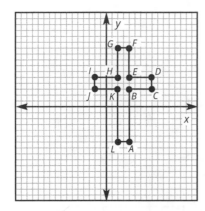

1.8

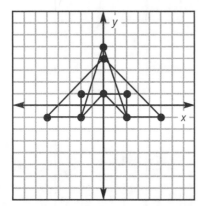

1.9   A (-4, -2)
B (2, -4)
C (4, -2)
D (2, 5)
E (-1, 1)
F (-5, 0)
G (4, 2)
H (0, -5)

1.10   (5, 6)

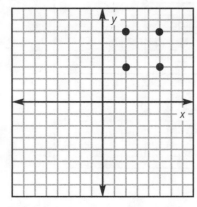

1.11   (6, 2)

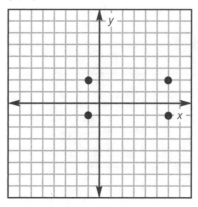

1.12   (5, 4)

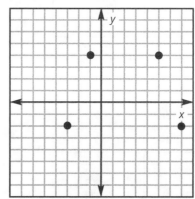

1.13   Either order:
a.   (11, -2), (11, 6)
b.   (-5, -2), (-5, 6)

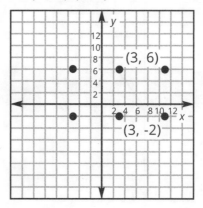

1.14   A (-4, -1)
B (2, -1)
C (6, 1)
D (6, 5)
E (3, 8)
F (-1, 6)
G (-4, 3)
H (2, 3)

1.15   A (0, 2)
           B (3, 5)
           C (6, 2)
           D (6, -4)
           E (0, -4)
           F (3, -2)
           G (4, 0)
           H (4, 2)
           I (2, 2)
           J (2, 0)
1.16   Teacher check
1.17   line, plane
1.18   line, plane
1.19   line, plane
1.20   line, plane
1.21   line, plane
1.22   none
1.23   point, line, plane
1.24   none
1.25   line, plane
1.26   point, line, plane
1.27   line, plane
1.28   line, plane
1.29   none
1.30

1.31

1.32

1.33   none
1.34

1.35

           equilateral
1.36   a.   (2, 1)

           b.   (3, -3)

           c.   (-4, 2)

           d.   (-3, -1)

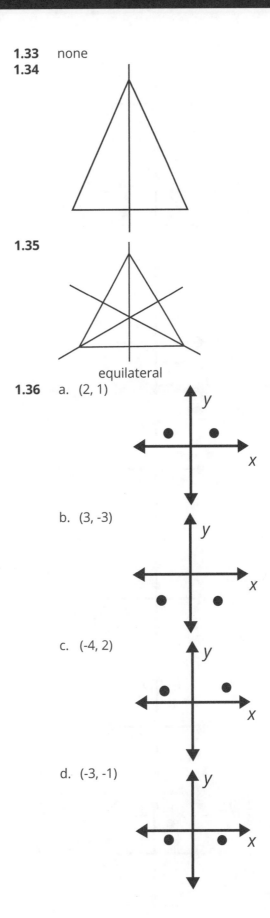

1.37   a.   (4, -3)

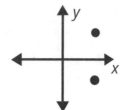

b.   (4, -1)

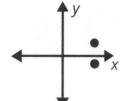

c.   (-3, -5)

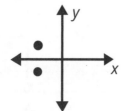

d.   (-3, 2)

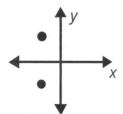

1.38   a.   (0, 3)

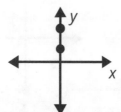

b.   (3, -1)

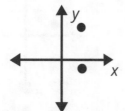

c.   (-2, 5)

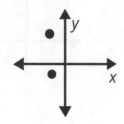

d.   (-4, 1)

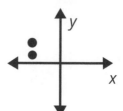

1.39   a.   (-5, 0)

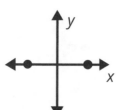

b.   (0, -2)

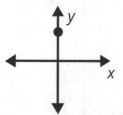

c.   (-3, -3)

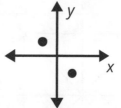

d.   (-2, 2)

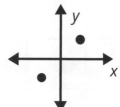

1.40   a.   (0, 4)

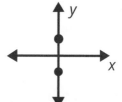

b.   (0, 6)

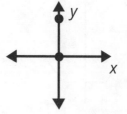

c. (1, 7)

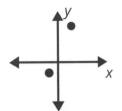

d. (-3, 3)

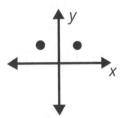

1.41 a. (3, 5)

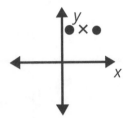

b. (-1, 5)

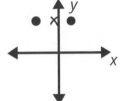

c. (0, 0)

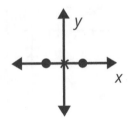

1.42

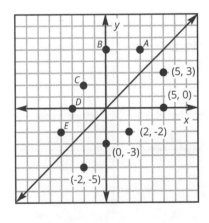

1.43

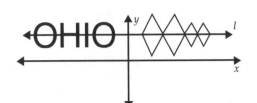

1.44

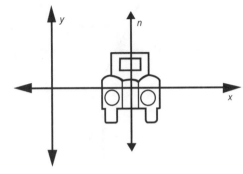

1.45

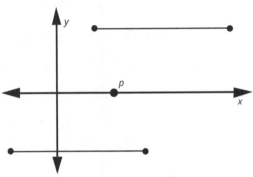

1.46

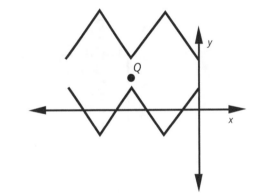

1.47

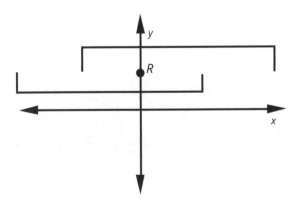

1.48

1.49

1.50

1.51

1.52

1.53

1.54

1.55

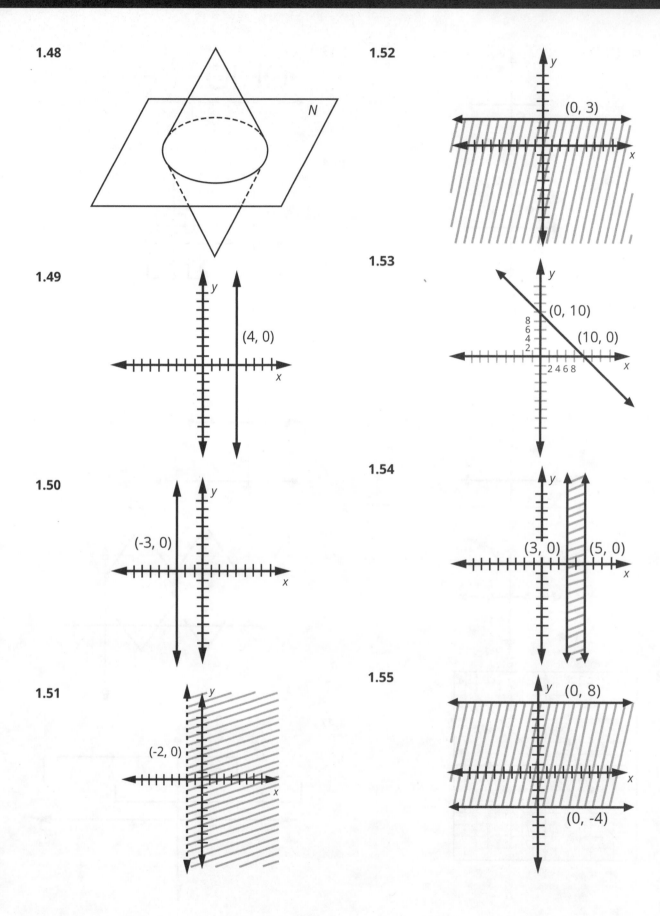

1.56

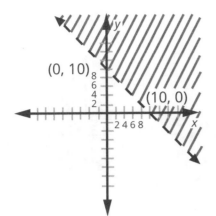

1.57

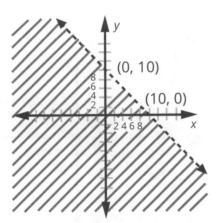

1.58

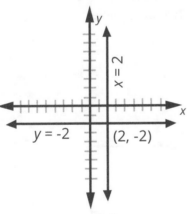

1.59

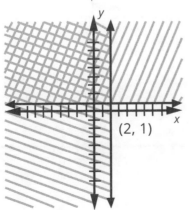

1.60

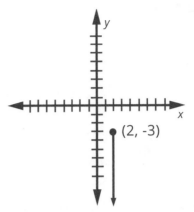

1.61

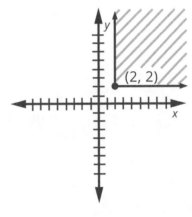

1.62

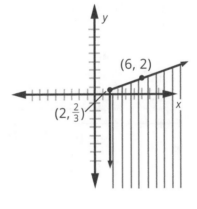

1.63 $y = 2$
1.64 $x \geq 2$
1.65 $x \leq 3$
1.66 $-3 \leq y \leq 3$
1.67 $\{(x, y): x \geq 2\}$
           $\{(x, y): x < -1\}$

SELF TEST 1

1.01   *A* (-5, -5)
            B (2, -3)
            C (2, 4)
            D (-2, 1)
            E (-1, 4)

1.02

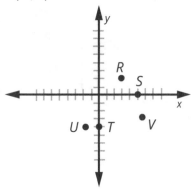

1.03   a. I
           b. IV
           c. III
           d. II
           e. I

1.04   line, plane
1.05   line, plane
1.06   point, line, plane
1.07   point, line, plane
1.08   point
1.09

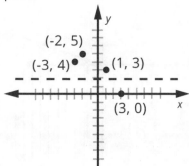

1.010

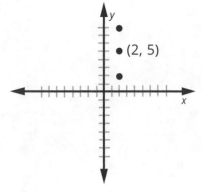

1.011

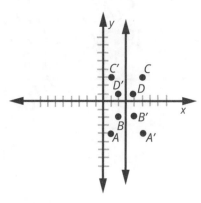

1.012   *x* = 2*y*
            Some points are (-6, -3), (-4, -2), (0, 0), and
            (2, 1).

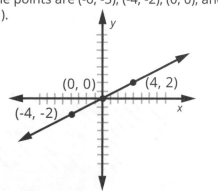

1.013   Two possibilities:

            (4, -1)

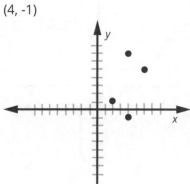

            (0, 3)

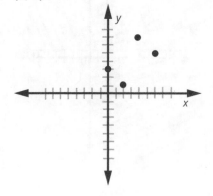

1.014 *x*-intercept: *x* – 0 = 8

                   x = 8

                (8, 0)

y-intercept: 0 – *y* = 8

                 -*y* = 8

                  y = -8

               (0, -8)

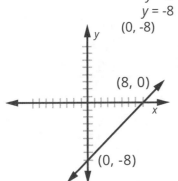

1.015

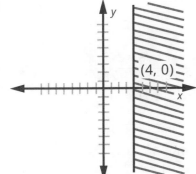

1.016

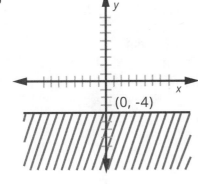

1.017

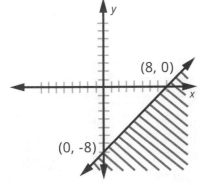

1.018 Solution graph:

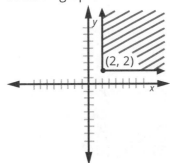

1.019

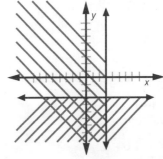

Solution graph:

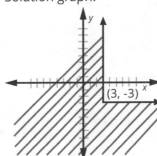

1.020

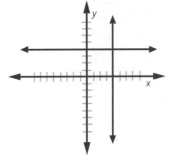

Solution graph:

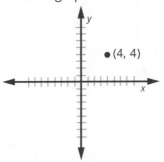

SECTION 2

2.1 $d = \sqrt{(2-6)^2 + (5-8)^2}$
$= \sqrt{(-4)^2 + (-3)^2}$
$= \sqrt{16 + 9} = \sqrt{25} = 5$

2.2 $d = \sqrt{(3-6)^2 + (4-8)^2}$
$= \sqrt{(-3)^2 + (-4)^2}$
$= \sqrt{9 + 16} = \sqrt{25} = 5$

2.3 $d = \sqrt{(-3-9)^2 + [2-(-3)]^2}$
$= \sqrt{(-12)^2 + 5^2}$
$= \sqrt{144 + 25} = \sqrt{169} = 13$

2.4 $d = \sqrt{(0-5)^2 + (6-12)^2}$
$= \sqrt{(-5)^2 + (-6)^2}$
$= \sqrt{25 + 36} = \sqrt{61}$

2.5 $d = \sqrt{(-3-0)^2 + (-4-0)^2}$
$= \sqrt{(-3)^2 + (-4)^2}$
$= \sqrt{9 + 16} = \sqrt{25} = 5$

2.6 $d = \sqrt{(0-9)^2 + (-6-6)^2}$
$= \sqrt{(-9)^2 + (-12)^2}$
$= \sqrt{81 + 144} = \sqrt{225} = 15$

2.7 $d = \sqrt{(4-7)^2 + (1-5)^2}$
$= \sqrt{(-3)^2 + (-4)^2}$
$= \sqrt{9 + 16} = \sqrt{25} = 5$

2.8 $d = \sqrt{(-3-3)^2 + (-6-2)^2}$
$= \sqrt{(-6)^2 + (-8)^2}$
$= \sqrt{36 + 64} = \sqrt{100} = 10$

2.9 $d = \sqrt{[2-(-10)]^2 + (3-12)^2}$
$= \sqrt{12^2 + (-9)^2}$
$= \sqrt{144 + 81} = \sqrt{225} = 15$

2.10 $d = \sqrt{(2-5)^2 + (2-5)^2}$
$= \sqrt{(-3)^2 + (-3)^2}$
$= \sqrt{9 + 9} = \sqrt{18} = 3\sqrt{2}$

2.11 $d = \sqrt{[0-(-5)]^2 + (5-0)^2}$
$= \sqrt{5^2 + 5^2} = \sqrt{25 + 25}$
$= \sqrt{50} = 5\sqrt{2}$

2.12 $d = \sqrt{(3-4)^2 + (4-7)^2}$
$= \sqrt{(-1)^2 + (-3)^2}$
$= \sqrt{1 + 9} = \sqrt{10}$

2.13 $d = \sqrt{(-1-1)^2 + (-1-3)^2}$
$= \sqrt{(-2)^2 + (-4)^2}$
$= \sqrt{4 + 16} = \sqrt{20} = 2\sqrt{5}$

2.14 $d = \sqrt{(-3-0)^2 + (0-\sqrt{7})^2}$
$= \sqrt{(-3)^2 + (\sqrt{7})^2}$
$= \sqrt{9 + 7} = \sqrt{16} = 4$

2.15 $d = \sqrt{(a-2a)^2 + (b-2b)^2}$
$= \sqrt{(-a)^2 + (-b)^2}$
$= \sqrt{a^2 + b^2}$

2.16 $AB = \sqrt{(3-6)^2 + (5-9)^2}$
$= \sqrt{(-3)^2 + (-4)^2}$
$= \sqrt{9 + 16} = \sqrt{25} = 5$
$BC = \sqrt{(6-2)^2 + (9-6)^2}$
$= \sqrt{4^2 + 3^2}$
$= \sqrt{16 + 9} = \sqrt{25} = 5$
$AC = \sqrt{(3-2)^2 + (5-6)^2}$
$= \sqrt{1^2 + (-1)^2}$
$= \sqrt{1 + 1} = \sqrt{2}$
isosceles

2.17 $RS = \sqrt{(1-3)^2 + (3-1)^2}$
$= \sqrt{(-2)^2 + 2^2}$
$= \sqrt{4 + 4} = \sqrt{8} = 2\sqrt{2}$
$ST = \sqrt{(3-5)^2 + (1-2)^2}$
$= \sqrt{(-2)^2 + (-1)^2}$
$= \sqrt{4 + 1} = \sqrt{5}$
$RT = \sqrt{(1-5)^2 + (3-2)^2}$
$= \sqrt{(-4)^2 + 1^2}$
$= \sqrt{16 + 1} = \sqrt{17}$
scalene

2.18 $WX = \sqrt{[5-(-2)]^2 + [-5-(-2)]^2}$
$= \sqrt{7^2 + (-3)^2}$
$= \sqrt{49 + 9} = \sqrt{58}$
$XY = \sqrt{(-2-8)^2 + (-2-2)^2}$
$= \sqrt{(-10)^2 + (-4)^2}$
$= \sqrt{100 + 16} = \sqrt{116} = 2\sqrt{29}$
$WY = \sqrt{(5-8)^2 + (-5-2)^2}$
$= \sqrt{(-3)^2 + (-7)^2}$
$= \sqrt{9 + 49} = \sqrt{58}$
isosceles

2.19 $PQ = \sqrt{(0-6)^2 + (0-0)^2}$
$= \sqrt{(-6)^2 + 0^2}$
$= \sqrt{36} = 6$
$QR = \sqrt{(6-3)^2 + (0-3\sqrt{3})^2}$
$= \sqrt{3^2 + (-3\sqrt{3})^2}$
$= \sqrt{9 + 27} = \sqrt{36} = 6$
$PR = \sqrt{(0-3)^2 + (0-3\sqrt{3})^2}$
$= \sqrt{(-3)^2 + (-3\sqrt{3})^2}$
$= \sqrt{9 + 27} = \sqrt{36} = 6$
equilateral

2.20 $RL = \sqrt{(7-3)^2 + (0-4)^2}$
$= \sqrt{4^2 + (-4)^2}$
$= \sqrt{16 + 16} = \sqrt{32} = 4\sqrt{2}$
$LM = \sqrt{(3-2)^2 + [4-(-1)]^2}$
$= \sqrt{1^2 + 5^2}$
$= \sqrt{1 + 25} = \sqrt{26}$
$RM = \sqrt{(7-2)^2 + [0-(-1)]^2}$
$= \sqrt{5^2 + 1^2}$
$= \sqrt{25 + 1} = \sqrt{26}$
isosceles

2.21

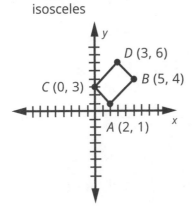

length $= AB$
$= \sqrt{(2-5)^2 + (1-4)^2}$
$= \sqrt{(-3)^2 + (-3)^2}$
$= \sqrt{9 + 9} = \sqrt{18} = 3\sqrt{2}$
width $= AC$
$= \sqrt{(2-0)^2 + (1-3)^2}$
$= \sqrt{(2)^2 + (-2)^2}$
$= \sqrt{4 + 4} = \sqrt{8} = 2\sqrt{2}$

2.22

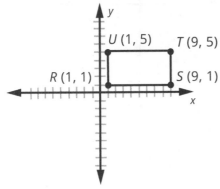

length $= RS = |9-1| = |8| = 8$
width $= UR = |5-1| = |4| = 4$

2.23

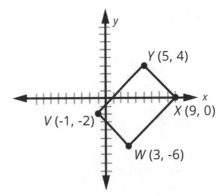

length $= VY$
$= \sqrt{(-1-5)^2 + (-2-4)^2}$
$= \sqrt{(-6)^2 + (-6)^2}$
$= \sqrt{36 + 36} = \sqrt{72} = 6\sqrt{2}$
width $= VW$
$= \sqrt{(-1-3)^2 + [-2-(-6)]^2}$
$= \sqrt{(-4)^2 + 4^2}$
$= \sqrt{16 + 16} = \sqrt{32} = 4\sqrt{2}$

2.24

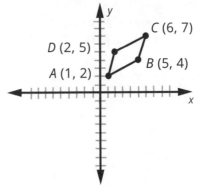

length $= AB$
$= \sqrt{(1-5)^2 + (2-4)^2}$
$= \sqrt{(-4)^2 + (-2)^2}$
$= \sqrt{16 + 4} = \sqrt{20} = 2\sqrt{5}$
width $= AD$
$= \sqrt{(1-2)^2 + (2-5)^2}$
$= \sqrt{(-1)^2 + (-3)^2}$
$= \sqrt{1 + 9} = \sqrt{10}$
$p = 2l + 2w$
$= 2(2\sqrt{5}) + 2\sqrt{10}$
$= 4\sqrt{5} + 2\sqrt{10}$
$d_1 = AC = \sqrt{(1-6)^2 + (2-7)^2}$
$= \sqrt{(-5)^2 + (-5)^2}$
$= \sqrt{25 + 25} = \sqrt{50} = 5\sqrt{2}$
$d_2 = BD = \sqrt{(5-2)^2 + (4-5)^2}$
$= \sqrt{3^2 + (-1)^2}$
$= \sqrt{9 + 1} = \sqrt{10}$

2.25

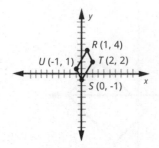

length = *ST*
$= \sqrt{(0 - 2)^2 + (-1 - 2)^2}$
$= \sqrt{(-2)^2 + (-3)^2}$
$= \sqrt{4 + 9} = \sqrt{13}$

width = *RT*
$= \sqrt{(1 - 2)^2 + (4 - 2)^2}$
$= \sqrt{(-1)^2 + 2^2}$
$= \sqrt{1 + 4} = \sqrt{5}$

$p = 2l + 2w$
$= 2\sqrt{13} + 2\sqrt{5}$

$d_1 = RS = \sqrt{(1 - 0)^2 + [4 - (-1)]^2}$
$= \sqrt{1^2 + 5^2}$
$= \sqrt{1 + 25} = \sqrt{26}$

$d_2 = TU = \sqrt{[2 - (-1)]^2 + (2 - 1)^2}$
$= \sqrt{3^2 + 1^2}$
$= \sqrt{9 + 1} = \sqrt{10}$

2.26

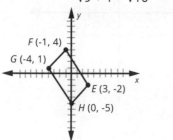

length = *GH*
$= \sqrt{(-4 - 0)^2 + [1 - (-5)]^2}$
$= \sqrt{(-4)^2 + 6^2}$
$= \sqrt{16 + 36} = \sqrt{52} = 2\sqrt{13}$

width = *EH*
$= \sqrt{(3 - 0)^2 + [-2 - (-5)]^2}$
$= \sqrt{3^2 + 3^2}$
$= \sqrt{9 + 9} = \sqrt{18} = 3\sqrt{2}$

$p = 2l + 2w$
$= 2(2\sqrt{13}) + 2(3\sqrt{2})$
$= 4\sqrt{13} + 6\sqrt{2}$

$d_1 = FH = \sqrt{(-1 - 0)^2 + [4 - (-5)]^2}$
$= \sqrt{(-1)^2 + 9^2}$
$= \sqrt{1 + 81} = \sqrt{82}$

$d_2 = EG = \sqrt{[3 - (-4)]^2 + (-2 - 1)^2}$
$= \sqrt{7^2 + (-3)^2}$
$= \sqrt{49 + 9} = \sqrt{58}$

2.27

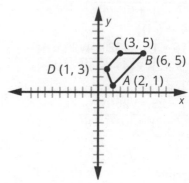

$AB = \sqrt{(2 - 6)^2 + (1 - 5)^2}$
$= \sqrt{(-4)^2 + (-4)^2}$
$= \sqrt{16 + 16} = \sqrt{32} = 4\sqrt{2}$

$BC = \sqrt{(6 - 3)^2 + (5 - 5)^2}$
$= \sqrt{3^2 + 0^2} = \sqrt{9} = 3$

$CD = \sqrt{(3 - 1)^2 + (5 - 3)^2}$
$= \sqrt{2^2 + 2^2}$
$= \sqrt{4 + 4} = \sqrt{8} = 2\sqrt{2}$

$AD = \sqrt{(2 - 1)^2 + (1 - 3)^2}$
$= \sqrt{1^2 + (-2)^2}$
$= \sqrt{1 + 4} = \sqrt{5}$

$P = 4\sqrt{2} + 3 + 2\sqrt{2} + \sqrt{5}$
$= 6\sqrt{2} + \sqrt{5} + 3$

2.28

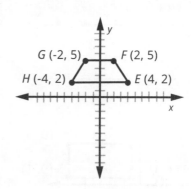

$EF = \sqrt{(4 - 2)^2 + (2 - 5)^2}$
$= \sqrt{2^2 + (-3)^2}$
$= \sqrt{4 + 9} = \sqrt{13}$

$FG = |2 - (-2)| = |2 + 2| = |4| = 4$

$GH = \sqrt{[-2 - (-4)]^2 + (5 - 2)^2}$
$= \sqrt{2^2 + 3^2}$
$= \sqrt{4 + 9} = \sqrt{13}$

$EH = |4 - (-4)| = |4 + 4| = |8| = 8$

$P = \sqrt{13} + 4 + \sqrt{13} + 8$
$= 12 + 2\sqrt{13}$

2.29

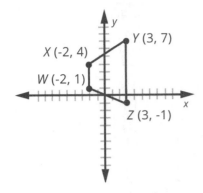

$WX = |1 - 4| = |-3| = 3$

$XY = \sqrt{(-2 - 3)^2 + (4 - 7)^2}$

$\quad = \sqrt{(-5)^2 + (-3)^2}$

$\quad = \sqrt{25 + 9} = \sqrt{34}$

$YZ = |7 - (-1)| = |7 + 1| = |8| = 8$

$WZ = \sqrt{(-2 - 3)^2 + [1 - (-1)]^2}$

$\quad = \sqrt{(-5)^2 + 2^2}$

$\quad = \sqrt{25 + 4} = \sqrt{29}$

$\;P = 3 + \sqrt{34} + 8 + \sqrt{29}$

$\quad = 11 + \sqrt{34} + \sqrt{29}$

2.30 $h = 5, k = 2, r = 3$

$(x - h)^2 + (y - k)^2 = r^2$

$(x - 5)^2 + (y - 2)^2 = 3^2$

$(x - 5)^2 + (y - 2)^2 = 9$

2.31 $h = 3, k = -2, r = 5$

$(x - h)^2 + (y - k)^2 = r^2$

$(x - 3)^2 + [y - (-2)]^2 = 5^2$

$(x - 3)^2 + (y + 2)^2 = 25$

2.32 $r = 4$

$x^2 + y^2 = r^2$

$x^2 + y^2 = 4^2$

$x^2 + y^2 = 16$

2.33 $h = 0, k = 4, r = \sqrt{3}$

$(x - h)^2 + (y - k)^2 = r^2$

$(x - 0)^2 + (y - 4)^2 = (\sqrt{3})^2$

$x^2 + (y - 4)^2 = 3$

2.34 $h = -3, k = 0, r = \sqrt{5}$

$(x - h)^2 + (y - k)^2 = r^2$

$[x - (-3)]^2 + (y - 0)^2 = (\sqrt{5})^2$

$(x + 3)^2 + y^2 = 5$

2.35 a. $(3, 7)$

b. $r = \sqrt{49} = 7$

2.36 a. $(5, -3)$

b. $r = \sqrt{25} = 5$

2.37 a. $(x + 2)^2 + y^2 = 10$

$(x + 2)^2 + (y - 0)^2 = 10$

$(-2, 0)$

b. $\sqrt{10}$

2.38 a. $x^2 + y^2 = 16$

$(x - 0)^2 + (y - 0)^2 = 16$

$(0, 0)$

b. $r = \sqrt{16} = 4$

2.39 a. $(-3, 6)$

b. $r = \sqrt{24} = 2\sqrt{6}$

2.40 a. $x^2 + (y - 3)^2 = 8$

$(x - 0)^2 + (y - 3)^2 = 8$

$(0, 3)$

b. $r = \sqrt{8} = 2\sqrt{2}$

2.41

$(3 - 5)^2 + (2 + 3)^2$	?	25
$(-2)^2 + 5^2$	?	25
$4 + 25$	?	25
29	>	25

exterior

2.42

$(2 - 5)^2 + (3 + 3)^2$	?	25
$(-3)^2 + 6^2$	?	25
$9 + 36$	?	25
45	>	25

exterior

2.43

$(-2 - 5)^2 + (4 + 3)^2$	?	25
$(-7)^2 + 7^2$	?	25
$49 + 49$	?	25
98	>	25

exterior

2.44

$(5 - 5)^2 + (-3 + 3)^2$	?	25
$0^2 + 0^2$	?	25
0	<	25

interior

2.45

$(5 - 5)^2 + (2 + 3)^2$	?	25
$0^2 + 5^2$	?	25
25	=	25

on the circle

2.46

$(0 - 5)^2 + (-3 + 3)^2$	?	25
$(-5)^2 + 0^2$	?	25
25	=	25

on the circle

2.47 Center = $(-2, 2)$

$r = \sqrt{25} = 5$

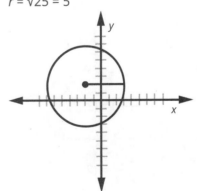

2.48 Center = (3, 0)
$r = \sqrt{4} = 2$

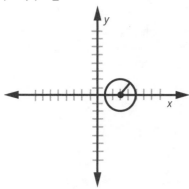

2.49 Center = (0, 0)
$r = \sqrt{16} = 4$

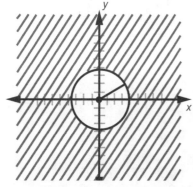

2.50 Center = (-1, 3)
$r = \sqrt{4} = 2$

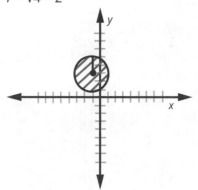

2.51 $M = (\dfrac{-2 + 3}{2}, \dfrac{0 + 5}{2}) = (\dfrac{1}{2}, \dfrac{5}{2})$

2.52 $M = (\dfrac{8 + 5}{2}, \dfrac{2 + 6}{2}) = (\dfrac{13}{2}, 4)$

2.53 $M = (\dfrac{-4 + 10}{2}, \dfrac{8 + 6}{2}) = (3, 7)$

2.54 $M = (\dfrac{0 - 16}{2}, \dfrac{-16 + 0}{2}) = (-8, -8)$

2.55 $M = (\dfrac{-8 + 12}{2}, \dfrac{8 + 4}{2}) = (2, 6)$

2.56
$-2 = \dfrac{1}{2}(3 + x_1)$
$-4 = 3 + x_1$ (multiply by 2)
$-4 - 3 = x_1$
$-7 = x_1$
$0 = \dfrac{1}{2}(5 + y_1)$
$0 = 5 + y_1$ (multiply by 2)
$0 - 5 = y_1$
$-5 = y_1$
$(-7, -5)$

2.57
$8 = \dfrac{1}{2}(5 + x_1)$
$16 = 5 + x_1$ (multiply by 2)
$16 - 5 = x_1$
$11 = x_1$
$2 = \dfrac{1}{2}(6 + y_1)$
$4 = 6 + y_1$ (multiply by 2)
$4 - 6 = y_1$
$-2 = y_1$
$(11, -2)$

2.58
$-4 = \dfrac{1}{2}(10 + x_1)$
$-8 = 10 + x_1$ (multiply by 2)
$-8 - 10 = x_1$
$-18 = x_1$
$8 = \dfrac{1}{2}(6 + y_1)$
$16 = 6 + y_1$ (multiply by 2)
$16 - 6 = y_1$
$10 = y_1$
$(-18, 10)$

2.59
$0 = \dfrac{1}{2}(-16 + x_1)$
$0 = -16 + x_1$ (multiply by 2)
$0 + 16 = x_1$
$16 = x_1$
$-16 = \dfrac{1}{2}(0 + y_1)$
$-32 = 0 + y_1$ (multiply by 2)
$-32 = y_1$
$(16, -32)$

2.60
$-8 = \dfrac{1}{2}(12 + x_1)$
$-16 = 12 + x_1$ (multiply by 2)
$-16 - 12 = x_1$
$-28 = x_1$
$8 = \dfrac{1}{2}(4 + y_1)$
$16 = 4 + y_1$ (multiply by 2)
$16 - 4 = y_1$
$12 = y_1$
$(-28, 12)$

2.61 $M_{AB} = (\frac{4+1}{2}, \frac{-1+4}{2}) = (\frac{5}{2}, \frac{3}{2})$

$M_{BC} = (\frac{-1+4}{2}, \frac{-4-1}{2}) = (\frac{3}{2}, -\frac{5}{2})$

$M_{CD} = (\frac{-4-1}{2}, \frac{1-4}{2}) = (-\frac{5}{2}, -\frac{3}{2})$

$M_{AD} = (\frac{-4+1}{2}, \frac{1+4}{2}) = (-\frac{3}{2}, \frac{5}{2})$

2.62 $M_{AB} = (\frac{5+0}{2}, \frac{7+0}{2}) = (\frac{5}{2}, \frac{7}{2})$

$M_{BC} = (\frac{3+5}{2}, \frac{9+7}{2}) = (\frac{8}{2}, \frac{16}{2}) = (4, 8)$

$M_{AC} = (\frac{3+0}{2}, \frac{9+0}{2}) = (\frac{3}{2}, \frac{9}{2})$

2.63 a. $M_{AC} = (\frac{-1+1}{2}, \frac{-4+4}{2}) = (\frac{0}{2}, \frac{0}{2}) = (0, 0)$

$M_{BD} = (\frac{-4+4}{2}, \frac{1-1}{2}) = (\frac{0}{2}, \frac{0}{2}) = (0, 0)$

b. The midpoints of the two diagonals are the same point.

2.64 $M_{AB} = (\frac{-3+5}{2}, \frac{1-1}{2}) = (\frac{2}{2}, \frac{0}{2}) = (1, 0)$

$d = |5 - 0| = |5| = 5$

$M_{BC} = (\frac{1-3}{2}, \frac{5+1}{2}) = (\frac{-2}{2}, \frac{6}{2}) = (-1, 3)$

$d = \sqrt{(-1-5)^2 + [3-(-1)]^2}$

$d = \sqrt{(-6)^2 + 4^2}$

$d = \sqrt{36 + 16} = \sqrt{52} = 2\sqrt{13}$

$M_{AC} = (\frac{1+5}{2}, \frac{5-1}{2}) = (\frac{6}{2}, \frac{4}{2}) = (3, 2)$

$d = \sqrt{[3-(-3)]^2 + (2-1)^2}$

$d = \sqrt{(6)^2 + 1^2}$

$d = \sqrt{36 + 1} = \sqrt{37}$

2.65 Sides: $M_{AB} = (\frac{3-2}{2}, \frac{6+5}{2}) = (\frac{1}{2}, \frac{11}{2})$

$M_{BC} = (\frac{4+3}{2}, \frac{1+6}{2}) = (\frac{7}{2}, \frac{7}{2})$

$M_{CD} = (\frac{-1+4}{2}, \frac{0+1}{2}) = (\frac{3}{2}, \frac{1}{2})$

$M_{AD} = (\frac{-1-2}{2}, \frac{0+5}{2}) = (-\frac{3}{2}, \frac{5}{2})$

Diagonals: $M_{AC} = (\frac{4-2}{2}, \frac{1+5}{2}) = (\frac{2}{2}, \frac{6}{2}) = (1, 3)$

$M_{BD} = (\frac{-1+3}{2}, \frac{0+6}{2}) = (\frac{2}{2}, \frac{6}{2}) = (1, 3)$

2.66 $M_{AB} = (\frac{8-1}{2}, \frac{4+1}{2}) = (\frac{7}{2}, \frac{5}{2})$

$= (\frac{\frac{7}{2}-1}{2}, \frac{\frac{5}{2}+1}{2}) = (\frac{\frac{5}{2}}{2}, \frac{\frac{7}{2}}{2}) = (\frac{5}{4}, \frac{7}{4})$

$= (\frac{8+\frac{7}{2}}{2}, \frac{4+\frac{5}{2}}{2}) = (\frac{\frac{23}{2}}{2}, \frac{\frac{13}{2}}{2}) = (\frac{23}{4}, \frac{13}{4})$

2.67 $M_{RS} = (\frac{4-2}{2}, \frac{2+2}{2}) = (\frac{2}{2}, \frac{4}{2}) = (1, 2)$

$d = |4 - (-2)| = |4 + 2| = |6| = 6$

$r = \frac{1}{2}d = \frac{1}{2} \cdot 6 = 3$

$(x-1)^2 + (y-2)^2 = 3^2$

$(x-1)^2 + (y-2)^2 = 9$

2.68

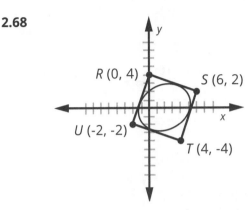

R (0, 4)   S (6, 2)

U (-2, -2)

T (4, -4)

$M_{RT} = $ ctr. $= (\frac{4+0}{2}, \frac{-4+4}{2}) = (\frac{4}{2}, \frac{0}{2}) = (2, 0)$

$r = \frac{d}{2} = \frac{RS}{2} = \frac{1}{2}\sqrt{(0-6)^2 + (4-2)^2}$

$= \frac{1}{2}\sqrt{(-6)^2 + 2^2}$

$= \frac{1}{2}\sqrt{36 + 4} = \frac{1}{2}\sqrt{40}$

$= \frac{1}{2}\sqrt{4 \cdot 10}$

$= \sqrt{10}$

Equation: $(x-2)^2 + (y-0)^2 = (\sqrt{10})^2$

$(x-2)^2 + y^2 = 10$

SELF TEST 2

2.01 $AB = \sqrt{[5 - (-3)]^2 + (8 - 4)^2}$
$= \sqrt{8^2 + 4^2}$
$= \sqrt{64 + 16} = \sqrt{80}$
$= \sqrt{5 \cdot 16} = \sqrt{5}\sqrt{16} = 4\sqrt{5}$

2.02 $RS = \sqrt{(-1 - 8)^2 + (0 - 6)^2}$
$= \sqrt{(-9)^2 + (-6)^2}$
$= \sqrt{81 + 36} = \sqrt{117}$

2.03 $WX = \sqrt{(-6 - 6)^2 + (-8 - 8)^2}$
$= \sqrt{(-12)^2 + (-16)^2}$
$= \sqrt{144 + 256} = \sqrt{400} = 20$

2.04 $CT = \sqrt{[0 - (-6)]^2 + [4 - (-3)]^2}$
$= \sqrt{6^2 + 7^2} = \sqrt{36 + 49} = \sqrt{85}$

2.05 $(x - 5)^2 + (y - 6)^2 = 3^2$
$(x - 5)^2 + (y - 6)^2 = 9$

2.06 $(x - 7)^2 + [y - (-3)]^2 = (\sqrt{7})^2$
$(x - 7)^2 + (y + 3)^2 = 7$

2.07 $(x - 0)^2 + (y - 8)^2 = 8^2$
$x^2 + (y - 8)^2 = 64$

2.08 $[x - (-2)]^2 + [y - (-5)]^2 = 1^2$
$(x + 2)^2 + (y + 5)^2 = 1$

2.09 a. $(-3, 5)$
b. $r = \sqrt{25} = 5$

2.010 a. $(3, 5)$
b. $r = \sqrt{8} = \sqrt{2 \cdot 4} = \sqrt{2}\sqrt{4} = 2\sqrt{2}$

2.011 a. $(-5, -7)$
b. $r = \sqrt{16} = 4$

2.012 a. $(4, 0)$
b. $r = \sqrt{12} = \sqrt{3 \cdot 4} = \sqrt{3}\sqrt{4} = 2\sqrt{3}$

2.013

$(8 + 2)^2 + (4 - 3)^2$	?	81
$10^2 + 1^2$	?	81
$100 + 1$	?	81
101	>	81

exterior

2.014

$(3 + 2)^2 + (0 - 3)^2$	?	81
$5^2 + (-3)^2$	?	81
$25 + 9$	?	81
34	<	81

interior

2.015

$(6 + 2)^2 + (3 - 3)^2$	?	81
$8^2 + 0^2$	?	81
$64 + 0$	?	81
64	<	81

interior

2.016

$(-2 + 2)^2 + (12 - 3)^2$	?	81
$0^2 + 9^2$	?	81
$0 + 81$	?	81
81	=	81

on the circle

2.017 $M = (\dfrac{2 + 6}{2}, \dfrac{3 + 11}{2}) = (\dfrac{8}{2}, \dfrac{14}{2}) = (4, 7)$

2.018 $M = (\dfrac{0 + 12}{2}, \dfrac{5 - 5}{2}) = (\dfrac{12}{2}, \dfrac{0}{2}) = (6, 0)$

2.019 $M = (\dfrac{-3 - 8}{2}, \dfrac{-7 - 4}{2}) = (-\dfrac{11}{2}, -\dfrac{11}{2})$

2.020 $M = (\dfrac{5 - 5}{2}, \dfrac{5 - 5}{2}) = (\dfrac{0}{2}, \dfrac{0}{2}) = (0, 0)$

2.021 $M_{AB} = (\dfrac{-1 + 3}{2}, \dfrac{-2 + 6}{2}) = (\dfrac{2}{2}, \dfrac{4}{2}) = (1, 2)$
$d = \sqrt{(1 - 1)^2 + (2 - 0)^2}$
$= \sqrt{0^2 + 2^2} = \sqrt{0 + 4} = \sqrt{4} = 2$

$M_{BC} = (\dfrac{3 + 1}{2}, \dfrac{6 + 0}{2}) = (\dfrac{4}{2}, \dfrac{6}{2}) = (2, 3)$
$d = \sqrt{[2 - (-1)]^2 + [3 - (-2)]^2}$
$= \sqrt{3^2 + 5^2}$
$= \sqrt{9 + 25} = \sqrt{34}$

$M_{AC} = (\dfrac{-1 + 1}{2}, \dfrac{-2 + 0}{2}) = (\dfrac{0}{2}, \dfrac{-2}{2}) = (0, -1)$
$d = \sqrt{(0 - 3)^2 + (-1 - 6)^2}$
$= \sqrt{(-3)^2 + (-7)^2}$
$= \sqrt{9 + 49} = \sqrt{58}$

2.022 $m_{RS} = \dfrac{7 - 3}{2 - 0} = \dfrac{4}{2} = 2$

$m_{ST} = \dfrac{7 - 7}{8 - 2} = \dfrac{0}{6} = 0$

$m_{TU} = \dfrac{3 - 7}{12 - 8} = \dfrac{-4}{4} = -1$

$m_{RU} = \dfrac{3 - 3}{12 - 0} = \dfrac{0}{12} = 0$

$\overline{ST} \parallel \overline{RU}$; $\therefore$ median goes from RS to TU.

$M_{RS} = (\dfrac{0 + 2}{2}, \dfrac{3 + 7}{2}) = (\dfrac{2}{2}, \dfrac{10}{2}) = (1, 5)$

$M_{TU} = (\dfrac{8 + 12}{2}, \dfrac{7 + 3}{2}) = (\dfrac{20}{2}, \dfrac{10}{2}) = (10, 5)$
$d = \sqrt{(10 - 1)^2 + (5 - 5)^2}$
$= \sqrt{9^2 + 0^2} = \sqrt{81 + 0}$
$= \sqrt{81} = 9$

2.023 center: $(0, -4)$

2.024 $d_{RT} = \sqrt{(1 - 8)^2 + (-1 - 5)^2}$
$= \sqrt{(-7)^2 + (-6)^2}$
$= \sqrt{49 + 36} = \sqrt{85}$
$d_{SU} = \sqrt{(6 - 3)^2 + (1 - 3)^2}$
$= \sqrt{3^2 + (-2)^2}$
$= \sqrt{9 + 4} = \sqrt{13}$
$\sqrt{13}$ is length of shorter diagonal

2.025 line, plane
2.026 line, plane
2.027 none
2.028 point, line, plane
2.029 none
2.030 line, plane
2.031 (4, 4)
2.032 (-4, -2)
2.033 (3, -6)
2.034 (-4, 6)
2.035 (1, 5)

SECTION 3

3.1 $m = \dfrac{8-2}{7-3} = \dfrac{6}{4} = \dfrac{3}{2}$

3.2 $m = \dfrac{0-4}{5-0} = -\dfrac{4}{5}$

3.3 $m = \dfrac{4-(-1)}{0-2} = \dfrac{4+1}{0-2} = -\dfrac{5}{2}$

3.4 $m = \dfrac{5-8}{-2-3} = \dfrac{-3}{-5} = \dfrac{3}{5}$

3.5 $m = \dfrac{1-(-4)}{3-1} = \dfrac{-1+4}{3-1} = \dfrac{3}{2}$

3.6 $m = \dfrac{-2-(-2)}{7-3} = \dfrac{-2+2}{7-3} = \dfrac{0}{4} = 0$

3.7 $m = \dfrac{b-0}{a-0} = \dfrac{b}{a}$

3.8 $m = \dfrac{0-d}{d-0} = \dfrac{-d}{d} = -1$

3.9 $m = \dfrac{(c+d)-(c-d)}{(c-d)-(c+d)}$

$= \dfrac{c+d-c+d}{c-d-c-d} = \dfrac{2d}{-2d} = -1$

3.10 $m = \dfrac{4-2}{3-1} = \dfrac{2}{2} = 1$

3.11 $\dfrac{3}{5} = \dfrac{y-2}{8-3}$

$\dfrac{3}{5} = \dfrac{y-2}{5}$

$3(5) = 5(y-2)$ (cross-multiply)
$3 = y - 2$
$3 + 2 = y$
$5 = y$

3.12 $5 = \dfrac{2-y}{-4-0}$

$5 = \dfrac{2-y}{-4}$

$\dfrac{5}{1} = \dfrac{2-y}{-4}$

$5(-4) = 1(2-y)$ (cross-multiply)
$-20 = 2 - y$
$-20 - 2 = -y$
$-22 = -y$
$22 = y$

3.13 $-\dfrac{7}{2} = \dfrac{-5-2}{x-13}$

$-\dfrac{7}{2} = \dfrac{-7}{x-13}$

$-7 = \dfrac{-14}{x-13}$ (multiply by 2)

$\dfrac{-7}{1} = \dfrac{-14}{x-13}$

$-7(x-13) = 1(-14)$ (cross-multiply)
$-7x + 91 = -14$
$-7x = -14 - 91$
$-7x = -105$
$x = 15$ (divide by -7)

3.14
$$2 = \frac{10 - 0}{5 - x}$$
$$\frac{2}{1} = \frac{10}{5 - x}$$
$$2(5 - x) = 1(10) \qquad \text{(cross-multiply)}$$
$$10 - 2x = 10$$
$$-2x = 10 - 10$$
$$2x = 0$$
$$x = 0$$

3.15
$$j = \frac{y - b}{c - a}$$
$$\frac{j}{1} = \frac{y - b}{c - a}$$
$$j(c - a) = 1(y - b) \text{ (cross-multiply)}$$
$$j(c - a) = y - b$$
$$j(c - a) + b = y$$

3.16
$$m_{RS} = \frac{4 - 1}{2 - (-1)} = \frac{4 - 1}{2 + 1} = \frac{3}{3} = 1$$
$$m_{ST} = \frac{8 - 4}{6 - 2} = \frac{4}{4} = 1$$
$$m_{PT} = \frac{8 - 1}{6 - (-1)} = \frac{8 - 1}{6 + 1} = \frac{7}{7} = 1$$
yes

3.17
$$m_{CD} = \frac{4 - (-1)}{3 - 1} = \frac{4 + 1}{3 - 1} = \frac{5}{2}$$
$$m_{DE} = \frac{8 - 4}{5 - 3} = \frac{4}{2} = 2$$
$$m_{CE} = \frac{8 - (-1)}{5 - 1} = \frac{8 + 1}{5 - 1} = \frac{9}{4}$$
no

3.18
$$m_{WX} = \frac{2 - 4}{6 - 4} = \frac{-2}{2} = -1$$
$$m_{XY} = \frac{16 - 2}{-8 - 6} = \frac{14}{-14} = -1$$
$$m_{WY} = \frac{16 - 4}{-8 - 4} = \frac{12}{-12} = -1$$
yes

3.19
$$m_{AB} = \frac{10 - 0}{-2 - 3} = \frac{10}{-5} = -2$$
$$m_{BC} = \frac{5 - 10}{0 - (-2)} = \frac{5 - 10}{0 + 2} = -\frac{5}{2}$$
$$m_{AC} = \frac{5 - 0}{0 - 3} = -\frac{5}{3}$$
no

3.20
$$m_{PQ} = \frac{0 - 3}{2 - 0} = -\frac{3}{2}$$
$$m_{QR} = \frac{-3 - 0}{4 - 2} = -\frac{3}{2}$$
$$m_{PR} = \frac{-3 - 3}{4 - 0} = \frac{-6}{4} = -\frac{3}{2}$$
yes

3.21
$$m_{AB} = \frac{4 - 0}{2 - 0} = \frac{4}{2} = 2$$
$$m_{BC} = \frac{4 - 4}{5 - 2} = \frac{0}{3} = 0$$
$$m_{CD} = \frac{0 - 4}{4 - 5} = \frac{-4}{-1} = 4$$
$$m_{DA} = \frac{0 - 0}{0 - 4} = \frac{0}{-4} = 0$$

3.22
$$m_{RS} = \frac{6 - 0}{-2 - (-4)} = \frac{6 - 0}{-2 + 4} = \frac{6}{2} = 3$$
$$m_{ST} = \frac{4 - 6}{4 - (-2)} = \frac{4 - 6}{4 + 2} = \frac{-2}{6} = -\frac{1}{3}$$
$$m_{TU} = \frac{-2 - 4}{2 - 4} = \frac{-6}{-2} = 3$$
$$m_{UR} = \frac{0 - (-2)}{-4 - 2} = \frac{0 + 2}{-4 - 2} = \frac{2}{-6} = -\frac{1}{3}$$

3.23
$$m_{MN} = \frac{4 - 0}{2 - 0} = \frac{4}{2} = 2$$
$$m_{NP} = \frac{4 - 4}{8 - 2} = \frac{0}{6} = 0$$
$$m_{PQ} = \frac{0 - 4}{12 - 8} = \frac{-4}{4} = -1$$
$$m_{QM} = \frac{0 - 0}{0 - 12} = \frac{0}{-12} = 0$$

3.24
$$m_{PQ} = \frac{5 - 3}{3 - 1} = \frac{2}{2} = 1$$
$$m_{QR} = \frac{2 - 5}{6 - 3} = \frac{-3}{3} = -1$$
$$m_{RP} = \frac{3 - 2}{1 - 6} = -\frac{1}{5}$$

3.25
$$M_{QR} = \left(\frac{6 + 3}{2}, \frac{2 + 5}{2}\right) = \left(\frac{9}{2}, \frac{7}{2}\right)$$
[to (1, 3)]
$$m = \frac{\frac{7}{2} - 3}{\frac{9}{2} - 1} = \frac{\frac{7}{2} - \frac{6}{2}}{\frac{9}{2} - \frac{2}{2}} = \frac{\frac{1}{2}}{\frac{7}{2}} = \frac{1}{7}$$
$$M_{PR} = \left(\frac{6 + 1}{2}, \frac{2 + 3}{2}\right) = \left(\frac{7}{2}, \frac{5}{2}\right)$$
[to (3, 5)]
$$m = \frac{\frac{5}{2} - 5}{\frac{7}{2} - 3} = \frac{\frac{5}{2} - \frac{10}{2}}{\frac{7}{2} - \frac{6}{2}} = \frac{-\frac{5}{2}}{\frac{1}{2}} = \frac{-5}{1} = -5$$
$$M_{PQ} = \left(\frac{3 + 1}{2}, \frac{5 + 3}{2}\right) = \left(\frac{4}{2}, \frac{8}{2}\right) = (2, 4)$$
[to (6, 2)]
$$m = \frac{4 - 2}{2 - 6} = \frac{2}{-4} = -\frac{1}{2}$$

3.26 $k \perp m$ because $\frac{2}{3}(-\frac{3}{2}) = -1$

$l \perp n$ because $-4(\frac{1}{4}) = -1$

3.27 $m_{AB} = \frac{2-(-2)}{-4-(-5)} = \frac{2+2}{-4+5} = \frac{4}{1} = 4$

$m_{BC} = \frac{5-2}{4-(-4)} = \frac{5-2}{4+4} = \frac{3}{8}$

$m_{CD} = \frac{1-5}{3-4} = \frac{-4}{-1} = 4$

$m_{AD} = \frac{1-(-2)}{3-(-5)} = \frac{1+2}{3+5} = \frac{3}{8}$

$m_{AB} = m_{CD}$; $\therefore \overline{AB} \, || \, \overline{CD}$.

$m_{BC} = m_{AD}$; $\therefore \overline{BC} \, || \, \overline{AD}$.

3.28 a. $m_{AB} = \frac{2-0}{9-16} = -\frac{2}{7}$

$m_{BC} = \frac{0-2}{0-9} = \frac{-2}{-9} = \frac{2}{9}$

$m_{AC} = \frac{0-0}{0-16} = \frac{0}{-16} = 0$

b. altitudes are perpendicular:

$m_{AB} = \frac{7}{2}$

$m_{BC} = -\frac{9}{2}$

$m_{AC} =$ no slope

3.29 $m_{AC} = \frac{2-2}{4-(-2)} = \frac{2-2}{4+2} = \frac{0}{6} = 0$

$m_{BD} = \frac{4-(-2)}{2-2} = \frac{4+2}{2-2} = \frac{6}{0} =$ no slope

$\therefore$ diagonals are $\perp$

3.30 $m_1 = \frac{d-0}{c-0} = \frac{d}{c}$

$m_2 = \frac{c-0}{-d-0} = -\frac{c}{d}$

$\therefore$ lines are $\perp$

3.31 $m_{AB} = \frac{5-1}{3-2} = \frac{4}{1} = 4$; $m_{alt} = -\frac{1}{4}$

$m_{BC} = \frac{2-5}{7-3} = -\frac{3}{4}$; $m_{alt} = \frac{4}{3}$

$m_{AC} = \frac{2-1}{7-2} = \frac{1}{5}$; $m_{alt} = -5$

3.32 $m_{RS} = \frac{3-0}{6-0} = \frac{3}{6} = \frac{1}{2}$

$m_{ST} = \frac{5-3}{5-6} = \frac{2}{-1} = -2$

$m_{TU} = \frac{2-5}{-1-5} = \frac{-3}{-6} = \frac{1}{2}$

$m_{RU} = \frac{2-0}{-1-0} = \frac{2}{-1} = -2$

$\overline{RS} \, || \, \overline{TU}$
$\overline{ST} \, || \, \overline{RU}$
$\overline{RS} \perp \overline{ST}$
$\overline{RS} \perp \overline{RU}$
$\overline{TU} \perp \overline{ST}$
$\overline{TU} \perp \overline{RU}$

3.33 $m_{RS} = \frac{-1-(-3)}{4-1} = \frac{-1+3}{4-1} = \frac{2}{3}$

$m_{ST} = \frac{2-(-1)}{2-4} = \frac{2+1}{2-4} = -\frac{3}{2}$

$m_{TU} = \frac{-2-2}{-4-2} = \frac{-4}{-6} = \frac{2}{3}$

$m_{RU} = \frac{-2-(-3)}{-4-1} = \frac{-2+3}{-4-1} = -\frac{1}{5}$

$\overline{RS} \, || \, \overline{TU}$
$\overline{RS} \perp \overline{ST}$
$\overline{TU} \perp \overline{ST}$

3.34 $m_{RS} = \frac{2-(-5)}{8-(-1)} = \frac{2+5}{8+1} = \frac{7}{9}$

$m_{ST} = \frac{5-2}{5-8} = \frac{3}{-3} = -1$

$m_{TU} = \frac{-2-5}{-4-5} = \frac{-7}{-9} = \frac{7}{9}$

$m_{RU} = \frac{-2-(-5)}{-4-(-1)} = \frac{-2+5}{-4+1} = \frac{3}{-3} = -1$

$\overline{RS} \, || \, \overline{TU}$
$\overline{ST} \, || \, \overline{RU}$

3.35 $m_{RS} = \frac{-2-1}{1-(-1)} = \frac{-2-1}{1+1} = -\frac{3}{2}$

$m_{ST} = \frac{0-(-2)}{4-1} = \frac{0+2}{4-1} = \frac{2}{3}$

$m_{TU} = \frac{3-0}{3-4} = \frac{3}{-1} = -3$

$m_{RU} = \frac{3-1}{3-(-1)} = \frac{3-1}{3+1} = \frac{2}{4} = \frac{1}{2}$

$\overline{RS} \perp \overline{ST}$

3.36 a. $m_{AB} = \dfrac{4-1}{3-0} = \dfrac{3}{3} = 1$

$m_{BC} = \dfrac{1-4}{6-3} = \dfrac{-3}{3} = -1$

$m_{CD} = \dfrac{-3-1}{3-6} = \dfrac{-4}{-3} = \dfrac{4}{3}$

$m_{AD} = \dfrac{1+3}{0-3} = \dfrac{4}{-3} = -\dfrac{4}{3}$

no special quadrilateral because only $\overline{AB} \perp \overline{BC}$

b. $m_{AC} = \dfrac{1-1}{6-0} = \dfrac{0}{6} = 0$

$m_{BD} = \dfrac{-3-4}{3-3} = \dfrac{-7}{0} =$ no slope

yes

3.37 $m_{AB} = \dfrac{1-1}{7-2} = \dfrac{0}{5} = 0$

$m_{BC} = \dfrac{4-1}{2-7} = -\dfrac{3}{5}$

$m_{AC} = \dfrac{4-1}{2-2} = \dfrac{3}{0} =$ no slope

yes, because $\overline{AB} \perp \overline{AC}$

3.38 $m_{RS} = \dfrac{-1-(-3)}{3-1} = \dfrac{-1+3}{3-1} = \dfrac{2}{2} = 1$

$m_{ST} = \dfrac{-7-(-1)}{5-3} = \dfrac{-7+1}{5-3} = \dfrac{-6}{2} = -3$

$m_{RT} = \dfrac{-7-(-3)}{5-1} = \dfrac{-7+3}{5-1} = \dfrac{-4}{4} = -1$

yes, because $\overline{RS} \perp \overline{RT}$

3.39 $m_{GH} = \dfrac{0-3}{9-7} = -\dfrac{3}{2}$

$m_{HI} = \dfrac{-1-0}{5-9} = \dfrac{-1}{-4} = \dfrac{1}{4}$

$m_{GI} = \dfrac{-1-3}{5-7} = \dfrac{-4}{-2} = 2$

no, because no $\perp$'s

3.40 $m_{JK} = \dfrac{3-2}{-1-2} = -\dfrac{1}{3}$

$m_{KL} = \dfrac{-1-3}{-2-(-1)} = \dfrac{-1-3}{-2+1} = \dfrac{-4}{-1} = 4$

$m_{JL} = \dfrac{-1-2}{-2-2} = \dfrac{-3}{-4} = \dfrac{3}{4}$

no, because no $\perp$'s

3.41 $m_{PQ} = \dfrac{2-1}{3-0} = \dfrac{1}{3}$

$m_{QR} = \dfrac{-4-2}{5-3} = \dfrac{-6}{2} = -3$

$m_{PR} = \dfrac{-4-1}{5-0} = \dfrac{-5}{5} = -1$

yes, because $\overline{PQ} \perp \overline{QR}$

3.42 $m = \dfrac{2-1}{5-4} = \dfrac{1}{1} = 1$

$y - 1 = 1(x - 4)$

$y - 1 = x - 4$

$y = x - 4 + 1$

$y = x - 3$

$-x + y = -3$ or $x - y = 3$

3.43 $m = \dfrac{-6-3}{-6-3} = \dfrac{-9}{-9} = 1$

$y - 3 = 1(x - 3)$

$y - 3 = x - 3$

$y = x - 3 + 3$

$y = x - 0$

$-x + y = 0$ or $x - y = 0$

3.44 $m = \dfrac{-4-0}{4-0} = \dfrac{-4}{4} = -1$

$y - 0 = -1(x - 0)$

$y = -x + 0$

$x + y = 0$

3.45 $m = \dfrac{-4-2}{8-6} = \dfrac{-6}{2} = -3$

$y - 2 = -3(x - 6)$

$y - 2 = -3x + 18$

$y = -3x + 18 + 2$

$y = -3x + 20$

$3x + y = 20$

3.46 $m = \dfrac{0-6}{6-0} = \dfrac{-6}{6} = -1$

$y - 6 = -1(x - 0)$

$y - 6 = -x + 0$

$y = -x + 6$

$x + y = 6$

3.47 $m = \dfrac{1-2}{5-(-2)} = \dfrac{1-2}{5+2} = -\dfrac{1}{7}$

$y - 2 = -\dfrac{1}{7}(x + 2)$

$y - 2 = -\dfrac{1}{7}x - \dfrac{2}{7}$

$y = -\dfrac{1}{7}x - \dfrac{2}{7} + 2$

$\dfrac{1}{7}x + y = \dfrac{12}{7}$

$x + 7y = 12$ (multiply by 7)

3.48 $m = \dfrac{5-6}{1-4} = \dfrac{-1}{-3} = \dfrac{1}{3}$

$y - 6 = \dfrac{1}{3}(x - 4)$

$y - 6 = \dfrac{1}{3}x - \dfrac{4}{3}$

$y = \dfrac{1}{3}x - \dfrac{4}{3} + 6$

$-\dfrac{1}{3}x + y = \dfrac{14}{3}$

$-x + 3y = 14$ or   (multiply by 3)

$x - 3y = -14$

3.49 $m = \dfrac{4-1}{\dfrac{1}{2} - \dfrac{1}{2}} = \dfrac{3}{0} = $ no slope

$x = \dfrac{1}{2}$ (line parallel to the y-axis)

3.50 $m = \dfrac{5-0}{0-5} = \dfrac{5}{-5} = -1$

$y - 0 = -1(x - 5)$

$y - 0 = -x + 5$

$x + y = 5$

3.51 $m = \dfrac{6-6}{5-0} = \dfrac{0}{5} = 0$

$y - 6 = 0(x - 0)$

$y = 6$

3.52 $y - 5 = 3(x - 5)$

$y - 5 = 3x - 15$

$-3x + y - 5 = -15$

$-3x + y = -15 + 5$

$-3x + y = -10$

$3x - y = 10$

3.53 $y - 2 = -\dfrac{1}{2}(x - 6)$

$y - 2 = -\dfrac{1}{2}x + 3$

$\dfrac{1}{2}x + y - 2 = 3$

$\dfrac{1}{2}x + y = 3 + 2$

$\dfrac{1}{2}x + y = 5$

$x + 2y = 10$ (multiply by 2)

3.54 $y - 4 = 0(x - 0)$

$y - 4 = 0$

$y = 4$

3.55 $y + 2 = \dfrac{2}{5}(x - 5)$

$y + 2 = \dfrac{2}{5}x - 2$

$-\dfrac{2}{5}x + y + 2 = -2$

$-\dfrac{2}{5}x + y = -2 - 2$

$-\dfrac{2}{5}x + y = -4$

$2x - 5y = 20$ (multiply by -5)

3.56 no slope; $\therefore x = 3$

3.57 $y + 1 = \dfrac{3}{4}(x - 2)$

$y + 1 = \dfrac{3}{4}x - \dfrac{6}{4}$

$-\dfrac{3}{4}x + y + 1 = -\dfrac{6}{4}$

$-\dfrac{3}{4}x + y = -\dfrac{6}{4} - 1$

$-\dfrac{3}{4}x + y = -\dfrac{10}{4}$

$3x + 4y = 10$ (multiply by -4)

3.58 $y - 4 = -\dfrac{5}{2}(x + 3)$

$y - 4 = -\dfrac{5}{2}x - \dfrac{15}{2}$

$\dfrac{5}{2}x + y - 4 = -\dfrac{15}{2}$

$\dfrac{5}{2}x + y = -\dfrac{15}{2} + 4$

$\dfrac{5}{2}x + y = -\dfrac{7}{2}$

$5x + 2y = -7$ (multiply by 2)

3.59 $M = (\dfrac{-6 + 2}{2}, \dfrac{5 - 3}{2}) = (\dfrac{-4}{2}, \dfrac{2}{2}) = (-2, 1)$

$y - 1 = \dfrac{9}{7}(x + 2)$

$y - 1 = \dfrac{9}{7}x + \dfrac{18}{7}$

$-\dfrac{9}{7}x + y - 1 = \dfrac{18}{7}$

$-\dfrac{9}{7}x + y = \dfrac{18}{7} + 1$

$-\dfrac{9}{7}x + y = \dfrac{25}{7}$

$9x - 7y = -25$ (multiply by -7)

3.60

$$M = (\frac{5+1}{2}, \frac{-2+0}{2}) = (\frac{6}{2}, \frac{-2}{2}) = (3, -1)$$

$$m = \frac{-2-0}{5-1} = \frac{-2}{4} = -\frac{1}{2}$$

$$y + 1 = 2(x - 3)$$
$$y + 1 = 2x - 6$$
$$y = 2x - 7$$
$$-2x + y = -7$$
$$2x - y = 7 \qquad \text{(multiply by -1)}$$

3.61

$$m_{AB} = \frac{1-5}{1-(-5)} = \frac{1-5}{1+5} = \frac{-4}{6} = -\frac{2}{3}$$

$$m_{BC} = \frac{4-1}{3-1} = \frac{3}{2}$$

$$m_{AC} = \frac{4-5}{3-(-5)} = \frac{4-5}{3+5} = -\frac{1}{8}$$

$\overline{AB} \perp \overline{BC}, \therefore AB$ and BC are legs.

$$M_{AB} = (\frac{1-5}{2}, \frac{1+5}{2}) = (\frac{-4}{2}, \frac{6}{2}) = (-2, 3)$$

$$M_{BC} = (\frac{3+1}{2}, \frac{4+1}{2}) = (\frac{4}{2}, \frac{5}{2}) = (2, \frac{5}{2})$$

$$m = \frac{\frac{5}{2} - 3}{2 - (-2)} = \frac{\frac{5}{2} - 3}{2 + 2} = \frac{\frac{1}{2}}{4} = -\frac{1}{8}$$

$$y - 3 = -\frac{1}{8}(x + 2)$$
$$y - 3 = -\frac{1}{8}x - \frac{1}{4}$$
$$\frac{1}{8}x + y - 3 = -\frac{1}{4}$$
$$\frac{1}{8}x + y = -\frac{1}{4} + 3$$
$$\frac{1}{8}x + y = \frac{11}{4}$$
$$x + 8y = 22 \qquad \text{(multiply by 8)}$$

3.62

$$m_{AB} = \frac{1-5}{1-(-5)} = \frac{1-5}{1+5} = \frac{-4}{6} = -\frac{2}{3}$$

$$m_{BC} = \frac{4-1}{3-1} = \frac{3}{2}$$

$$m_{AC} = \frac{4-5}{3-(-5)} = \frac{4-5}{3+5} = -\frac{1}{8}$$

$\overline{AB} \perp \overline{BC}, \therefore AC$ is hypotenuse.

$$y - 4 = \frac{1}{8}(x - 3)$$
$$y - 4 = -\frac{1}{8}x + \frac{3}{8}$$
$$\frac{1}{8}x + y - 4 = \frac{3}{8}$$
$$\frac{1}{8}x + y = \frac{3}{8} + 4$$
$$\frac{1}{8}x + y = \frac{35}{8}$$
$$x + 8y = 35 \qquad \text{(multiply by 8)}$$

3.63

$$d_{AC} = \sqrt{(2-1)^2 + [2-(-1)]^2}$$
$$= \sqrt{1^2 + 3^2}$$
$$= \sqrt{1 + 9} = \sqrt{10}$$
$$d_{BD} = \sqrt{(-2-6)^2 + (-2-4)^2}$$
$$= \sqrt{(-8)^2 + (-6)^2}$$
$$= \sqrt{64 + 36} = \sqrt{100} = 10$$

$\therefore BD$ is longer diagonal.

$$m_{BD} = \frac{4-(-2)}{6-(-2)} = \frac{4+2}{6+2} = \frac{6}{8} = \frac{3}{4}$$

$$y + 2 = \frac{3}{4}(x + 2)$$
$$y + 2 = \frac{3}{4}x + \frac{6}{4}$$
$$-\frac{3}{4}x + y + 2 = \frac{6}{4}$$
$$-\frac{3}{4}x + y = \frac{6}{4} - 2$$
$$-\frac{3}{4}x + y = -\frac{2}{4}$$
$$3x - 4y = 2 \qquad \text{(multiply by -4)}$$

3.64

$$m_{RS} = \frac{8-5}{1-(-1)} = \frac{8-5}{1+1} = \frac{3}{2}$$

$$m_{ST} = \frac{-2-8}{7-1} = \frac{-10}{6} = -\frac{5}{3}$$

$$m_{TU} = \frac{0-(-2)}{2-7} = \frac{0+2}{2-7} = -\frac{2}{5}$$

$$m_{RU} = \frac{0-5}{2-(-1)} = \frac{0-5}{2+1} = -\frac{5}{3}$$

$\overline{ST} \parallel \overline{RU}; \therefore$ median goes from $\overline{RS}$ to $\overline{TU}$.

$$M_{RS} = (\frac{1-1}{2}, \frac{8+5}{2}) = (\frac{0}{2}, \frac{13}{2}) = (0, \frac{13}{2})$$

$$M_{TU} = (\frac{2+7}{2}, \frac{0-2}{2}) = (\frac{9}{2}, \frac{-2}{2}) = (\frac{9}{2}, -1)$$

$$m = \frac{-1 - \frac{13}{2}}{\frac{9}{2} - 0} = \frac{-\frac{15}{2}}{\frac{9}{2}} = -\frac{15}{9} = -\frac{5}{3}$$

$$y + 1 = -\frac{5}{3}(x - \frac{9}{2})$$
$$y + 1 = -\frac{5}{3}x + \frac{15}{2}$$
$$\frac{5}{3}x + y + 1 = \frac{15}{2}$$
$$\frac{5}{3}x + y = \frac{15}{2} - 1$$
$$\frac{5}{3}x + y = \frac{13}{2}$$
$$10x + 6y = 39 \qquad \text{(multiply by 6)}$$

3.65

$$m_{PQ} = \frac{5-1}{3-(-1)} = \frac{5-1}{3+1} = \frac{4}{4} = 1$$

$$m_{QR} = \frac{-5-5}{5-3} = \frac{-10}{2} = -5$$

$$m_{PR} = \frac{-5-1}{5-(-1)} = \frac{-5-1}{5+1} = \frac{-6}{6} = -1$$

$$m_{alt} = \frac{1}{5}$$

$$y - 1 = \frac{1}{5}(x + 1)$$

$$y - 1 = \frac{1}{5}x + \frac{1}{5}$$

$$-\frac{1}{5}x + y - 1 = \frac{1}{5}$$

$$-\frac{1}{5}x + y = \frac{1}{5} + 1$$

$$-\frac{1}{5}x + y = \frac{6}{5}$$

$$x - 5y = -6 \qquad \text{(multiply by -5)}$$

3.66

$$m_{AC} = \frac{-3-3}{3-(-3)} = \frac{-3-3}{3+3} = \frac{-6}{6} = -1$$

$$y - 3 = -1(x - 3)$$

$$y - 3 = -x - 3$$

$$x + y - 3 = -3$$

$$x + y = -3 + 3$$

$$x + y = 0$$

$$m_{BD} = \frac{-3-3}{-3-3} = \frac{-6}{-6} = 1$$

$$y - 3 = 1(x - 3)$$

$$y - 3 = x - 3$$

$$-x + y - 3 = -3$$

$$-x + y = -3 + 3$$

$$-x + y = 0$$

$$x - y = 0 \qquad \text{(multiply by -1)}$$

SELF TEST 3

3.01 $m = \dfrac{8-6}{10-5} = \dfrac{2}{5}$

3.02 $m = \dfrac{-2-5}{3-(-3)} = \dfrac{-2-5}{3+3} = -\dfrac{7}{6}$

3.03 $m = \dfrac{4-6}{-2-0} = \dfrac{-2}{-2} = 1$

3.04 $m = \dfrac{6-3}{4-0} = \dfrac{3}{4}$

3.05 $m = \dfrac{-2-5}{6-5} = \dfrac{-7}{1} = -7$

3.06 $m = \dfrac{-2-4}{6-(-2)} = \dfrac{-2-4}{6+2} = \dfrac{-6}{8} = -\dfrac{3}{4}$

3.07 $m = \dfrac{1-7}{3-5} = \dfrac{-6}{-2} = 3$

$m\perp = -\dfrac{1}{3}$

3.08 $m = \dfrac{0-(-2)}{8-4} = \dfrac{0+2}{8-4} = \dfrac{2}{4} = \dfrac{1}{2}$

$m\perp = -2$

3.09 $m = \dfrac{4-6}{4-6} = \dfrac{-2}{-2} = 1$

$m\perp = -1$

3.010 $m = \dfrac{1-(-4)}{5-0} = \dfrac{1+4}{5-0} = \dfrac{5}{5} = 1$

$$y + 4 = 1(x - 0)$$

$$y + 4 = x$$

$$-x + y + 4 = 0$$

$$-x + y = -4$$

$$x - y = 4 \qquad \text{(multiply by -1)}$$

3.011 $m = \dfrac{0-2}{5-(-3)} = \dfrac{0-2}{5+3} = \dfrac{-2}{8} = -\dfrac{1}{4}$

$$y - 2 = -\frac{1}{4}(x + 3)$$

$$y - 2 = -\frac{1}{4}x - \frac{3}{4}$$

$$\frac{1}{4}x + y - 2 = -\frac{3}{4}$$

$$\frac{1}{4}x + y = -\frac{3}{4} + 2$$

$$\frac{1}{4}x + y = \frac{5}{4}$$

$$x + 4y = 5 \qquad \text{(multiply by 4)}$$

3.012 $m = \dfrac{4-4}{-6-6} = \dfrac{0}{-12} = 0$

$y = 4$

3.013 $y - 0 = 5(x - 4)$

$y - 0 = 5x - 20$

$-5x + y = -20$

$5x - y = 20$ (multiply by -1)

3.014 $y - 1 = \dfrac{1}{2}(x + 6)$

$y - 1 = \dfrac{1}{2}x + 3$

$-\dfrac{1}{2}x + y - 1 = 3$

$-\dfrac{1}{2}x + y = 3 + 1$

$-\dfrac{1}{2}x + y = 4$

$x - 2y = -8$ (multiply by -2)

3.015 $y - 5 = \dfrac{3}{2}(x - 2)$

$y - 5 = \dfrac{3}{2}x - 3$

$-\dfrac{3}{2}x + y - 5 = -3$

$-\dfrac{3}{2}x + y = -3 + 5$

$-\dfrac{3}{2}x + y = 2$

$3x - 2y = -4$ (multiply by -2)

3.016 $d_{AB} = \sqrt{(2-8)^2 + (1-4)^2}$

$= \sqrt{(-6)^2 + (-3)^2}$

$= \sqrt{36 + 9} = \sqrt{45} = 3\sqrt{5}$

$d_{BC} = \sqrt{(8-5)^2 + (4-7)^2}$

$= \sqrt{3^2 + (-3)^2}$

$= \sqrt{9 + 9} = \sqrt{18} = 3\sqrt{2}$

$d_{AC} = \sqrt{(2-5)^2 + (1-7)^2}$

$= \sqrt{(-3)^2 + (-6)^2}$

$= \sqrt{9 + 36} = \sqrt{45} = 3\sqrt{5}$

$\therefore \overline{BC}$ is base.

$M_{BC} = \left(\dfrac{8+5}{2}, \dfrac{4+7}{2}\right) = \left(\dfrac{13}{2}, \dfrac{11}{2}\right)$

[to (2, 1)]

$m = \dfrac{1 - \dfrac{11}{2}}{2 - \dfrac{13}{2}} = \dfrac{-\dfrac{9}{2}}{-\dfrac{9}{2}} = 1$

$y - 1 = 1(x - 2)$

$y - 1 = x - 2$

$-x + y - 1 = -2$

$-x + y = -2 + 1$

$-x + y = -1$

$x - y = 1$ (multiply by -1)

3.017 $M_{RS} = \left(\dfrac{-1+5}{2}, \dfrac{6+5}{2}\right) = \left(\dfrac{4}{2}, \dfrac{11}{2}\right) = \left(2, \dfrac{11}{2}\right)$

$m_{RS} = \dfrac{5-6}{5-(-1)} = \dfrac{5-6}{5+1} = -\dfrac{1}{6}; \therefore m\perp = 6$

$y - \dfrac{11}{2} = 6(x - 2)$

$y - \dfrac{11}{2} = 6x - 12$

$-6x + y - \dfrac{11}{2} = -12$

$-6x + y = -12 + \dfrac{11}{2}$

$-6x + y = -\dfrac{13}{2}$

$12x - 2y = 13$ (multiply by -2)

3.018 $m \parallel = \dfrac{2}{3}$

$y + 2 = \dfrac{2}{3}(x - 1)$

$y + 2 = \dfrac{2}{3}x - \dfrac{2}{3}$

$-\dfrac{2}{3}x + y + 2 = -\dfrac{2}{3}$

$-\dfrac{2}{3}x + y = -\dfrac{2}{3} - 2$

$-\dfrac{2}{3}x + y = -\dfrac{8}{3}$

$2x - 3y = 8$ (multiply by -3)

3.019 $m_{PS} = \dfrac{-4-(-2)}{7-2} = \dfrac{-4+2}{7-2} = -\dfrac{2}{5}$

$m_{QR} = \dfrac{-2-(-4)}{7-2} = \dfrac{-2+4}{7-2} = \dfrac{2}{5}$

$\overline{PS}$ has negative slope.

$y + 2 = -\dfrac{2}{5}(x - 2)$

$y + 2 = -\dfrac{2}{5}x + \dfrac{4}{5}$

$\dfrac{2}{5}x + y + 2 = \dfrac{4}{5}$

$\dfrac{2}{5}x + y = \dfrac{4}{5} - 2$

$\dfrac{2}{5}x + y = -\dfrac{6}{5}$

$2x + 5y = -6$ (multiply by 5)

3.020 positive

3.021 negative

3.022 zero

3.023 no slope

3.024 positive

3.025 $x = 0$:

$0 + y = 5$
$y = 5$
$(0, 5)$

$y = 0$:

$x + 0 = 5$
$x = 5$
$(5, 0)$

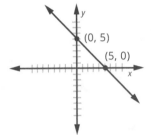

3.026 $x = 0$:

$0 + 2y = 6$
$\dfrac{2y}{2} = \dfrac{6}{2}$
$y = 3$
$(0, 3)$

$y = 0$:

$x + 0 = 6$
$x = 6$
$(6, 0)$

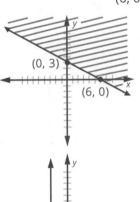

3.027

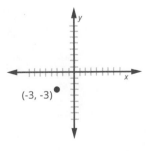

Solution graph:

3.028

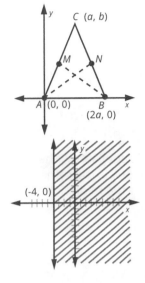

3.029 a. $(3, 7)$

b. $r = \sqrt{49} = 7$

3.030 a. $(-2, 0)$

b. $r = \sqrt{10}$

3.031 a. $(-3, 6)$

b. $r = \sqrt{24} = \sqrt{4 \cdot 6} = \sqrt{4}\sqrt{6} = 2\sqrt{6}$

3.032 $M = (\dfrac{3-2}{2}, \dfrac{5+0}{2}) = (\dfrac{1}{2}, \dfrac{5}{2})$

3.033 $M = (\dfrac{10-4}{2}, \dfrac{6+8}{2}) = (\dfrac{6}{2}, \dfrac{14}{2}) = (3, 7)$

3.034 $M = (\dfrac{3-7}{2}, \dfrac{5-5}{2}) = (\dfrac{-4}{2}, \dfrac{0}{2}) = (-2, 0)$

SECTION 4

4.1 a

4.2 b

4.3 a

4.4 b

4.5 a

4.6 a. $M = (\dfrac{0 + 2h}{2}, \dfrac{0 + 0}{2}) = (\dfrac{2h}{2}, \dfrac{0}{2}) = (h, 0)$

b. Since $\triangle RST$ is equilateral, the x-coordinate of R is the same coordinate as the one for the midpoint of ST; x-coordinate $= h$.

c.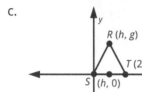

4.7 a. $C\,(a, 0),\ D\,(a, a)$

b. $C\,(-a, 0),\ D\,(-a, a)$

c.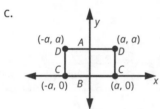

4.8 a. $(a, -b),\ (-a, -b),\ (-a, b)$

b.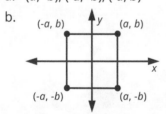

4.9 a. $M = (\dfrac{0 + j}{2}, \dfrac{t + t}{2}) = (\dfrac{j}{2}, \dfrac{2t}{2}) = (\dfrac{1}{2}j, t)$

x-coordinate is $\dfrac{1}{2}j$

b.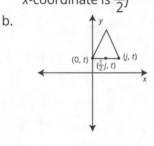

4.10 a. j

b. $d = |h - 0| = |h| = h$

c. h

d. $d = |h + k| = h + k = k + h$

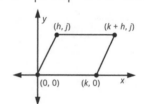

4.11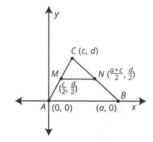

$M_{AC} = (\dfrac{0 + c}{2}, \dfrac{0 + d}{2}) = (\dfrac{c}{2}, \dfrac{d}{2})$

$M_{BC} = (\dfrac{a + c}{2}, \dfrac{0 + d}{2}) = (\dfrac{a + c}{2}, \dfrac{d}{2})$

$m_{MN} = \dfrac{\dfrac{d}{2} - \dfrac{d}{2}}{\dfrac{a + c}{2} - \dfrac{c}{2}} = \dfrac{0}{\dfrac{a + c}{2} - \dfrac{c}{2}} = 0$

$m_{AB} = \dfrac{0 - 0}{a} = \dfrac{0}{a} = 0$

Slopes are equal; therefore, $\overline{MN} \parallel \overline{AB}$.

4.12

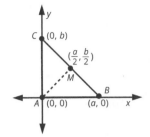

$$M_{BC} = (\frac{0+a}{2}, \frac{b+0}{2}) = (\frac{a}{2}, \frac{b}{2})$$

$$MB = \sqrt{(\frac{a}{2} - a)^2 + (\frac{b}{2} - 0)^2}$$

$$= \sqrt{(\frac{a}{2} - \frac{2a}{2})^2 + (\frac{b}{2})^2}$$

$$= \sqrt{(\frac{a}{2})^2 + (\frac{b}{2})^2} = \sqrt{\frac{a^2}{4} + \frac{b^2}{4}}$$

$$MC = \sqrt{(\frac{a}{2} - 0)^2 + (\frac{b}{2} - b)^2}$$

$$= \sqrt{(\frac{a}{2})^2 + (\frac{b}{2} - \frac{2b}{2})^2}$$

$$= \sqrt{(-\frac{a}{2})^2 + (-\frac{b}{2})^2} = \sqrt{\frac{a^2}{4} + \frac{b^2}{4}}$$

$$MA = \sqrt{(\frac{a}{2} - 0)^2 + (\frac{b}{2} - 0)^2}$$

$$= \sqrt{(\frac{a}{2})^2 + (\frac{b}{2})^2} = \sqrt{\frac{a^2}{4} + \frac{b^2}{4}}$$

$$7 \therefore MB = MC = MA$$

4.13

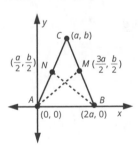

$$M_{AB} = (\frac{0+2a}{2}, \frac{0+0}{2}) = (\frac{2a}{2}, \frac{0}{2}) = (a, 0)$$

x-coordinate of point $C = a$

$$M_{AC} = (\frac{0+a}{2}, \frac{0+b}{2}) = (\frac{a}{2}, \frac{b}{2})$$

$$M_{BC} = (\frac{2a+a}{2}, \frac{0+b}{2}) = (\frac{3a}{2}, \frac{b}{2})$$

$$MA = \sqrt{(\frac{3a}{2} - 0)^2 + (\frac{b}{2} - 0)^2}$$

$$= \sqrt{(\frac{3a}{2})^2 + (\frac{b}{2})^2} = \sqrt{\frac{9a^2}{4} + \frac{b^2}{4}}$$

$$NB = \sqrt{(\frac{a}{2} - 2a)^2 + (\frac{b}{2} - 0)^2}$$

$$= \sqrt{(\frac{a}{2} - \frac{4a}{2})^2 + (\frac{b}{2} - 0)^2}$$

$$= \sqrt{(\frac{-3a}{2})^2 + (\frac{b}{2})^2} = \sqrt{\frac{9a^2}{4} + \frac{b^2}{4}}$$

$$\therefore MA = NB$$

4.14

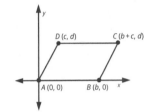

$$AD = \sqrt{(c - 0)^2 + (d - 0)^2} = \sqrt{c^2 + d^2}$$
$$BC = \sqrt{[(b + c) - b]^2 + (d - 0)^2} = \sqrt{c^2 + d^2}$$
$$AB = \sqrt{(b - 0)^2 + (0 - 0)^2} = \sqrt{b^2 + 0^2} = \sqrt{b^2}$$
$$CD = \sqrt{[c - (b + c)]^2 + (d - d)^2} = \sqrt{b^2 + 0^2} = \sqrt{b^2}$$
$$\therefore AD = BC; AB = CD$$

4.15

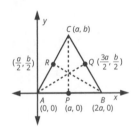

$$M_{AB} = (\frac{0+2a}{2}, \frac{0+0}{2}) = (\frac{2a}{2}, \frac{0}{2}) = (a, 0)$$

$$M_{BC} = (\frac{2a+a}{2}, \frac{0+b}{2}) = (\frac{3a}{2}, \frac{b}{2})$$

$$M_{AC} = (\frac{0+a}{2}, \frac{0+b}{2}) = (\frac{a}{2}, \frac{b}{2})$$

$$PC = \sqrt{(a - a)^2 + (0 - b)^2}$$
$$= \sqrt{(-b)^2} \quad \text{(Height of equilateral } \triangle = b$$
$$= a\sqrt{3} \quad \text{with side} = 2a)$$

$$QA = \sqrt{(0 - \frac{3a}{2})^2 + (0 - \frac{b}{2})^2}$$

$$= \sqrt{(\frac{-3a}{2})^2 + (-\frac{b}{2})^2}$$

$$= \sqrt{\frac{9a^2}{4} + \frac{b^2}{4}}$$

$$= \sqrt{\frac{9a^2}{4} + \frac{(a\sqrt{3})^2}{4}}$$

$$= \sqrt{\frac{9a^2}{4} + \frac{3a^2}{4}}$$

$$= \sqrt{\frac{12a^2}{4}} = \sqrt{3a^2} = a\sqrt{3}$$

$$RB = \sqrt{(2a - \frac{a}{2})^2 + (0 - \frac{b}{2})^2}$$

$$= \sqrt{(\frac{4a}{2} - \frac{a}{2})^2 + (0 - \frac{b}{2})^2}$$

$$= \sqrt{(\frac{3a}{2})^2 + (-\frac{b}{2})^2} = \sqrt{\frac{9a^2}{4} + \frac{b^2}{4}}$$

$$= \sqrt{\frac{9a^2}{4} + \frac{(a\sqrt{3})^2}{4}}$$

$$= \sqrt{\frac{9a^2}{4} + \frac{3a^2}{4}}$$

$$= \sqrt{\frac{12a^2}{4}} = \sqrt{3a^2} = a\sqrt{3}$$

$$\therefore PC = QA = RB$$

4.16

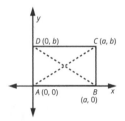

$$AC = \sqrt{(a - 0)^2 + (b - 0)^2} = \sqrt{a^2 + b^2}$$
$$BD = \sqrt{(0 - a)^2 + (b - 0)^2} = \sqrt{(-a)^2 + b^2}$$
$$= \sqrt{a^2 + b^2}$$
$$\therefore AC = BD$$

4.17

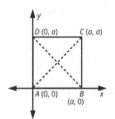

$$m_{AC} = \frac{a - 0}{a - 0} = 1$$

$$m_{BD} = \frac{0 - a}{a - 0} = \frac{-a}{a} = -1$$

$$m_{AC} \cdot m_{BD} = 1(-1) = -1$$

$$\therefore \overline{AC} \perp \overline{BD}$$

4.18

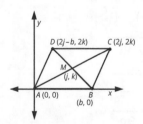

Since M is midpoint of BD, D $(2j - b, 2k)$.

Since M is midpoint of AC, C $(2j, 2k)$.

$$m_{AD} = \frac{2k - 0}{(2j - b) - 0} = \frac{2k}{2j - b}$$

$$m_{BC} = \frac{2k - 0}{2j - b} = \frac{2k}{2j - b}$$

$$\overline{AD} \parallel \overline{BC}$$

$$m_{AB} = \frac{0 - 0}{b - 0} = \frac{0}{b} = 0$$

$$m_{DC} = \frac{2k - 2k}{2j - (2j - b)} = \frac{0}{-b} = 0$$

$$\overline{AB} \parallel \overline{DC}$$

$\therefore ABCD$ is a parallelogram.

4.19

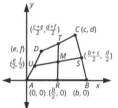

$$M_{AB} = (\frac{b + 0}{2}, \frac{0 + 0}{2}) = (\frac{b}{2}, \frac{0}{2}) = (\frac{b}{2}, 0)$$

$$M_{BC} = (\frac{c + b}{2}, \frac{d + 0}{2}) = (\frac{c + b}{2}, \frac{d}{2})$$

$$M_{CD} = (\frac{c + e}{2}, \frac{d + f}{2})$$

$$M_{AD} = (\frac{e + 0}{2}, \frac{f + 0}{2}) = (\frac{e}{2}, \frac{f}{2})$$

$$M_{SU} = (\frac{\frac{b + c}{2} + \frac{e}{2}}{2}, \frac{\frac{d}{2} + \frac{f}{2}}{2})$$

$$= (\frac{\frac{b + c + e}{2}}{2}, \frac{\frac{d + f}{2}}{2})$$

$$= (\frac{b + c + e}{4}, \frac{d + f}{4})$$

$$M_{RT} = (\frac{\frac{c + e}{2} + \frac{b}{2}}{2}, \frac{\frac{d + f}{2} + 0}{2})$$

$$= (\frac{\frac{c + e + b}{2}}{2}, \frac{\frac{d + f}{2}}{2})$$

$$= (\frac{c + e + b}{4}, \frac{d + f}{4})$$

Midpoints of both segments are the same point.

∴ Segments bisect each other.

4.20

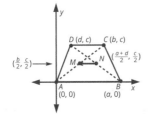

$$M_{AC} = \left(\frac{b+0}{2}, \frac{c+0}{2}\right) = \left(\frac{b}{2}, \frac{c}{2}\right)$$

$$M_{BC} = \left(\frac{a+d}{2}, \frac{0+c}{2}\right) = \left(\frac{a+d}{2}, \frac{c}{2}\right)$$

$$m_{AB} = \frac{0-0}{a-0} = \frac{0}{a} = 0$$

$$m_{MN} = \frac{\frac{c}{2} - \frac{c}{2}}{\frac{a+d}{2} - \frac{b}{2}} = \frac{0}{\frac{a+d}{2} - \frac{b}{2}} = 0$$

Slopes are equal;
∴ segments ||.

4.21

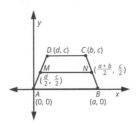

$$M_{AD} = \left(\frac{d+0}{2}, \frac{c+0}{2}\right) = \left(\frac{d}{2}, \frac{c}{2}\right)$$

$$M_{BC} = \left(\frac{a+b}{2}, \frac{0+c}{2}\right) = \left(\frac{a+b}{2}, \frac{c}{2}\right)$$

$$MN = \sqrt{\left(\frac{a+b}{2} - \frac{d}{2}\right)^2 + \left(\frac{c}{2} - \frac{c}{2}\right)^2}$$

$$= \sqrt{\left(\frac{a+b-d}{2}\right)^2 + 0^2}$$

$$= \sqrt{\left(\frac{a+b-d}{2}\right)^2} = \frac{a+b-d}{2}$$

$$AB = \sqrt{(a-0)^2 + (0-0)^2} = \sqrt{a^2 + 0^2} = \sqrt{a^2} = a$$

$$CD = \sqrt{(b-d)^2 + (c-c)^2}$$

$$= \sqrt{(b-d)^2 + 0^2}$$

$$= \sqrt{(b-d)^2} = b - d$$

$$MN = \frac{1}{2}(AB + CD)$$

$$\frac{1}{2}(a+b-d) = \frac{1}{2}(a+b-d)$$

4.22

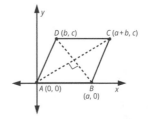

$$m_{AC} = \frac{c-0}{a+b-0} = \frac{c}{a+b}$$

$$m_{BD} = \frac{c-0}{b-a} = \frac{c}{b-a}$$

$$\frac{c}{a+b} = -\frac{b-a}{c}$$

$$c(c) = (a+b)(-b+a) \quad \text{(cross-multiply)}$$

$$c^2 = (a+b)(a-b)$$

$$c^2 = a^2 - b^2$$

$$c^2 + b^2 = a^2$$

$$a^2 = b^2 + c^2$$

$$\sqrt{a^2} = \sqrt{b^2 + c^2}$$

$$a = \sqrt{b^2 + c^2}$$

$$AB = \sqrt{(a-0)^2 + (0-0)^2} = \sqrt{a^2 + 0^2} = \sqrt{a^2} = a$$

$$AB = \sqrt{b^2 + c^2}$$

$$BC = \sqrt{(a+b-a)^2 + (c-0)^2} = \sqrt{b^2 + c^2}$$

∴ $AB = BC$ and $ABCD$ is a rhombus.

4.23

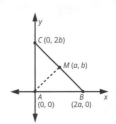

$$M_{BC} = \left(\frac{0+2a}{2}, \frac{2b+0}{2}\right) = \left(\frac{2a}{2}, \frac{2b}{2}\right) = (a, b)$$

$$AM = \sqrt{(0-a)^2 + (0-b)^2} = \sqrt{(-a)^2 + (-b)^2}$$

$$= \sqrt{a^2 + b^2}$$

$$BC = \sqrt{(0-2a)^2 + (2b-0)^2}$$

$$= \sqrt{(-2a)^2 + (2b)^2} = \sqrt{4a^2 + 4b^2}$$

$$= \sqrt{4(a^2 + b^2)} = 2\sqrt{a^2 + b^2}$$

$$= \sqrt{a^2 + b^2} = \frac{1}{2}(2\sqrt{a^2 + b^2})$$

$$AM = \frac{1}{2}BC$$

4.24

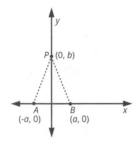

$AP = \sqrt{[0 - (-a)]^2 + (b - 0)^2} = \sqrt{a^2 + b^2}$

$BP = \sqrt{(0 - a)^2 + (b - 0)^2}$

$= \sqrt{(-a)^2 + b^2} = \sqrt{a^2 + b^2}$

$\therefore AP = BP$

4.25

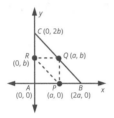

$M_{AB} = \left(\dfrac{2a + 0}{2}, \dfrac{0 + 0}{2}\right) = \left(\dfrac{2a}{2}, \dfrac{0}{2}\right) = (a, 0)$

$M_{BC} = \left(\dfrac{0 + 2a}{2}, \dfrac{2b + 0}{2}\right) = \left(\dfrac{2a}{2}, \dfrac{2b}{2}\right) = (a, b)$

$M_{AC} = \left(\dfrac{0 + 0}{2}, \dfrac{2b + 0}{2}\right) = \left(\dfrac{0}{2}, \dfrac{2b}{2}\right) = (0, b)$

$m_{PQ} = \dfrac{b - 0}{a - a} = \dfrac{b}{0} = $ no slope

$m_{RQ} = \dfrac{b - b}{a - 0} = \dfrac{0}{a} = 0$

$\therefore \overline{PQ} \perp \overline{RQ}$ and $\triangle PQR$ is a right $\triangle$.

SELF TEST 4

4.01 $B(0, s)$
$D(r, 0)$

4.02 x-coordinate $= \dfrac{1}{2}RT$

$RT = \sqrt{(2a - 0)^2 + (0 - 0)^2}$

$= \sqrt{(2a)^2 + 0^2}$

$= \sqrt{4a^2} = 2a$

$= \dfrac{1}{2}(2a) = a$

Let y-coordinate $= c$

$TS = \sqrt{(2a - a)^2 + (0 - c)^2}$

$= \sqrt{a^2 + (-c)^2}$

$= \sqrt{a^2 + c^2}$

$RT = TS$

$\sqrt{a^2 + c^2} = \sqrt{4a^2}$

$a^2 + c^2 = 4a^2$

$c^2 = 4a^2 - a^2$

$c^2 = 3a^2$

$\sqrt{c^2} = \sqrt{3a^2}$

$c = \sqrt{3}\sqrt{a^2}$

$c = a\sqrt{3}$

Point $S = (a, a\sqrt{3})$

4.03 $(a + c, b)$

4.04

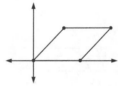

$m_{BD} = \dfrac{b - 0}{a - c} = \dfrac{b}{a - c}$

$m_{AC} = \dfrac{b - 0}{a + c - 0} = \dfrac{b}{a + c}$

4.05 c

4.06 $(r, 0); (0, r)$

4.07

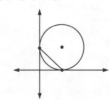

$d = \sqrt{(r - 0)^2 + (0 - r)^2}$

$= \sqrt{r^2 + (-r)^2}$

$= \sqrt{r^2 + r^2}$

$= \sqrt{2r^2} = \sqrt{2}\sqrt{r^2}$

$= r\sqrt{2}$

4.08 $m = \dfrac{r - 0}{0 - r} = \dfrac{r}{-r} = -1$

$y - 0 = -1(x - r)$

$y = -x + r$

$x + y = r$

4.09   Points are $(0, 0)$ and (r, r).

$m_{BD} = \dfrac{r - 0}{r - 0} = \dfrac{r}{r} = 1$

4.010

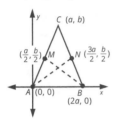

$M_{AC} = (\dfrac{a + 0}{2}, \dfrac{b + 0}{2}) = (\dfrac{a}{2}, \dfrac{b}{2})$

$M_{BC} = (\dfrac{a + 2a}{2}, \dfrac{b + 0}{2}) = (\dfrac{3a}{2}, \dfrac{b}{2})$

$BM = \sqrt{(\dfrac{a}{2} - 2a)^2 + (\dfrac{b}{2} - 0)^2}$

$= \sqrt{(\dfrac{a}{2} - \dfrac{4a}{2})^2 + (\dfrac{b}{2})^2}$

$= \sqrt{(-\dfrac{3a}{2})^2 + (\dfrac{b}{2})^2} = \sqrt{\dfrac{9a^2}{4} + \dfrac{b^2}{4}}$

$AN = \sqrt{(0 - \dfrac{3a}{2})^2 + (0 - \dfrac{b}{2})^2}$

$= \sqrt{(-\dfrac{3a}{2})^2 + (-\dfrac{b}{2})^2}$

$= \sqrt{(\dfrac{9a^2}{4})^2 + \dfrac{b^2}{4}}$

$\therefore BM = AN$

4.011

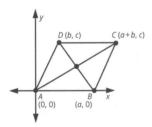

$m_{AC} = \dfrac{c - 0}{a + b - 0} = \dfrac{c}{a + b}$

$m_{BD} = \dfrac{c - 0}{b - a} = \dfrac{c}{b - a}$

$AB = AD$

$AB = \sqrt{(a - 0)^2 + (0 - 0)^2}$

$= \sqrt{a^2 + 0^2}$

$= \sqrt{a^2} = a$

$AD = \sqrt{(b - 0)^2 + (c - 0)^2}$

$= \sqrt{b^2 + c^2}$

$a = \sqrt{b^2 + c^2}$

$(a)^2 = (\sqrt{b^2 + c^2})^2$

$a^2 = b^2 + c^2$

$a^2 - b^2 = c^2$

$c^2 = a^2 - b^2$

$\dfrac{c}{a + b} = \dfrac{a - b}{c}$

$\dfrac{c}{a + b} = -\dfrac{b - a}{c}$

$m_{AC} = -m_{BD}$

$\therefore \overline{AC} \perp \overline{BD}$

4.012

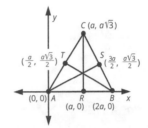

Refer to Problem 4.02 to find coordinates of point C.

$M_{AB} = (\dfrac{2a + 0}{2}, \dfrac{0 + 0}{2}) = (\dfrac{2a}{2}, \dfrac{0}{2}) = (a, 0)$

$M_{BC} = (\dfrac{a + 2a}{2}, \dfrac{a\sqrt{3} + 0}{2}) = (\dfrac{3a}{2}, \dfrac{a\sqrt{3}}{2})$

$M_{AC} = (\dfrac{a + 0}{2}, \dfrac{a\sqrt{3}}{2}) = (\dfrac{a}{2}, \dfrac{a\sqrt{3}}{2})$

$AS = \sqrt{(\dfrac{3a}{2} - 0)^2 + (\dfrac{a\sqrt{3}}{2} - 0)^2}$

$= \sqrt{(\dfrac{3a}{2})^2 + (\dfrac{a\sqrt{3}}{2})^2}$

$= \sqrt{\dfrac{9a^2}{4} + \dfrac{3a^2}{4}} = \sqrt{\dfrac{12a^2}{4}}$

$= \sqrt{3a^2} = \sqrt{3}\sqrt{a^2} = a\sqrt{3}$

$BT = \sqrt{(\dfrac{a}{2} - 2a)^2 + (\dfrac{a\sqrt{3}}{2} - 0)^2}$

$= \sqrt{(\dfrac{a}{2} - \dfrac{4a}{2})^2 + (\dfrac{a\sqrt{3}}{2})^2}$

$= \sqrt{(-\dfrac{3a}{2})^2 + (\dfrac{a\sqrt{3}}{2})^2}$

$= \sqrt{\dfrac{9a^2}{4} + \dfrac{3a^2}{4}} = \sqrt{\dfrac{12a^2}{4}}$

$= \sqrt{3a^2} = \sqrt{3}\sqrt{a^2} = a\sqrt{3}$

$CR = \sqrt{(a-a)^2 + (0 - a\sqrt{3})^2}$

$\quad = \sqrt{0^2 + (-a\sqrt{3})^2}$

$\quad = \sqrt{3a^2} = \sqrt{3}\sqrt{a^2} = a\sqrt{3}$

$\therefore AS = BT = CR$

4.013

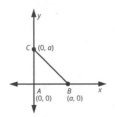

$AB = \sqrt{(0-a)^2 + (0-0)^2}$

$\quad = \sqrt{(-a)^2 + 0^2}$

$\quad = \sqrt{a^2} = a$

$BC = \sqrt{(a-0)^2 + (0-a)^2}$

$\quad = \sqrt{a^2 + (-a)^2}$

$\quad = \sqrt{a^2 + a^2}$

$\quad = \sqrt{2a^2} = \sqrt{2}\sqrt{a^2} = a\sqrt{2}$

$BC = AB\sqrt{2}$

4.014

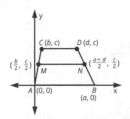

$M_{AC} = \left(\dfrac{b+0}{2}, \dfrac{c+0}{2}\right) = \left(\dfrac{b}{2}, \dfrac{c}{2}\right)$

$M_{BD} = \left(\dfrac{a+d}{2}, \dfrac{0+c}{2}\right) = \left(\dfrac{a+d}{2}, \dfrac{c}{2}\right)$

$m_{AB} = \dfrac{0-0}{a-0} = \dfrac{0}{a} = 0$

$m_{CD} = \dfrac{c-c}{d-b} = \dfrac{0}{d-b} = 0$

$m_{MN} = \dfrac{\dfrac{c}{2} - \dfrac{c}{2}}{\dfrac{a+d}{2} - \dfrac{b}{2}} = \dfrac{0}{\dfrac{a+d}{2} - \dfrac{b}{2}} = 0$

Slopes are equal; $\therefore$ median || to bases.

4.015 line, plane

4.016 line, plane

4.017 line, plane

4.018 point, line, plane

4.019 line, plane

4.020 none

4.021 Some points are (-4, -4), (0, 0), and (2, 2)

$\qquad x = y$

4.022 $y \geq -4$

4.023 $y \geq -2 \;\cup\; y < 2$

$\qquad -2 \leq y < 2$

4.024 Points given are (0, 4) and (4, 0).

$m = \dfrac{0-4}{4-0} = \dfrac{-4}{4} = -1$

$y - 4 = -1(x - 0)$

$y - 4 = -x + 0$

$x + y - 4 = 0$

$x + y = 4$

4.025 a. (5, -3)

$\qquad$ b. $r = \sqrt{25} = 5$

4.026 a. (0, 0)

$\qquad$ b. $r = \sqrt{16} = 4$

4.027 a. (0, 3)

$\qquad$ b. $r = \sqrt{8} = 2\sqrt{2}$

4.028

8	$= \frac{1}{2}(x + 5)$	
16	$= x + 5$	(multiply by 2)
16 – 5	$= x$	
11	$= x$	
2	$= \frac{1}{2}(y + 6)$	
4	$= y + 6$	(multiply by 2)
4 – 6	$= y$	
-2	$= y$	

(11, -2)

4.029

0	$= \frac{1}{2}(x - 16)$	
0	$= x - 16$	(multiply by 2)
16	$= x$	
-16	$= \frac{1}{2}(y + 0)$	
-32	$= y + 0$	(multiply by 2)
-32	$= y$	

(16, -32)

4.030

2	$= \frac{1}{2}(x + 12)$	
4	$= x + 12$	(multiply by 2)
4 – 12	$= x$	
-8	$= x$	
6	$= \frac{1}{2}(y + 4)$	
12	$= y + 4$	(multiply by 2)
12 – 4	$= y$	
8	$= y$	

(-8, 8)

4.031 $d = \sqrt{(0-5)^2 + (6-12)^2}$

$\quad = \sqrt{(-5)^2 + (-6)^2}$

$\quad = \sqrt{25 + 36} = \sqrt{61}$

4.032 $d = \sqrt{(4-7)^2 + (1-5)^2}$
$= \sqrt{(-3)^2 + (-4)^2}$
$= \sqrt{9 + 16} = \sqrt{25} = 5$

4.033 $d = \sqrt{(-3-0)^2 + (0-\sqrt{7})^2}$
$= \sqrt{(-3)^2 + (-\sqrt{7})^2}$
$= \sqrt{9 + 7} = \sqrt{16} = 4$

4.034 $m = \dfrac{5-8}{-2-3} = \dfrac{-3}{-5} = \dfrac{3}{5}$

4.035 $m = \dfrac{2-22}{-4-0} = \dfrac{-20}{-4} = 5$

4.036 $m = \dfrac{10-0}{5-0} = \dfrac{10}{5} = 2$

4.037 $m = \dfrac{-5-2}{15-13} = -\dfrac{7}{2}$
$m\perp = \dfrac{2}{7}$

4.038 $m = \dfrac{4-(-1)}{0-2} = -\dfrac{5}{2}$
$m\perp = \dfrac{2}{5}$

4.039 $m = \dfrac{5-2}{8-3} = \dfrac{3}{5}$
$m\perp = -\dfrac{5}{3}$

4.040 $m = \dfrac{-4-0}{4-0} = \dfrac{-4}{4} = -1$
$y - 0 = -1(x - 0)$
$y = -x$
$x + y = 0$

4.041 $m = \dfrac{1-2}{5-(-2)} = -\dfrac{1}{7}$
$y - 2 = -\dfrac{1}{7}(x + 2)$
$y - 2 = -\dfrac{1}{7}x - \dfrac{2}{7}$
$\dfrac{1}{7}x + y - 2 = -\dfrac{2}{7}$
$\dfrac{1}{7}x + y = -\dfrac{2}{7} + 2$
$\dfrac{1}{7}x + y = \dfrac{12}{7}$
$x = 7y = 12$ (multiply by 7)

4.042 $m = \dfrac{6-6}{5-0} = \dfrac{0}{5} = 0$
$y = 6$

4.043 $y - 5 = 3(x - 5)$
$y - 5 = 3x - 15$
$-3x + y - 5 = -15$
$-3x + y = -15 + 5$
$-3x + y = -10$
$3x - y = 10$ (multiply by -1)

4.044 $y - 4 = 0(x - 0)$
$y - 4 = 0$
$y = 4$

4.045 $x = 3$

LIFEPAC TEST

1. ‖

2. y

3. y

4. $5x - y = 8$
   $5x - 7 = 8$
   $5x = 8 + 7$
   $5x = 15$
   $\dfrac{5x}{5} = \dfrac{15}{5}$
   $x = 3$

5. a. $(-4, 6)$
   b. $r = \sqrt{25} = 5$

6. $(x - 2)^2 + (y - 6)^2 \quad = \quad 4$
   $(5 - 2)^2 + (6 + 0)^2 \quad ? \quad 4$
   $3^2 + 0^2 \quad ? \quad 4$
   $9 \quad \neq \quad 4$
   no

7. $d = \sqrt{(-4 - 4)^2 + (2 - 2)^2}$
   $= \sqrt{(-8)^2 + (0)^2}$
   $= \sqrt{64} = 8$

8. $M = \left(\dfrac{4 - 4}{2}, \dfrac{2 + 2}{2}\right) = \left(\dfrac{0}{2}, \dfrac{4}{2}\right) = (0, 2)$

9. $m = \dfrac{2 - 2}{4 - (-4)} = \dfrac{0}{8} = 0$

10. ‖ lines have equal slopes; $\therefore m = 0$.

11. no slope

12. $x = -5$

13. $y + 4 = \dfrac{3}{5}(x - 2)$
    $y + 4 = \dfrac{3}{5}x - \dfrac{6}{5}$
    $-\dfrac{3}{5}x + y + 4 = -\dfrac{6}{5}$
    $-\dfrac{3}{5}x + y = -\dfrac{6}{5} - 4$
    $-\dfrac{3}{5}x + y = \dfrac{26}{5}$
    $3x - 5y = 26$ (multiply by -5)

14. ctr. $= m = \left(\dfrac{6 - 2}{2}, \dfrac{7 + 1}{2}\right) = \left(\dfrac{4}{2}, \dfrac{8}{2}\right) = (2, 4)$
    diameter $= d = \sqrt{(-2 - 6)^2 + (1 - 7)^2}$
    $= \sqrt{(-8)^2 + (-6)^2}$
    $= \sqrt{64 + 36}$
    $= \sqrt{100} = 10$
    radius $= \dfrac{1}{2}d = \dfrac{1}{2}(10) = 5$
    $(x - 2)^2 + (y - 4)^2 = 5^2$
    $(x - 2)^2 + (y - 4)^2 = 25$

15. $M = \left(\dfrac{2 + 4}{2}, \dfrac{-5 + 1}{2}\right) = \left(\dfrac{6}{2}, \dfrac{-4}{2}\right) = (3, -2)$
    $m = \dfrac{-5 - 1}{2 - 4} = \dfrac{-6}{-2} = 3$
    $m = -\dfrac{1}{3}$
    $y + 2 = \dfrac{1}{3}(x - 3)$
    $y + 2 = \dfrac{1}{3}x + 1$
    $\dfrac{1}{3}x + y + 2 = 1$
    $\dfrac{1}{3}x + y = 1 - 2$
    $\dfrac{1}{3}x + y = -1$
    $x + 3y = -3$ (multiply by 3)

16. $M_{RT} = \left(\dfrac{2c + 2a}{2}, \dfrac{2d + 0}{2}\right) = (a + c, d)$
    $M_{ST} = \left(\dfrac{2c + 2b}{2}, \dfrac{2d + 0}{2}\right) = (b + c, d)$
    $MN = \sqrt{[(a + c) - (b + c)]^2 + (d - d)^2}$
    $= \sqrt{(a + c - b - c)^2 + 0^2}$
    $= \sqrt{(a - b)^2} = a - b$

17. x-intercept: $\quad 4x - 0 = 12$
    $4x = 12$
    $\dfrac{4x}{4} = \dfrac{12}{4}$
    $x = 3$
    $(3, 0)$

    y-intercept: $\quad 0 - 3y = 12$
    $-3y = 12$
    $\dfrac{-3y}{-3} = \dfrac{12}{-3}$
    $y = -4$
    $(0, -4)$

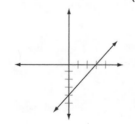

18. $|x| > 2$
$x > 2 \quad x < -2$

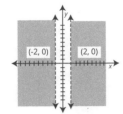

19. $x \geq -1 \cup x \leq 3$

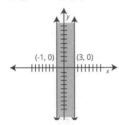

20. false
21. true
22. true
23. true
24. false
25.

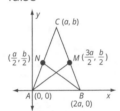

$$M_{AC} = \left(\frac{a + 0}{2}, \frac{b + 0}{2}\right) = \left(\frac{a}{2}, \frac{b}{2}\right)$$

$$M_{BC} = \left(\frac{a + 2a}{2}, \frac{b + 0}{2}\right) = \left(\frac{3a}{2}, \frac{b}{2}\right)$$

$$AM = \sqrt{\left(0 - \frac{3a}{2}\right)^2 + \left(0 - \frac{b}{2}\right)^2}$$

$$= \sqrt{\left(-\frac{3a}{2}\right)^2 + \left(-\frac{b}{2}\right)^2}$$

$$= \sqrt{\frac{9a^2}{4} + \frac{b^2}{4}}$$

$$BN = \sqrt{\left(\frac{a}{2} - 2a\right)^2 + \left(\frac{b}{2} - 0\right)^2}$$

$$= \sqrt{\left(\frac{a}{2} - \frac{4a}{2}\right)^2 + \left(\frac{b}{2}\right)^2}$$

$$= \sqrt{\left(-\frac{3a}{2}\right)^2 + \left(\frac{b}{2}\right)^2}$$

$$= \sqrt{\frac{9a^2}{4} + \frac{b^2}{4}}$$

$\therefore AM = BN$

ALTERNATE LIFEPAC TEST

1 through 5.

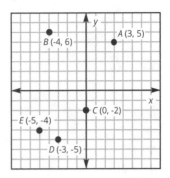

6. $d = \sqrt{(x_1 - x_2)^2 + (y_1 - y_2)^2}$
$d = \sqrt{(3 - 5)^2 + [4 - (-2)]^2}$
$d = \sqrt{(-2)^2 + (6)^2}$
$d = \sqrt{4 + 36}$
$d = \sqrt{40}$
$d = \sqrt{4 \cdot 10} = \sqrt{4} \cdot \sqrt{10}$
$d = 2\sqrt{10}$

7. $d = \sqrt{(x_1 - x_2)^2 + (y_1 - y_2)^2}$
$d = \sqrt{(0 - 8)^2 + (0 - 4)^2}$
$d = \sqrt{(-8)^2 + (-4)^2}$
$d = \sqrt{64 + 16}$
$d = \sqrt{80}$
$d = \sqrt{16 \cdot 5} = \sqrt{16} \cdot \sqrt{5}$
$d = 4\sqrt{5}$

8. $d = \sqrt{(x_1 - x_2)^2 + (y_1 - y_2)^2}$
$d = \sqrt{(1 - 4)^2 + [3 - (-4)]^2}$
$d = \sqrt{(-3)^2 + (7)^2}$
$d = \sqrt{9 + 49}$
$d = \sqrt{58}$

9. $d = \sqrt{(x_1 - x_2)^2 + (y_1 - y_2)^2}$
$d = \sqrt{(0 - 5)^2 + (-8 - 4)^2}$
$d = \sqrt{(-5)^2 + (-12)^2}$
$d = \sqrt{25 + 144}$
$d = \sqrt{169}$
$d = 13$

10. $d = \sqrt{(x_1 - x_2)^2 + (y_1 - y_2)^2}$
    $d = \sqrt{[0 - (-6)]^2 + (6 - 0)^2}$
    $d = \sqrt{(6)^2 + (6)^2}$
    $d = \sqrt{36 + 36}$
    $d = \sqrt{72}$
    $d = \sqrt{36 \cdot 2} = \sqrt{36} \cdot \sqrt{2}$
    $d = 6\sqrt{2}$

11. $h = 3$, $k = 5$, and $r = 5$
    $(x - h)^2 + (y - k)^2 = r^2$
    $(x - 3)^2 + (y - 4)^2 = 5^2$
    $(x - 3)^2 + (y - 4)^2 = 25$

12. $h = -2$, $k = -6$, and $r = 4$
    $(x - h)^2 + (y - k)^2 = r^2$
    $[x - (-2)]^2 + [y - (-6)]^2 = 4^2$
    $(x + 2)^2 + (y + 6)^2 = 16$

13. $h = 0$, $k = 0$, and $r = 3$
    $(x - h)^2 + (y - k)^2 = r^2$
    $(x - 0)^2 + (y - 0)^2 = 3^2$
    $x^2 + y^2 = 9$

14. $h = 5$, $k = -3$, and $r = 5$
    $(x - h)^2 + (y - k)^2 = r^2$
    $(x - 5)^2 + [y - (-3)]^2 = 5^2$
    $(x - 5)^2 + (y + 3)^2 = 25$

15. $d = \sqrt{(x_1 - x_2)^2 + (y_1 - y_2)^2}$
    $d = \sqrt{(2 - 8)^2 + [-3 - (-3)]^2}$
    $d = \sqrt{(-6)^2 + (0)^2}$
    $d = \sqrt{36}$
    $d = 6$

    diameter of circle = 6; therefore, radius = 3
    and center = (5, -3)

    $h = 5$, $k = -3$, and $r = 3$
    $(x - h)^2 + (y - k)^2 = r^2$
    $(x - 5)^2 + [y - (-3)]^2 = 3^2$
    $(x - 5)^2 + (y + 3)^2 = 9$

16. $x = \dfrac{1}{2}(x_2 + x_1)$

    $x = \dfrac{1}{2}(0 + 0)$

    $x = \dfrac{1}{2}(0)$

    $x = 0$

    $y = \dfrac{1}{2}(y_2 + y_1)$

    $y = \dfrac{1}{2}(8 + 0)$

    $y = \dfrac{1}{2}(8)$

    $y = 4$

    The midpoint is (0, 4).

17. $x = \dfrac{1}{2}(x_2 + x_1)$

    $x = \dfrac{1}{2}(8 + 0)$

    $x = \dfrac{1}{2}(8)$

    $x = 4$

    $y = \dfrac{1}{2}(y_2 + y_1)$

    $y = \dfrac{1}{2}(8 + 0)$

    $y = \dfrac{1}{2}(8)$

    $y = 4$

    The midpoint is (4, 4).

18. $x = \dfrac{1}{2}(x_2 + x_1)$

    $x = \dfrac{1}{2}(0 + 8)$

    $x = \dfrac{1}{2}(8)$

    $x = 4$

    $y = \dfrac{1}{2}(y_2 + y_1)$

    $y = \dfrac{1}{2}(8 + 0)$

    $y = \dfrac{1}{2}(8)$

    $y = 4$

    The midpoint is (4, 4).

19. $x = \frac{1}{2}(x_2 + x_1)$

$x = \frac{1}{2}(-8 + 8)$

$x = \frac{1}{2}(0)$

$x = 0$

$y = \frac{1}{2}(y_2 + y_1)$

$y = \frac{1}{2}[8 + (-8)]$

$y = \frac{1}{2}(0)$

$y = 0$

The midpoint is (0, 0).

20. $x = \frac{1}{2}(x_2 + x_1)$

$x = \frac{1}{2}[8 + (-8)]$

$x = \frac{1}{2}(0)$

$x = 0$

$y = \frac{1}{2}(y_2 + y_1)$

$y = \frac{1}{2}[8 + (-8)]$

$y = \frac{1}{2}(0)$

$y = 0$

The midpoint is (0, 0).

21. Both points lie on the y-axis; therefore, the line has no slope. The equation is $x = 0$.

22. $y - y_1 = \frac{y_2 - y_1}{x_2 - x_1}(x - x_1)$

$y - 3 = \frac{-4 - 3}{4 - 1}(x - 1)$

$y - 3 = \frac{-7}{3}(x - 1)$

$3y - 9 = -7(x - 1)$

$3y - 9 = -7x + 7$

$3y - 9 + 9 + 7x$

$\qquad = \cancel{-7x} + \cancel{7x} + 7 + 9$

$7x + 3y = 16$

23. $y - y_1 = \frac{y_2 - y_1}{x_2 - x_1}(x - x_1)$

$y - 3 = \frac{1 - 3}{-2 - 5}(x - 5)$

$y - 3 = \frac{-2}{-7}(x - 5)$

$y - 3 = \frac{2}{7}(x - 5)$

$7y - 21 = 2(x - 5)$

$7y - 21 = 2x - 10$

$7y - \cancel{21} + \cancel{21} - 2x = \cancel{2x} - \cancel{2x} - 10 + 21$

$-2x + 7y = 11$

24. m of the line through (5, 2):

$m_1 = -\frac{1}{m_2}$

$m_1 = \frac{-1}{-2}$

$m_1 = \frac{1}{2}$

$y - y_1 = m(x - x_1)$

$y - 2 = \frac{1}{2}(x - 5)$

$2y - 4 = 1(x - 5)$

$2y - 4 = x - 5$

$\cancel{2y} - \cancel{2y} - 4 + 5$

$\qquad = x - 2y - 5 + 5$

$\qquad 1 = x - 2y$

$x - 2y = 1$

25. Slope of parallel lines are equal.

$y - y_1 = m(x - x_1)$

$y - 1 = \frac{1}{5}(x - 3)$

$5y - 5 = 1(x - 3)$

$5y - 5 = x - 3$

$\cancel{5y} - \cancel{5y} - 5 + 3$

$\qquad = x - 5y - 3 + 3$

$\qquad -2 = x - 5y$

$x - 5y = -2$

26. midpoint of $\overline{AB}$:

$x = \frac{1}{2}(x_2 + x_1)$

$x = \frac{1}{2}(7 + 3)$

$x = \frac{1}{2}(10)$

$x = 5$

$y = \frac{1}{2}(y_2 + y_1)$

$y = \frac{1}{2}(6 + 2)$

$y = \frac{1}{2}(8)$

$y = 4$

The midpoint is (5, 4).

slope of $\overline{AB} = \frac{y_2 - y_1}{x_2 - x_1}$

$= \frac{6 - 2}{7 - 3}$

$= \frac{4}{4} = 1$

The slope of *l* is -1.

Equation of *l*:

$y - y_1 = m(x - x_1)$

$y - 4 = -1(x - 5)$

$y - 4 = -1(x - 5)$

$y - 4 = -x + 5$

$y + x - 4 + 4$

$\quad = -x + x + 5 + 4$

$y + x = 9$

$x + y = 9$

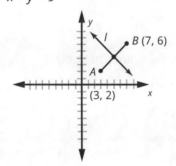

27. $M_{AC} = (\frac{a}{2}, \frac{b}{2})$

$M_{BD} = (\frac{a}{2}, \frac{b}{2})$

$M_{AC} = M_{BD}$

∴ *AC* and *BD* bisect each other.

MATH 1009

ALTERNATE LIFEPAC TEST

NAME _____

DATE _____

SCORE _____

Graph the given points on one set of axes (each answer, 2 points).

1. A (3, 5)

2. B (-4, 6)

3. C (0, -2)

4. D (-3, -5)

5. E (5, -4)

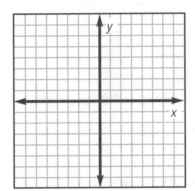

Find the distance between these points (each answer, 3 points).

6. A (3, 4), B (5, -2)   AB = _____

7. C (0, 0) , D (8, 4)   CD = _____

8. E (1, 3), F (4, -4)   EF = _____

9. H (0, -8), I (5, 4)   HI = _____

10. J (0, 6), K (-6, 0)   JK = _____

Write the equation of a circle whose center and other information are given (each answer, 3 points).

11. A (3, 4), r = 5   _____

12. B (-2, -6) , r = 4   _____

13. C (0, 0), r = 3   _____

14. D (5, -3), r = 5   _____

15. end points of diameter are
D (2, -3) and E (8, -3)   _____

Find the coordinates of the midpoint of the segment whose end points are given (each answer, 3 points).

16. M (0, 0) and N (0, 8)   _____

17. R (0, 0) and S (8, 8)   _____

18. P (8, 0) and Q (0, 8)   _____

19. W (8, -8) and X (-8, 8)   _____

20. A (-8, -8) and B (8, 8)   _____

Write the equation of a circle whose center and other information are given (each answer, 3 points).

21. A (0, 0), B (0, 8)   _____

22. C (1, 3), D (4, -4)   _____

23. E (5, 3), F (-2, 1)   _____

Write the equation of the given line in standard form (each answer, 4 points).

24.   The line through A (5, 2) and perpendicular to a line with slope of -2

25.   The line through B (3, 1) and parallel to a line with slope of $\frac{1}{5}$

26.   The line that is the perpendicular bisector of a segment whose end points are A (3, 2) and B (7, 6)

Sketch and complete the following proof (complete proof, 5 points).

27.   Prove: The diagonals of a rectangle bisect each other.

MATH 1010

Unit 10: Review

TEACHER NOTES

MATERIALS NEEDED FOR LIFEPAC	
Required	**Suggested**
• compasses and straightedges	(None)

ADDITIONAL LEARNING ACTIVITIES

Section 1: Geometry, Proof, and Angles

1. Read each of the following statements and have the students tell (without seeing a truth table) whether each statement is true or false. If a student answers with false, have him tell why it is false. Answers are given for the teacher's information.

    a. If two or more points are all on the same line, then the points are collinear. (true)

    b. If $AB + BC = AC$, then B is between points A and C. (true)

    c. If two planes intersect, then their intersection is a plane. (false; their intersection is a line)

    d. If a line containing two points lies in a plane, then the points lie in the plane. (true)

    e. If a plane contains at least three points, then a line contains at least one point. (false; a plane does contain at least three points, but a line contains at least two points)

    f. If a line contains at least one point, then a plane contains at least three points. (true; since the "If" part of the statement is false and the "then" part of the statement is true, the statement is true)

    g. If a postulate is a statement accepted without proof, then a theorem is a statement that can be proved. (true)

    h. If a postulate is a statement that can be proved, then a theorem is a statement accepted without proof. (true; since both the "If" part and the "then" part of the statement are false, the statement is true)

    i. If the hypothesis is not the "then" clause in a conditional statement, then the conclusion is not the "if" clause in a conditional statement. (true)

    j. If a two-column proof is a formal proof of a theorem composed of two standard parts, then an indirect proof is a proof of a theorem by indirect means. (true; since the "If" part of the statement is false and the "then" part of the statement is true, the statement is true)

    k. If an acute angle equals 45°, then a right angle equals 180°. (false; since the "If" part of the statement is true but the "then" part of the statement is false, the statement is false)

    l. If two complementary angles equal 90°, then two right angles are supplementary. (true)

    m. If a triangle does not contain 180°, then a quadrilateral does not contain 540°. (false; since the "If" part of the statement is false but the "then" part of the statement is true, the statement is false)

n. If two adjacent angles have their exterior sides in perpendicular lines, then the angles are complementary. (false; the angles are supplementary)

o. If all right angles are not equal, then all obtuse angles are equal. (true; since both the "If" part and the "then" part of the statement are false, the statement is true)

p. If the measure of an exterior angle of a triangle equals the sum of the interior angles, then the sum of the measures of the angles of a triangle equals 260°. (true; since both the "If" part and the "then" part of the statement are false, the statement is true)

2. An interior angle of a polygon equals $\frac{(n-2)180°}{n}$, where n is the number of sides of the polygon. Have the students copy the following regular octagon and draw the two lines through the center as shown. Then have the students find the number of degrees in $\angle 1$, $\angle 2$, and $\angle 3$.

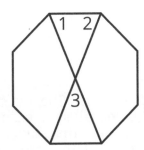

3. Have the student draw and label a figure for each of the following conditions. Then have he or she draw and label a figure such that all of the conditions given are true.

a. points P, A, and B are collinear

b. point P is between points A and B

c. point P is midpoint of $\overline{AB}$

d. $\vec{PA}$ and $\vec{PB}$ are opposite rays

Section 2: Triangles, Quadrilaterals, Polygons, and Circles

1. Draw the following figure on the chalkboard with the stated conditions. Have the students find the lengths of each of the other segments.

Given: $\triangle ABC$ is a 45°-45°-90° $\triangle$
            $\overline{BD}$ is bisector of $\angle ABC$
            $\triangle AED$ is a 30°-60°-90° $\triangle$
            $\overline{BC} = 4$

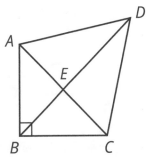

Administer the LIFEPAC Test.

The test is to be administered in one session. Give no help except with directions.
Evaluate the tests and review areas where the students have done poorly.
Review the pages and activities that stress the concepts tested.
If necessary, administer the Alternate LIFEPAC Test.

2. This activity is for two students to do together. Have both students draw and label an example of each of the theorems from Theorem 4-1 through Theorem 4-25 and from Theorem 5-1 through Theorem 5-13 without referring to previous LIFEPACs. They may draw and label five to ten examples at a time. The theorems may or may not be written out. Then have both students trade examples and check each others work. They may check their examples with the ones given in the corresponding LIFEPACs.

Examples: Theorem 4-1: If two angles and a not included side of one triangle are equal to the corresponding parts of another triangle, then the triangles are congruent. (AAS)

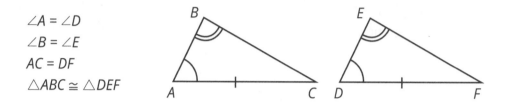

$\angle A = \angle D$

$\angle B = \angle E$

$AC = DF$

$\triangle ABC \cong \triangle DEF$

3. This activity is for two students to do together. The first student chooses any theorem from Theorem 6-1 through 6-18 and draws and labels an example of the theorem. Then he gives the figure to the second student to examine; that student tells what the theorem states that corresponds to the figure. If he answers with the correct theorem, he chooses a theorem and proceeds in the same manner as the first student. If he answers with an incorrect theorem, the first student may give him more time to think or he may give him a clue, whichever the second student prefers. The students alternate turns. Each student should be sure he draws the examples accurately and labels any parts necessary for the other student to understand the meaning of the figure. For example, the figure for Theorem 6-1: "A radius drawn to a point of tangency is perpendicular to the tangent" should have the radius and tangent labeled as in the following diagram.

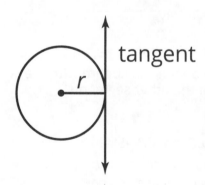

tangent

r

Section 3: Construction, Measurement, and Coordinate Geometry

1. Draw the given figure on the chalkboard. The cube is divided into six square-based pyramids of equal size. If each edge of the cube measures 4 inches, have the class find the altitude, slant height, lateral area, total area, and volume of each pyramid.

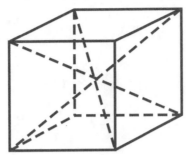

The pyramid that is the base of the cube is shown (with the altitude and slant height) for the teacher's information. The lateral area, total area, and volume may be found by using their formulas after the altitude and slant height are found.

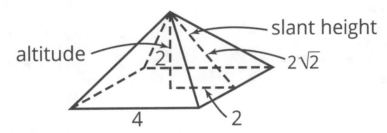

2. Have the class solve this problem. If a cone whose slant height is 6" and radius is 3" is rolled around a cylinder whose altitude is 6" and radius is 3", how much of the cylinder will be covered by one complete turn of the cone? two complete turns of the cone?

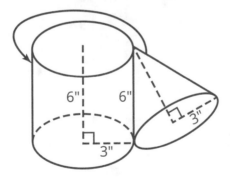

3. Name two points on the coordinate axes. Then have one student find the distance between the two points; one student find the slope of the line containing the given points; one student find the midpoint of the segment with the given points as end points; and one student graph and write the equation of the line containing the given points.

    You may want to prepare the answers to several problems beforehand so the students' answers may be checked quickly. Or, you may have each student find the answers to two parts of one problem (such as finding the distance and the slope) and then compare the students' answers.

ANSWER KEYS

SECTION 1

1.1 $\overline{AB}$
1.2 $\overleftrightarrow{AB}$
1.3 $\overrightarrow{AB}$
1.4 plane m
1.5 point p
1.6 space
1.7 R
1.8 RT
1.9 three
1.10 two
1.11 proof
1.12 one
1.13 four
1.14 six
1.15 line

1.16 [diagram: line with points B U N T]

1.17 [diagram: segment W M X]

1.18 [diagram: point P with lines m, n, T]

1.19 [diagram: line with points G O P]

1.20 [diagram: intersecting planes with points P Q A B]

1.21 conditional; true
1.22 conjunction; true
1.23 negation; true
1.24 disjunction; true
1.25 conditional; true
1.26 a. If the alternate interior angles are equal, then the two lines are parallel; true.
   b. If the lines are not parallel, then the alternate interior angles are not equal; true.
   c. If the alternate interior angles are not equal, then the lines are not parallel; true.
1.27 a. If the vertical angles are equal, then the two lines intersect; true.

b. If two lines do not intersect, then the vertical angles are not equal; true.
c. If the vertical angles are not equal, then the lines do not intersect; true.
1.28 a. If diagonals bisect each other, then the figure is a parallelogram; true.
   b. If the figure is not a parallelogram, then the diagonals do not bisect each other; true.
   c. If diagonals do not bisect each other, then the figure is not a parallelogram; true.
1.29 a. If base ∠'s are =, then △ is isosceles; true.
   b. If △ is not isosceles, then base ∠'s are not =; true.
   c. If base ∠'s are not =, then △ is not isosceles; true.
1.30 a. If rights ∠'s are formed, then lines are ⊥; true.
   b. If lines are not ⊥, then right ∠'s are not formed; true.
   c. If right ∠'s are not formed, then lines are not ⊥; true.

1.31 [diagram: perpendicular lines m and l]

1.32 [diagram: parallel lines l and m crossing t]

1.33 [diagram: two triangles ABC and RST]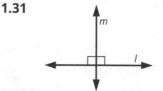

1.34 [diagram: transversal crossing lines l and m with angles 1 and 2]

1.35 [diagram: angle with rays l, m and angles 1, 2]

1.36 a. F
b. T

1.37 a. F
b. T
c. T
d. T

1.38 a. T
b. T
c. T
d. F

1.39 a. T
b. T
c. T
d. F

1.40 a. T
b. F
c. F
d. F

1.41 ∠1, ∠7; ∠2, ∠8; ∠3, ∠5; ∠4, ∠6

1.42 ∠4, ∠5; ∠1, ∠8

1.43 ∠2, ∠7; ∠3, ∠6

1.44 ∠1, ∠2; ∠3, ∠4; ∠5, ∠6; ∠7, ∠8

1.45 Any twelve:
∠1, ∠4; ∠1, ∠3; ∠1, ∠5; ∠1, ∠6; ∠2, ∠3;
∠2, ∠4; ∠2, ∠5; ∠2, ∠6; ∠6, ∠8; ∠6, ∠7;
∠5, ∠8; ∠5, ∠7; ∠4, ∠8; ∠3, ∠7; ∠3, ∠8;
∠4, ∠7

1.46 quadrilateral

1.47 pentagon

1.48 hexagon

1.49 octagon

1.50 *n*-gon

1.51 1. **STATEMENT**
$r \parallel s$
REASON
Given

2. **STATEMENT**
∠2, ∠4 are supplementary
REASON
Exterior sides in opposite rays

3. **STATEMENT**
∠4 = ∠8
REASON
Corresponding ∠'s

4. **STATEMENT**
∠2 + ∠4 = 180°
REASON
Definition of supplementary ∠'s

5. **STATEMENT**
∠2 + ∠8 = 180°
REASON
Substitution

6. **STATEMENT**
∠2, ∠8 are supplementary
REASON
Definition of supplementary ∠'s

1.52 1. **STATEMENT**
$l \parallel m$, ∠1 = ∠4
REASON
Given

2. **STATEMENT**
∠1 = ∠2
REASON
Alternate interior ∠'s

3. **STATEMENT**
∠3 = ∠4
REASON
Vertical ∠'s

4. **STATEMENT**
∠2 = ∠3
REASON
Substitution

1.53 1. **STATEMENT**
∠1 = ∠3
REASON
Given

2. **STATEMENT**
∠1 = ∠2
REASON
Vertical ∠'s

3. **STATEMENT**
∠2 = ∠3
REASON
Substitution

4. **STATEMENT**
$a \parallel b$
REASON
If corresponding ∠'s =, then lines ∥.

1.54   m ∠2 = 180 – m ∠1
             = 180 – 120
             = 60°
1.55   m ∠4 = 180 – m ∠3
             = 180 – 40
             = 140°
1.56   m ∠5 = m ∠2 = 60°
1.57   m ∠6 = 180 – (m ∠5 + m ∠7)
           m ∠5 = 60°
           m ∠7 = m ∠3 = 40°
           m ∠6 = 180 – (60 + 40)
             = 180 – 100
             = 80°
1.58   m ∠7 = m ∠3 = 40°
1.59   (n – 2)180 = (3 – 2)180 = (1)180 = 180°
1.60   (n – 2)180 = (4 – 2)180 = (2)180 = 360°
1.61   (n – 2)180 = (5 – 2)180 = (3)180 = 540°
1.62   (n – 2)180 = (6 – 2)180 = (4)180 = 720°
1.63   (n – 2)180 = (20 – 2)180 = (18)180 = 3,240°
1.64   (n – 2)180 = (50 – 2)180 = (48)180 = 8,640°
1.65   360°

SELF TEST 1

1.01   e
1.02   f
1.03   b
1.04   d
1.05   a
1.06   a. F
           b. T
           c. T
           d. T
1.07   a. T
           b. F
           c. F
           d. F
1.08   ∠3 = 180 – (∠1 + ∠2)
             = 180 – (30 + 30)
             = 180 – 60
             = 120°
1.09   ∠1 = 180 – (∠2 + ∠3)
             = 180 – (20 + 130)
             = 180 – 150
             = 30°
1.010 ∠2 = 180 – (∠1 + ∠3)
             = 180 – (40 + 110)
             = 180 – 150
             = 30°
1.011 ∠3 = 180 – (∠1 + ∠2)
             = 180 – (45 + 45)
             = 180 – 90
             = 90°
1.012 ∠1 = 180 – (∠2 + ∠3)
             = 180 – (15 + 118)
             = 180 – 133
             = 47°
1.013 c
           (n – 2)180 = (3 – 2)180 = (1)180 = 180°
1.014 c
           (n – 2)180 = (4 – 2)180 = (2)180 = 360°
1.015 a
           (n – 2)180 = (5 – 2)180 = (3)180 = 540°
1.016 d
           (n – 2)180 = (20 – 2)180 = (18)180 = 3,240°
1.017 1. **STATEMENT**
               $\overline{JK} \perp \overline{MN}$
               REASON
               Given

           2. **STATEMENT**
               ∠MKJ is rt. ∠
               REASON
               ⊥'s form rt. ∠'s

3. **STATEMENT**
△*MKJ* is rt. △
REASON
Definition of rt. △

4. **STATEMENT**
∠1, ∠2 are complementary
REASON
Acute ∠'s of rt. △ are complementary

1.018 1. **STATEMENT**
m ∠5 = m ∠6
REASON
Given

2. **STATEMENT**
m ∠1 = m ∠2
REASON
Vertical ∠'s are =.

3. **STATEMENT**
m ∠3 = m ∠4
REASON
If 2 ∠'s of one △ =
then third ∠'s are =.

1.019 1. **STATEMENT**
$\overline{AC} \perp \overline{CD}, \overline{DB} \perp \overline{AB}$
REASON
Given

2. **STATEMENT**
∠*C*, ∠*B* are rt. ∠'s
REASON
⊥'s form rt. ∠'s

3. **STATEMENT**
m ∠*C* = m ∠*B*
REASON
All rt. ∠'s are =.

4. **STATEMENT**
m ∠1 + m ∠2
REASON
Vertical ∠'s are =.

5. **STATEMENT**
m ∠*A* = m ∠*D*
REASON
If 2 ∠'s of one △ = 2 ∠'s of another △,
then third ∠'s are =.

SECTION 2

2.1 ∠*T*
2.2 ∠*R*
2.3 ∠*B*
2.4 *AC*
2.5 *AB*
2.6 *SR*

2.7 1. **STATEMENT**
$\overline{AB} \parallel \overline{DE}, AC = CE$
REASON
Given

2. **STATEMENT**
∠*A* = ∠*E*, ∠*B* = ∠*D*
REASON
Alternate interior ∠'s

3. **STATEMENT**
△*ABC* ≅ △*EDC*
REASON
AAS

2.8 1. **STATEMENT**
$\overline{UT} \parallel \overline{RS}, UT = RS$
REASON
Given

2. **STATEMENT**
∠2 = ∠4
REASON
Alternate interior ∠'s

3. **STATEMENT**
RT = *RT*
REASON
Reflexive

4. **STATEMENT**
△*RST* ≅ △*TUR*
REASON
SAS

5. **STATEMENT**
∠*S* = ∠*U*
REASON
CPCTE

2.9 1. **STATEMENT**
∠B = ∠C, AE = DE
REASON
Given

2. **STATEMENT**
∠BEA = ∠CED
REASON
Vertical ∠'s =.

3. **STATEMENT**
△ABE ≅ △DCE
REASON
AAS

4. **STATEMENT**
AB = DC
REASON
CPCTE

2.10 1. **STATEMENT**
AC = BC, MC = NC
REASON
Given

2. **STATEMENT**
∠C = ∠C
REASON
Reflexive

3. **STATEMENT**
△ANC ≅ △BMC
REASON
SAS

4. **STATEMENT**
∠ANC = ∠BMC
REASON
CPCTE

2.11 AB > BC > AC
2.12 6 + 12 = 18; 18 > 17
6 + 17 = 23; 23 > 17
12 + 17 = 29; 29 > 17
yes

2.13 1 + 2 = 3; 3 ≯ 3
1 + 3 = 4; 4 > 3
2 + 3 = 5; 5 > 3
no

2.14 6 + 8 = 14; 14 > 10
6 + 10 = 16; 16 > 10
8 + 10 = 18; 18 > 10
yes

2.15 $\overline{BC}$
2.16 $\overline{AC}$
2.17 $\overline{AB}$
2.18 AB
2.19 AC
2.20 NO
2.21 parallelogram

For Problems 2.22 through 2.25, ∠A and ∠D are supplementary.

2.22
$$x + 30 + 2x + 60 = 180$$
$$3x + 90 = 180$$
$$3x = 180 - 90$$
$$3x = 90$$
$$\frac{3x}{3} = \frac{90}{3}$$
$$x = 30°$$
$$\angle A = 30 + 30 = 60°$$

2.23 ∠B = ∠D
∠D = 2x + 60 = 2(30) + 60 = 60 + 60 = 120°
∠B = 120°
2.24 ∠C = ∠A
∠C = 60°
2.25 ∠D = 2x + 60 = 2(30) + 60 = 60 + 60 = 120°

2.26
$$\frac{x}{8} = \frac{5}{4}$$
$$x(4) = 8(5)$$
$$4x = 40$$
$$\frac{4x}{4} = \frac{40}{4}$$
$$x = 10$$

2.27
$$\frac{3}{x} = \frac{x}{4}$$
$$3(4) = x(x)$$
$$12 = x^2$$
$$x^2 = 12$$
$$\sqrt{x^2} = \sqrt{12}$$
$$x = \sqrt{4 \cdot 3} = 2\sqrt{3}$$

2.28
$$\frac{x}{3} = \frac{x + 2}{2}$$
$$x(2) = 3(x + 2)$$
$$2x = 3x + 6$$
$$2x - 3x = 6$$
$$-x = 6$$
$$x = -6$$

2.29 1. **STATEMENT**
a || b
REASON
Given

2. **STATEMENT**
$\angle 1 \cong \angle 2, \angle 3 \cong \angle 4$
REASON
Alternate interior $\angle$'s

3. **STATEMENT**
$\triangle MOP \sim \triangle RON$
REASON
AA

2.30 1. **STATEMENT**
$\overline{EC} \perp \overline{AC}, \overline{DB} \perp \overline{AC}, \angle A = \angle F$
REASON
Given

2. **STATEMENT**
$\overline{EC} \parallel \overline{DB}$
REASON
Two lines $\perp$ to same line are $\parallel$.

3. **STATEMENT**
$\angle 1 = \angle 2$
REASON
Alternate interior $\angle$'s

4. **STATEMENT**
$\angle A = \angle F$
REASON
Given

5. **STATEMENT**
$\triangle MDF \cong \triangle NEF$
REASON
AA

2.31 1. **STATEMENT**
$AB \parallel CD$
REASON
Given

2. **STATEMENT**
$\angle C = \angle B, \angle A = \angle D$
REASON
Alternate interior $\angle$'s

3. **STATEMENT**
$\triangle ABM \sim \triangle DCM$
REASON
AA

4. **STATEMENT**
$\dfrac{MC}{MB} = \dfrac{CD}{AB}$
REASON
Definition of similar $\triangle$'s

2.32 1. **STATEMENT**
$\overline{RS} \parallel \overline{AB}, \angle 1 = \angle 2$
REASON
Given

2. **STATEMENT**
$\dfrac{CR}{RA} = \dfrac{CS}{SB}$
REASON
Segment $\parallel$ to sides of $\triangle$ divides other sides proportionally.

3. **STATEMENT**
$\angle 2 = \angle 3$
REASON
Alternate interior $\angle$'s

4. **STATEMENT**
$\angle 1 = \angle 3$
REASON
Substitution

5. **STATEMENT**
$SB = RS$
REASON
Sides opposite = $\angle$'s are =.

6. **STATEMENT**
$\dfrac{CR}{RA} = \dfrac{CS}{RS}$
REASON
Substitution

2.33 1. **STATEMENT**
$\triangle ABC$ is rt. $\triangle$, $\overline{BD} \perp \overline{AC}$, $AB = \sqrt{17}$
REASON
Given

2. **STATEMENT**
$\dfrac{AC}{AB} = \dfrac{AB}{AD}$
REASON
Leg is geometric mean between hypotenuse and projection of leg on hypotenuse.

3. **STATEMENT**
$(AD)(AC) = (AB)^2$
REASON
POP

4. **STATEMENT**
$(AD)(AC) = 17$
REASON
Substitution

2.34 $AC = \sqrt{6^2 + 8^2}$
$= \sqrt{36 + 64}$
$= \sqrt{100} = 10$

2.35 $(AB)^2 + (BC)^2 = (AC)^2$
$(AB)^2 + 5^2 = 20^2$
$(AB)^2 + 25 = 400$
$(AB)^2 = 400 - 25$
$(AB)^2 = 375$
$\sqrt{(AB)^2} = \sqrt{375}$
$AB = \sqrt{25 \cdot 15} = 5\sqrt{15}$

2.36 $(AB)^2 + (BC)^2 = (AC)^2$
$(5\sqrt{2})^2 + (BC)^2 = 10^2$
$50 + (BC)^2 = 100$
$(BC)^2 = 100 - 50$
$(BC)^2 = 50$
$\sqrt{(BC)^2} = \sqrt{50}$
$BC = \sqrt{25 \cdot 2} = 5\sqrt{2}$

2.37   diagonal $= \sqrt{5^2 + 5^2 + 5^2}$
$= \sqrt{25 + 25 + 25}$
$= \sqrt{25 \cdot 3}$
$= 5\sqrt{3}$

2.38

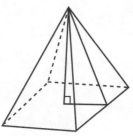

$3^2 + l^2 = 6^2$
$9 + l^2 = 36$
$l^2 = 36 - 9$
$l^2 = 27$
$\sqrt{l^2} = \sqrt{27}$
$l = \sqrt{9 \cdot 3} = 3\sqrt{3}$

2.39 $\tan 20° = \dfrac{x}{12}$

2.40 $\sin 70° = \dfrac{x}{8}$

2.41 $\tan 35° = \dfrac{9}{x}$

2.42 $\sin 80° = \dfrac{9}{x}$

2.43 $\cos 65° = \dfrac{x}{12}$

2.44 $\sin 30° = \dfrac{x}{8}$
$\dfrac{1}{2} = \dfrac{x}{8}$
$2(x) = 1(8)$
$2x = 8$
$\dfrac{2x}{2} = \dfrac{8}{2}$
$x = 4$

$\cos 30° = \dfrac{y}{8}$
$\dfrac{\sqrt{3}}{2} = \dfrac{y}{8}$
$2(y) = \sqrt{3}(8)$
$2y = 8\sqrt{3}$
$\dfrac{2y}{2} = \dfrac{8\sqrt{3}}{2}$
$y = 4\sqrt{3}$

2.45 $\sin 30° = \dfrac{5}{x}$
$\dfrac{1}{2} = \dfrac{5}{x}$
$1(x) = 2(5)$
$x = 10$

$\tan 30° = \dfrac{5}{y}$
$\dfrac{1}{\sqrt{3}} = \dfrac{5}{y}$
$1(y) = \sqrt{3}(5)$
$y = 5\sqrt{3}$

2.46 $\tan 30° = \dfrac{x}{7}$
$\dfrac{1}{\sqrt{3}} = \dfrac{x}{7}$
$\sqrt{3}(x) = 1(7)$
$x\sqrt{3} = 7$
$\dfrac{x\sqrt{3}}{\sqrt{3}} = \dfrac{7}{\sqrt{3}}$
$x = \dfrac{7}{\sqrt{3}} = \dfrac{7}{\sqrt{3}} \cdot \dfrac{\sqrt{3}}{\sqrt{3}} = \dfrac{7\sqrt{3}}{3}$ or $\dfrac{7}{3}\sqrt{3}$

$\cos 30° = \dfrac{7}{y}$
$\dfrac{\sqrt{3}}{2} = \dfrac{7}{y}$
$\sqrt{3}(y) = 2(7)$
$y\sqrt{3} = 14$
$\dfrac{y\sqrt{3}}{\sqrt{3}} = \dfrac{14}{\sqrt{3}}$
$x = \dfrac{14}{\sqrt{3}} = \dfrac{14}{\sqrt{3}} \cdot \dfrac{\sqrt{3}}{\sqrt{3}} = \dfrac{14\sqrt{3}}{3}$ or $\dfrac{14}{3}\sqrt{3}$

2.47 $x = \dfrac{8}{\sqrt{2}} = \dfrac{8}{\sqrt{2}} \cdot \dfrac{\sqrt{2}}{\sqrt{2}} = \dfrac{8\sqrt{2}}{2}$ or $4\sqrt{2}$

2.48 $x = 8\sqrt{2}$

2.49 $x = \dfrac{3\sqrt{2}}{\sqrt{2}} = 3$

2.50 $x = \dfrac{6\sqrt{2}}{\sqrt{2}} = 6$

2.51 $\overline{OB}, \overline{OA}, \overline{OD}$

2.52 $\overleftrightarrow{AC}$

2.53 $\overline{AE}, \overline{BE}$

2.54 $\overleftrightarrow{BC}$

2.55 $\overline{BA}$

2.56 $\angle B, \angle E, \angle BAE$

2.57 $\angle BOD, \angle DOA$

2.58 $\overset{\frown}{BD}, \overset{\frown}{DA}, \overset{\frown}{AE}, \overset{\frown}{BE}$

2.59 $\overset{\frown}{BDA}, \overset{\frown}{BEA}$

2.60 $\triangle BEA, \triangle BAC$

2.61 $60°$

2.62 $50°$

2.63 $m\overset{\frown}{AB} = 180 - m\overset{\frown}{BC}$
$m\overset{\frown}{BC} = 70°$
$m\overset{\frown}{AB} = 180 - 70 = 110°$

2.64 $m\overset{\frown}{ABD} = 360 - m\overset{\frown}{AD}$
$\quad\quad\quad = 360 - 120$
$\quad\quad\quad = 240°$

2.65 $m\overset{\frown}{BC} = m\angle 1 = 48°$
$m\overset{\frown}{CD} = m\,BC = 48°$
$m\overset{\frown}{BAD} = 360 - (m\overset{\frown}{BC} + m\overset{\frown}{CD})$
$\quad\quad\quad = 360 - (48 + 48)$
$\quad\quad\quad = 360 - 96$
$\quad\quad\quad = 264°$

2.66 $3 \cdot 6 = 6 \cdot BP$
$\quad 12 = 6BP$
$\quad 6BP = 12$
$\quad \dfrac{6BP}{6} = \dfrac{12}{6}$
$\quad BP = 2$

2.67 $m\angle 1 = \dfrac{1}{2}(m\overset{\frown}{AD} + m\overset{\frown}{BC})$
$\quad\quad = \dfrac{1}{2}(20 + 30)$
$\quad\quad = \dfrac{1}{2}(50)$
$\quad\quad = 25°$

2.68 $m\angle 2 = \dfrac{1}{2}(m\overset{\frown}{AB} + m\overset{\frown}{DC})$
$\quad 115 = \dfrac{1}{2}(m\overset{\frown}{AB} + 120)$
$\quad 230 = m\overset{\frown}{AB} + 120 \quad$ (multiply by 2)
$230 - 120 = m\overset{\frown}{AB}$
$\quad 110° = m\overset{\frown}{AB}$

2.69 $AC \cdot BC = EC \cdot DC$
$12 \cdot 6 = EC \cdot 4$
$\quad 72 = 4EC$
$\quad \dfrac{72}{4} = \dfrac{4EC}{4}$
$\quad 18 = EC$

2.70 $m\angle C = \dfrac{1}{2}(m\overset{\frown}{AE} - m\overset{\frown}{BD})$
$\quad\quad = \dfrac{1}{2}(90 - 30)$
$\quad\quad = \dfrac{1}{2}(60)$
$\quad\quad = 30°$

2.71 $m\angle C = \dfrac{1}{2}(m\overset{\frown}{AE} - m\overset{\frown}{BD})$
$\quad 25 = \dfrac{1}{2}(100 - m\overset{\frown}{BD})$
$\quad 50 = 100 - m\overset{\frown}{BD} \quad$ (multiply by 2)
$50 + m\overset{\frown}{BD} = 100$
$\quad m\overset{\frown}{BD} = 100 - 50$
$\quad m\overset{\frown}{BD} = 50°$

2.72 $\dfrac{8 + 4}{x} = \dfrac{x}{4}$
$\quad \dfrac{12}{x} = \dfrac{x}{4}$
$\quad x(x) = 12(4)$
$\quad x^2 = 48$
$\quad \sqrt{x^2} = \sqrt{48}$
$\quad x = \sqrt{48} = \sqrt{16 \cdot 3} = 4\sqrt{3}$

2.73 $x \cdot x = 2 \cdot 6$
$\quad x^2 = 12$
$\quad \sqrt{x^2} = \sqrt{12}$
$\quad x = \sqrt{12} = \sqrt{4 \cdot 3} = 2\sqrt{3}$

2.74 $99 + x = 180$
$\quad x = 180 - 99$
$\quad x = 81°$

2.75 $(5 + 4)4 = (x + 3)3$
$\quad (9)4 = (x + 3)3$
$\quad 36 = 3x + 9$
$\quad 36 - 9 = 3x$
$\quad 27 = 3x$
$\quad \dfrac{27}{3} = \dfrac{3x}{3}$
$\quad 9 = x$

SELF TEST 2

2.01 $\angle P$

2.02 QR

2.03 $\angle Y$

2.04 WZ

2.05 $\angle Z$

2.06 RS

2.07 $\angle Q$

2.08 XW

2.09 $\dfrac{x}{25} = \dfrac{2}{5}$

  $x(5) = 25(2)$

  $5x = 50$

  $\dfrac{5x}{5} = \dfrac{50}{5}$

  $x = 10$

2.010 $\dfrac{9}{x} = \dfrac{3}{12}$

  $x(3) = 9(12)$

  $3x = 108$

  $\dfrac{3x}{3} = \dfrac{108}{3}$

  $x = 36$

2.011 $\dfrac{3}{2} = \dfrac{x}{4}$

  $2(x) = 3(4)$

  $2x = 12$

  $\dfrac{2x}{2} = \dfrac{12}{2}$

  $x = 6$

2.012 $\dfrac{16}{x} = \dfrac{x}{4}$

  $x(x) = 16(4)$

  $x^2 = 64$

  $\sqrt{x^2} = \sqrt{64}$

  $x = 8$

2.013 $x = \dfrac{22}{\sqrt{2}} = \dfrac{22}{\sqrt{2}} \cdot \dfrac{\sqrt{2}}{\sqrt{2}} = \dfrac{22\sqrt{2}}{2} = 11\sqrt{2}$

2.014 $x = \dfrac{12}{\sqrt{2}} = \dfrac{12}{\sqrt{2}} \cdot \dfrac{\sqrt{2}}{\sqrt{2}} = \dfrac{12\sqrt{2}}{2} = 6\sqrt{2}$

2.015 $x = 1.2\sqrt{2}$

2.016 $x = \dfrac{9\sqrt{2}}{\sqrt{2}} = 9$

2.017 $x = 10\sqrt{2}$

2.018 $x = \dfrac{24\sqrt{2}}{\sqrt{2}} = 24$

2.019 $m \angle 1 = \dfrac{1}{2}(m \overset{\frown}{VU} - m \overset{\frown}{ST})$

  $= \dfrac{1}{2}(80 - 40)$

  $= \dfrac{1}{2}(40)$

  $= 20°$

2.020 $m \angle 2 = \dfrac{1}{2}(m \overset{\frown}{UV} + m \overset{\frown}{ST})$

  $= \dfrac{1}{2}(70 + 30)$

  $= \dfrac{1}{2}(100)$

  $= 50°$

2.021 $m \angle 3 = \dfrac{1}{2}(m \overset{\frown}{VB} - m \overset{\frown}{BS})$

  $= \dfrac{1}{2}(60 - 30)$

  $= \dfrac{1}{2}(30)$

  $= 15°$

2.022 $m \angle 1 = \dfrac{1}{2}(m \overset{\frown}{UV} - m \overset{\frown}{ST})$

  $30 = \dfrac{1}{2}(m \overset{\frown}{UV} - 20)$

  $60 = m \overset{\frown}{UV} - 20$ (multiply by 2)

  $60 + 20 = m \overset{\frown}{UV}$

  $80° = m \overset{\frown}{UV}$

2.023 $m \overset{\frown}{DB} = m \angle DPB = 60°$

2.024 $m \overset{\frown}{DB} = m \overset{\frown}{BF}$

  $m \overset{\frown}{BF} = 180 - m \overset{\frown}{AF}$

  $= 180 - 110$

  $= 70$

  $m \overset{\frown}{DB} = 70°$

2.025   The center of the circle is P.
  Since $AC = CD = DB$, $\triangle CPD$ is equilateral and $\angle CPD = 60°$.

2.026   Since $\overline{AB}$ is also $\perp$ to line t, $\overline{DF} \parallel t$.

2.027 $m \angle DPB = m \overset{\frown}{DB} = 60°$
  $\triangle DPB$ is equilateral.
  $\therefore \overline{DE}$ is $\perp$ bisector of $\overline{PB}$.
  $PE = EB = 3$
  $PB = PE + EB$
  $= 3 + 3$
  $= 6$

2.028   1.   **STATEMENT**
    $\overline{RA} \perp \overline{AE}, \overline{CE} \perp \overline{AE}$
    REASON
    Radii $\perp$ to segment

   2.   **STATEMENT**
    $\overline{RA} \parallel \overline{SE}$
    REASON
    2 lines $\perp$ to same line are $\parallel$.

   3.   **STATEMENT**
    $\angle R = \angle S$
    REASON
    Alternate interior $\angle$'s

2.029 1. **STATEMENT**
$\overline{XZ} \parallel \overline{BC}$; $\angle 1 = \angle 2$
REASON
Given

2. **STATEMENT**
$YC = ZC$
REASON
Sides opposite = $\angle$'s are =.

3. **STATEMENT**
$\dfrac{AX}{XB} = \dfrac{AY}{YC}$
REASON
Segment $\parallel$ to side of $\triangle$ divides other sides proportionally.

4. **STATEMENT**
$\dfrac{AX}{XB} = \dfrac{AY}{ZC}$
REASON
Substitution

2.030 1. **STATEMENT**
$\overline{RS} \parallel \overline{BC}$; $\angle 1 = \angle 2$
REASON
Given

2. **STATEMENT**
$\angle 2 = \angle 3$
REASON
Alternate interior $\angle$'s

3. **STATEMENT**
$\angle 1 = \angle 3$
REASON
Substitution

4. **STATEMENT**
$RB = RS$
REASON
Sides opposite = $\angle$'s are =.

5. **STATEMENT**
$\dfrac{AR}{RB} = \dfrac{AS}{SC}$
REASON
Segment $\parallel$ to side of $\triangle$ divides other sides proportionally.

6. **STATEMENT**
$\dfrac{AR}{RS} = \dfrac{AS}{SC}$
REASON
Substitution

SECTION 3

3.1

3.2
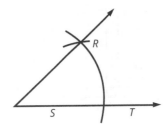

3.3
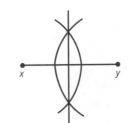

3.4
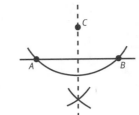

3.5
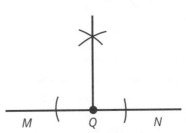

3.6
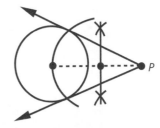

3.7
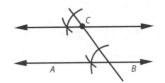

3.8

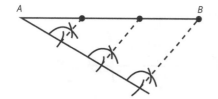

3.9

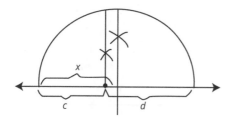

3.10

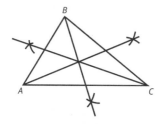

3.11

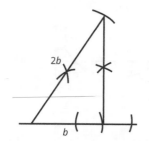

3.12 a line parallel to the given line

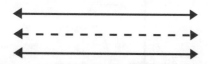

3.13 a line that is the perpendicular bisector of segment AB

3.14 a sphere

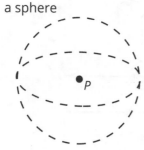

3.15 a cylinder

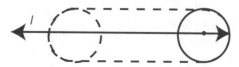

3.16 $A = lw$
$= 5(6)$
$= 30$

3.17 $L.A. = ph$
$= 22(2)$
$= 44$

3.18 $T.A. = L.A. + 2B$
$= 44 + 2(30)$
$= 44 + 60$
$= 104$

3.19 $V = Bh$
$= 30(2)$
$= 60$

3.20 $l = \sqrt{5^2 - 3^2}$
$= \sqrt{25 - 9}$
$= \sqrt{16}$
$= 4$

3.21 $L.A. = \dfrac{1}{2}pl$
$= \dfrac{1}{2}(24)(4)$
$= 48$

3.22 $h = \sqrt{4^2 - 3^2}$
$= \sqrt{16 - 9}$
$= \sqrt{7}$

3.23 $T.A. = L.A. + B$
$= 48 + 36$
$= 84$

3.24 $V = \dfrac{1}{3}Bh$
$= \dfrac{1}{3}(36)(\sqrt{7})$
$= 12\sqrt{7}$

3.25 $L.A. = 2\pi rh$
$= 2\pi(2)(3)$
$= 12\pi$

3.26 $T.A. = L.A. + 2B$
$= L.A. + 2\pi r^2$
$= 12\pi + 2\pi(2)^2$
$= 12\pi + 8\pi$
$= 20\pi$

3.27 $V = \pi r^2 h$
$= \pi(2)^2(3)$
$= 12\pi$

3.28 $I = \sqrt{3^2 + 4^2}$
$\quad = \sqrt{9 + 16}$
$\quad = \sqrt{25}$
$\quad = 5$

3.29 $L.A. = \pi r l$
$\quad = \pi(3)(5)$
$\quad = 15\pi$

3.30 $T.A. = L.A. + \pi r^2$
$\quad = 15\pi + \pi(3)^2$
$\quad = 15\pi + 9\pi$
$\quad = 24\pi$

3.31 $V = \frac{1}{3}\pi r^2 h$
$\quad = \frac{1}{3}\pi(3)^2(4)$
$\quad = 12\pi$

3.32 $S.A. = 4\pi r^2$
$\quad = 4\pi(4)^2$
$\quad = 4\pi(16)$
$\quad = 64\pi$

3.33 $V = \frac{4}{3}\pi r^3$
$\quad = \frac{4}{3}\pi(4)^3$
$\quad = \frac{4}{3}\pi(64)$
$\quad = \frac{256}{3}\pi$

3.34 $A = \pi r^2$
$\quad = \pi(6)^2$
$\quad = 36\pi$

3.35 $A_{O-AXB} = \frac{90}{360}\pi(6)^2$
$\quad = \frac{1}{4}\pi(36)$
$\quad = 9\pi$

3.36 $A_{AXB} = A_{sector} - A_{\triangle}$
$\quad = 9\pi - \frac{1}{2}bh$
$\quad = 9\pi - \frac{1}{2}(6)(6)$
$\quad = 9\pi - 18$

3.37 $C = 2\pi r$
$\quad = 2\pi(6)$
$\quad = 12\pi$

3.38 apothem $= \frac{4}{2}\sqrt{3} = 2\sqrt{3}$

3.39 4

3.40 central $\angle = \frac{360°}{6} = 60°$

3.41 $A = \frac{1}{2}ap$
$\quad = \frac{1}{2}(2\sqrt{3})24$
$\quad = 24\sqrt{3}$

3.42 $\frac{A_{\triangle ABC}}{A_{\triangle DEF}} = (\frac{s_1}{s_2})^2$
$\quad \frac{12}{A_{\triangle DEF}} = (\frac{4}{1})^2$
$\quad \frac{12}{A_{\triangle DEF}} = 16$
$\quad 16A_{\triangle DEF} = 12 \qquad$ (cross-multiply)
$\quad A_{\triangle DEF} = \frac{12}{16} = \frac{3}{4}$

3.43 $\frac{A_1}{A_2} = (\frac{s_1}{s_2})^2$
$\quad \frac{20}{4} = (\frac{5}{x})^2$
$\quad \frac{20}{4} = \frac{25}{x^2}$
$\quad 20x^2 = 100 \qquad$ (cross-multiply)
$\quad x^2 = 5 \qquad$ (divide by 20)
$\quad \sqrt{x^2} = \sqrt{5}$
$\quad x = \sqrt{5}$

3.44 through 3.48

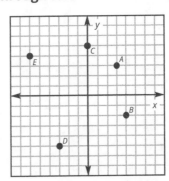

3.49 $d = \sqrt{(5-7)^2 + [3-(-4)]^2}$
$\quad = \sqrt{(-2)^2 + 7^2}$
$\quad = \sqrt{4 + 49}$
$\quad = \sqrt{53}$

3.50 $d = \sqrt{(0-6)^2 + (0-8)^2}$
$\quad = \sqrt{(-6)^2 + (-8)^2}$
$\quad = \sqrt{36 + 64}$
$\quad = \sqrt{100}$
$\quad = 10$

3.51 $d = \sqrt{(0-0)^2 + (8-12)^2}$
$\quad = \sqrt{0^2 + (-4)^2}$
$\quad = \sqrt{16}$
$\quad = 4$

3.52 $d = \sqrt{(7-4)^2 + [1-(-6)]^2}$
$\quad = \sqrt{3^2 + 7^2}$
$\quad = \sqrt{9 + 49}$
$\quad = \sqrt{58}$

3.53 $d = \sqrt{[-6 - (-12)^2 + (4 - 4)^2}$
     $= \sqrt{6^2 + 0^2}$
     $= \sqrt{36}$
     $= 6$

3.54 $(x - 5)^2 + (y - 7)^2 = 4^2$
     $(x - 5)^2 + (y - 7)^2 = 16$

3.55 $(x + 3)^2 + (y - 5)^2 = 1^2$
     $(x + 3)^2 + (y - 5)^2 = 1$

3.56 $(x - 0)^2 + (y - 8)^2 = (\sqrt{3})^2$
     $x^2 + (y - 8)^2 = 3$

3.57 $(x - 0)^2 + (y - 0)^2 = (\sqrt{5})^2$
     $x^2 + y^2 = 5$

3.58 $(x + 3)^2 + (y + 8)^2 = (2\sqrt{3})^2$
     $(x + 3)^2 + (y + 8)^2 = 12$

3.59 $m = \dfrac{2 - 3}{0 - 1} = \dfrac{-1}{-1} = 1$
     $y - 2 = 1(x - 0)$
     $y - 2 = x$
     $-x + y - 2 = 0$
      $-x + y = 2$ or
      $x - y = -2$ (multiply by -1)

3.60 $m = \dfrac{2 - 3}{-3 - 3} = \dfrac{-1}{-6} = \dfrac{1}{6}$
     $y - 3 = \dfrac{1}{6}(x - 3)$
     $y - 3 = \dfrac{1}{6}x - \dfrac{1}{2}$
     $-\dfrac{1}{6}x + y - 3 = -\dfrac{1}{2}$
      $-\dfrac{1}{6}x + y = -\dfrac{1}{2} + 3$
      $-\dfrac{1}{6}x + y = \dfrac{5}{2}$
      $x - 6y = -15$ (multiply by -6)

3.61 $m = \dfrac{1 - 3}{6 - 4} = \dfrac{-2}{2} = -1$
     $y - 3 = -1(x - 4)$
     $y - 3 = -x + 4$
     $x + y - 3 = 4$
      $x + y = 4 + 3$
      $x + y = 7$

3.62 $m \perp = \dfrac{1}{2}$
     $y - 3 = \dfrac{1}{2}(x - 5)$
     $y - 3 = \dfrac{1}{2}x - \dfrac{5}{2}$
     $-\dfrac{1}{2}x + y - 3 = -\dfrac{5}{2}$
      $-\dfrac{1}{2}x + y = -\dfrac{5}{2} + 3$
      $-\dfrac{1}{2}x + y = \dfrac{1}{2}$
      $x - 2y = -1$ (multiply by -2)

3.63 $m \,||\, = \dfrac{1}{5}$
     $y - 1 = \dfrac{1}{5}(x - 3)$
     $y - 1 = \dfrac{1}{5}x - \dfrac{3}{5}$
     $-\dfrac{1}{5}x + y - 1 = -\dfrac{3}{5}$
      $-\dfrac{1}{5}x + y = -\dfrac{3}{5} + 1$
      $-\dfrac{1}{5}x + y = \dfrac{2}{5}$
      $x - 5y = -2$ (multiply by -5)

3.64

$M_{AB} = (\dfrac{-2 + 4}{2}, \dfrac{2 + 8}{2}) = (\dfrac{2}{2}, \dfrac{10}{2}) = (1, 5)$

$M_{BC} = (\dfrac{-2 + 6}{2}, \dfrac{2 + 0}{2}) = (\dfrac{4}{2}, \dfrac{2}{2}) = (2, 1)$

$M_{AC} = (\dfrac{6 + 4}{2}, \dfrac{0 + 8}{2}) = (\dfrac{10}{2}, \dfrac{8}{2}) = (5, 4)$

$m_{AP} = \dfrac{1 - 8}{2 - 4} = \dfrac{-7}{-2} = \dfrac{7}{2}$

$m_{BQ} = \dfrac{4 - 2}{5 - (-2)} = \dfrac{2}{7}$

$m_{CR} = \dfrac{5 - 0}{1 - 6} = \dfrac{5}{-5} = -1$

AP: $y - 8 = \dfrac{7}{2}(x - 4)$
     $y - 8 = \dfrac{7}{2}x - 14$
     $-\dfrac{7}{2}x + y - 8 = -14$
     $-\dfrac{7}{2}x + y = -14 + 8$
     $-\dfrac{7}{2}x + y = -6$
     $7x - 2y = 12$ (multiply by -2)

BQ: $y - 2 = \dfrac{2}{7}(x + 2)$
     $y - 2 = \dfrac{2}{7}x + \dfrac{4}{7}$
     $-\dfrac{2}{7}x + y - 2 = \dfrac{4}{7}$
     $-\dfrac{2}{7}x + y = \dfrac{4}{7} + 2$
     $-\dfrac{2}{7}x + y = \dfrac{18}{7}$
     $2x - 7y = -18$ (multiply by -7)

CR: $y - 0 = -1(x - 6)$
     $y = -x + 6$
     $x + y = 6$

3.65 $x = 0$:

$$0 - 3y = 12$$
$$-3y = 12$$
$$\frac{-3y}{-3} = \frac{12}{-3}$$
$$y = -4$$

$(0, -4)$

$y = 0$:

$$4x - 0 = 12$$
$$4x = 12$$
$$\frac{4x}{4} = \frac{12}{4}$$
$$x = 3$$

$(3, 0)$

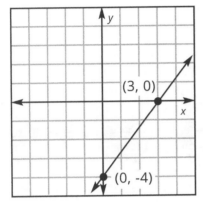

3.66 $|x| \leq 4$
$x \leq 4$ or $x \geq -4$

3.67 $4 \geq y > -3$
$y \leq 4$ and $y > -3$

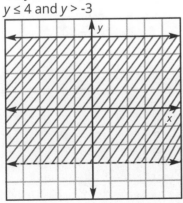

3.68

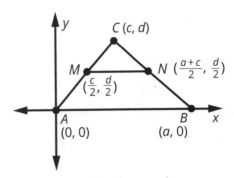

$$M_{AC} = \left(\frac{c + 0}{2}, \frac{d + 0}{2}\right) = \left(\frac{c}{2}, \frac{d}{2}\right)$$

$$M_{BC} = \left(\frac{a + c}{2}, \frac{0 + d}{2}\right) = \left(\frac{a + c}{2}, \frac{d}{2}\right)$$

$$MN = \sqrt{\left(\frac{c}{2} - \frac{a + c}{2}\right)^2 + \left(\frac{d}{2} - \frac{d}{2}\right)^2}$$

$$= \sqrt{\left(-\frac{a}{2}\right)^2 + 0^2}$$

$$= \frac{a}{2}$$

$$AB = \sqrt{(0 - a)^2 + (0 - 0)^2}$$

$$= \sqrt{(-a)^2 + 0^2}$$

$$= \sqrt{a^2}$$

$$= a$$

$$\therefore MN = \frac{1}{2}AB$$

SELF TEST 3

3.01

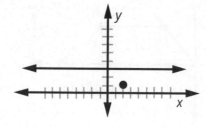

$A' = (2, 1)$

3.02

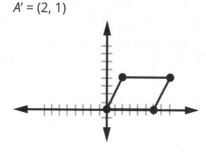

x-coordinate = 6 + 2 = 8
y-coordinate = 4
(8, 4)

3.03 $\frac{2}{5} = \frac{20}{x}$

$2(x) = 5(20)$

$2x = 100$

$\frac{2x}{2} = \frac{100}{2}$

$x = 50$

3.04 $4 \cdot 6 = 3 \cdot x$

$24 = 3x$

$\frac{24}{3} = \frac{3x}{3}$

$8 = x$

3.05 $(x - 3)^2 + (y + 2)^2 = 7^2$
$(x - 3)^2 + (y + 2)^2 = 49$

3.06

$y + 5 = -\frac{2}{3}(x - 2)$

$y + 5 = -\frac{2}{3}x + \frac{4}{3}$

$\frac{2}{3}x + y + 5 = \frac{4}{3}$

$\frac{2}{3}x + y = \frac{4}{3} - 5$

$\frac{2}{3}x + y = -\frac{11}{3}$

$2x + 3y = -11$ (multiply by 3)

3.07   Cylinder:

$V = Bh$

$B = \pi r^2$

$\quad = \pi(4)^2$

$\quad = 16\pi$

$V = 16\pi(10)$

$\quad = 160\pi$

Cone:

$V = \frac{1}{3}Bh$

$B = \pi r^2$

$\quad = \pi(1)^2$

$\quad = \pi$

$V = \frac{1}{3}\pi(2)$

$\quad = \frac{1}{3}\pi$

$\quad = \dfrac{160\pi}{\frac{2}{3}\pi} = \dfrac{160}{\frac{2}{3}} = 160(\frac{3}{2}) = 240$ cones

3.08 $m_{AB} = \dfrac{9 - (-3)}{4 - 0} = \dfrac{12}{4} = 3$

$m \perp = -\dfrac{1}{3}$

3.09 $V = \frac{4}{3}\pi r^3$

$\quad = \frac{4}{3}\pi(10)^3$

$\quad = \frac{4}{3}\pi(1{,}000)$

$\quad = \frac{4{,}000}{3}\pi$

3.010 (-3, 4)
3.011 acute
3.012 diameter
3.013 collinear
3.014 disjunction
3.015 deductive
3.016

$3x + 50 + 2x - 20$ =	180	
$5x + 30$	=	180
$5x$	=	180 − 30
$5x$	=	150
$\frac{5x}{5}$	=	$\frac{150}{5}$
x	=	30°

3.017 $\angle B + \angle C = 180 - \angle A$
$= 180 - 80$
$= 100°$

$\angle BPC = 180 - \dfrac{1}{2}(\angle B + \angle C)$

$= 180 - \dfrac{1}{2}(100)$

$= 180 - 50$

$= 130°$

3.018 $P_{square} = 4(x + 2) = 4x + 8$

$P_\triangle = 3(2x) = 6x$

$4x + 8$	$= 6x$
8	$= 6x - 4x$
8	$= 2x$
$\dfrac{8}{2}$	$= \dfrac{2x}{2}$
4	$= x$

3.019

$\dfrac{6}{4}$	$= \dfrac{7}{x}$
$6(x)$	$= 4(7)$
$6x$	$= 28$
$\dfrac{6x}{6}$	$= \dfrac{28}{6}$
x	$= \dfrac{28}{6} = \dfrac{14}{3}$
$\dfrac{6}{4}$	$= \dfrac{9}{x}$
$6(x)$	$= 4(9)$
$6x$	$= 36$
$\dfrac{6x}{6}$	$= \dfrac{36}{6}$
x	$= 6$

3.020 hypotenuse $= \sqrt{8^2 + 10^2}$
$= \sqrt{64 + 100}$
$= \sqrt{164}$
$= \sqrt{4 \cdot 41}$
$= 2\sqrt{41}$

3.021

$m\overset{\frown}{BC} = \angle CAB = 70°$

$m\angle CDB = \dfrac{1}{2}m\,BC$

$= \dfrac{1}{2}(70)$

$= 35°$

3.022 $A = \dfrac{1}{2}d_1 d_2$

$= \dfrac{1}{2}(6)(12)$

$= 36$

3.023

1. **STATEMENT**
   $\angle 1 = \angle 2; AP = BP$
   REASON
   Given

2. **STATEMENT**
   $\angle APD = \angle BPC$
   REASON
   Vertical $\angle$'s are =.

3. **STATEMENT**
   $\triangle APD \cong \triangle BPC$
   REASON
   ASA

3.024

1. **STATEMENT**
   $\overline{AB} \perp \overline{CD}$
   REASON
   Given

2. **STATEMENT**
   $m\angle 1 = m\angle COB$
   REASON
   Definition of $\perp$

3. **STATEMENT**
   $m\angle COB = m\angle 2 + m\angle 3 + m\angle 4$
   REASON
   Angle addition theorem

4. **STATEMENT**
   $m\angle 1 = m\angle 2 + m\angle 3 + m\angle 4$
   REASON
   Substitution

5. **STATEMENT**
   $m\angle 3 = m\angle 7$
   REASON
   Vertical $\angle$'s are =.

6. **STATEMENT**
   $m\angle 1 = m\angle 2 + m\angle 4 + m\angle 7$
   REASON
   Substitution

3.025

1. **STATEMENT**
   $\overline{XA} \perp \overleftrightarrow{RS}; \angle 1 = \angle 2$
   REASON
   Given

2. **STATEMENT**
   $\angle 1, \angle 3$ are complementary
   $\angle 2, \angle 4$ are complementary
   REASON
   Adjacent $\angle$'s with exterior sides in $\perp$'s are complementary

3. **STATEMENT**
$\angle 3 = \angle 4$
REASON
Two $\angle$'s complementary to = $\angle$'s are =.

4. **STATEMENT**
$\dfrac{BX}{XC} = \dfrac{AB}{AC}$
REASON
$\angle$ bisector proportion theorem

3.026 1. **STATEMENT**
$\angle 1 = \angle 2$, $\angle 5 = \angle 6$
REASON
Given

2. **STATEMENT**
$AB = AB$
REASON
Reflexive

3. **STATEMENT**
$\triangle ABD \cong \triangle BAC$
REASON
AAS

4. **STATEMENT**
$AD = BC$
REASON
CPCTE

5. **STATEMENT**
$\angle 3 = \angle 4$
REASON
Vertical $\angle$'s

6. **STATEMENT**
$\triangle APD \cong \triangle BPC$
REASON
AAS

7. **STATEMENT**
$DP = CP$
REASON
CPCTE

8. **STATEMENT**
$\angle 7 = \angle 8$
REASON
Base $\angle$'s of isosceles $\triangle$ =.

3.027 1. **STATEMENT**
$\overline{AB}$ diameter
$\overline{BC}$ tangent to $\odot O$
REASON
Given

2. **STATEMENT**
$\angle A = \angle A$
REASON
Reflexive

3. **STATEMENT**
$\angle CBA$ is rt. $\angle$
REASON
Radius $\perp$ to tangent

4. **STATEMENT**
$\angle BXA = 90°$
REASON
Inscribed in semicircle

5. **STATEMENT**
$\angle CBA = \angle BXA$
REASON
All rt. $\angle$'s are =.

6. **STATEMENT**
$\triangle AXB \sim \triangle ABC$
REASON
AA

3.028 1. **STATEMENT**
$\overline{AB} \parallel \overline{CD}$
REASON
Given

2. **STATEMENT**
m $\angle 1$ = m $\angle 2$ + m $\angle 4$
REASON
Exterior $\angle$ = sum of remote interior $\angle$'s

3. **STATEMENT**
m $\angle 3$ = m $\angle 4$
REASON
Alternate interior $\angle$'s

4. **STATEMENT**
m $\angle 1$ = m $\angle 2$ + m $\angle 3$
REASON
Substitution

LIFEPAC TEST

1. c

$C = \pi d$

$\dfrac{C}{d} = \pi$

2. b

$m = \dfrac{8-3}{3-(-1)} = \dfrac{8-3}{3+1} = \dfrac{5}{4}$

3. d

4. b

$7\sqrt{3}\left(\dfrac{2}{\sqrt{3}}\right) = 14$

5. b

$s = \sqrt{36} = 6$

diagonal $= 6\sqrt{2}$

6. b

7. a

8. d

9. b

m $\angle AOC$ = m $\angle AOX$ + m $\angle XOC$

m $\angle AOX$ = m $\angle XOC$

m $\angle AOC$ = 42 + 42 = 84°

10. c

$\angle c = 180 - (m \angle A + m \angle B)$

$= 180 - 47 + 62)$

$= 180 - 109$

$= 71°$

11. c

$\angle A = \angle B$

$\angle A = \angle B = 180 - \angle C$

$2\angle A = 180 - \angle C$

$= 180 - 62$

$= 118°$

$A = \dfrac{118}{2} = 59°$

Longest side = side opposite largest $\angle$ = AB

12. a

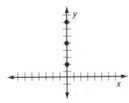

$TJ = |5 - 2| = 3$

$TH = |y - 5| = 3$

$y - 5 = 3$

$y = 3 + 5 = 8$

$H\,(0, 8)$

13. c

$(n - 2)180 = 1{,}260$

$180n - 360 = 1{,}260$

$180n = 1{,}260 + 360$

$180n = 1{,}620$

$\dfrac{180n}{180} = \dfrac{1{,}620}{180}$

$n = 9$

14. b

$(n - 2)180 = (5 - 2)180 =$

$(3)180 = 540°$

$85 + 90 + 95 + 110 + x = 540$

$380 + x = 540$

$x = 540 - 380 = 160°$

The largest $\angle$ is 160°

The exterior $\angle$ = 180 - 160 = 20°

15. a

$x + x + x + 15 + x + 45 = 4x + 60$

$4x + 60 = 360$

$4x = 360 - 60$

$4x = 300$

$\dfrac{4x}{4} = \dfrac{300}{4}$

$x = 75°$

16. true

17. true

18. true

19. true

20. true

21. false

22. false

23. false

24. false

25. true

26. true

27. false

28. false

$C = 2\pi r$

$10 = 2\pi r$

$\dfrac{10}{2\pi} = \dfrac{2\pi r}{2\pi}$

$\dfrac{5}{\pi} = r$

$A = \pi r^2$

$= \pi\left(\dfrac{5}{\pi}\right)^2$

$= \pi\left(\dfrac{25}{\pi^2}\right)$

$= \dfrac{25}{\pi}$

$100 \neq \dfrac{25}{\pi}$

29. true

30. true

31. $M_{AB} = (\frac{x_2 + x_1}{2}, \frac{y_2 + y_1}{2})$

$(-3, 2) = (\frac{0 + x_1}{2}, \frac{2 + y_1}{2})$

$-3 = \frac{0 + x_1}{2}$

$-6 = x_1$ (multiply by 2)

$2 = \frac{2 + y_1}{2}$

$4 = 2 + y_1$ (multiply by 2)

$4 - 2 = y_1$

$2 = y_1$

$B(-6, 2)$

32. $m\angle B + m\angle C = 180 - m\angle A$

$m\angle B = m\angle C$

$2m\angle B = 180 - 38$

$2m\angle B = 142$

$\frac{2m\angle B}{2} = \frac{142}{2}$

$m\angle B = 71°$

33. sum of exterior $\angle$'s $= 360°$

$\frac{360}{6} = 60°$

34. When "$p \to q$" is false:

$\frac{p\,q}{T\,F}$

When "p or q" is true:

$\frac{p\,q}{T\,T}$

T F

F T

$\therefore$ q must be false.

35. $(n - 2)180 = 900$

$180n - 360 = 900$

$180n = 900 + 360$

$180n = 1,260$

$\frac{180n}{180} = \frac{1,260}{180}$

$n = 7$

36. $y - 5 = \frac{3}{7}(x - 2)$

$y - 5 = \frac{3}{7}x - \frac{6}{7}$

$-\frac{3}{7}x + y - 5 = -\frac{6}{7}$

$-\frac{3}{7}x + y = -\frac{6}{7} + 5$

$-\frac{3}{7}x + y = \frac{29}{7}$

$3x - 7y = -29$ (multiply by -7)

37. $A = \frac{m\widehat{AB}}{360°}(\pi r^2)$

$m\,\widehat{AB} = 120°$

$A = \frac{120}{360}(\pi)(6)^2$

$= \frac{1}{3}(\pi)(36)$

$= 12\pi$

38.

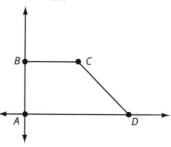

$AD = \sqrt{(b - 0)^2 + (0 - 0)^2}$

$= \sqrt{b^2 + 0^2}$

$= \sqrt{b^2}$

$= b$

$BC = \sqrt{(c - 0)^2 + (a - a)^2}$

$= \sqrt{c^2 + 0^2}$

$= \sqrt{c^2}$

$= c$

$A = \frac{1}{2}h(b_1 + b_2)$

$= \frac{1}{2}a(b + c)$

39. $x^2 < 4$

$\sqrt{x^2} < \sqrt{4}$

$x < 2$ and $x > -2$

40.

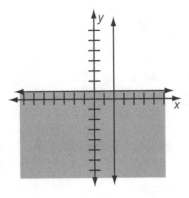

Solution graph:

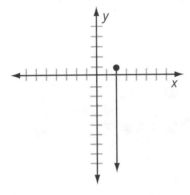

41.
1. **STATEMENT**
   $\angle 1 = \angle 2, \angle 5 = \angle 6$
   REASON
   Given

2. **STATEMENT**
   $AB = AB$
   REASON
   Reflexive

3. **STATEMENT**
   $\triangle ABD \cong \triangle BAC$
   REASON
   AAS

4. **STATEMENT**
   $AD = BC$
   REASON
   CPCTE

5. **STATEMENT**
   $\angle 3 = \angle 4$
   REASON
   Vertical $\angle$'s

6. **STATEMENT**
   $\triangle APD \cong \triangle BPC$
   REASON
   AAS

7. **STATEMENT**
   $DP = CP$
   REASON
   CPCTE

8. **STATEMENT**
   $\angle 7 = \angle 8$
   REASON
   Base $\angle$'s of isosceles $\triangle$ =.

42.
1. **STATEMENT**
   $\angle 1 = \angle 2, AP = BP$
   REASON
   Given

2. **STATEMENT**
   $\angle APD = \angle BPC$
   REASON
   Vertical $\angle$'s

3. **STATEMENT**
   $\triangle APD \cong \triangle BPC$
   REASON
   ASA

ALTERNATE LIFEPAC TEST

1. c

2. e

3. b

4. a

5. d

6.
a. If a quadrilateral is a parallelogram, then two sides of the quadrilateral are equal and parallel.
b. If two sides of a quadrilateral are not equal and parallel, then the quadrilateral is not a parallelogram.
c. If a quadrilateral is not a parallelogram, then two sides of the quadrilateral are not equal and parallel.

7.
a. T
b. F
c. T
d. T

8.
a. OA or OB or OC
b. $\overleftrightarrow{CE}$
c. $\overrightarrow{AD}$
d. $\angle A$ or $\angle D$ or $\angle DCA$
e. $\triangle ADC$

9.
a. $\angle 1$ and $\angle 2$ are vertical $\angle$'s.
   m $\angle 1$ = m $\angle 2$
   m $\angle 1$ = 120°
   m $\angle 2$ = 120°
b. $\angle 1$ and $\angle 3$ are corresponding $\angle$'s.
   m $\angle 1$ = m $\angle 3$
   m $\angle 1$ = 120°
   m $\angle 3$ = 120°

10.
a. m $\angle P$ = m $\angle J$
   m $\angle J$ = 30°
   m $\angle P$ = 30°
b. m $\angle K$ = m $\angle Q$
   m $\angle Q$ = 70°
   m $\angle K$ = 70°
c. $QR = KL$
   $KL = 5$
   $QR = 5$

11. $T.A. = \frac{1}{2}pl + B$

$p = 4(8) = 32$

$l^2 = \sqrt{8^2 - 4^2}$ (by the Pythagorean Theorem)

$l^2 = \sqrt{64 - 16}$

$l^2 = \sqrt{48}$

$l^2 = \sqrt{16 \cdot 3} = \sqrt{16} \cdot \sqrt{3}$

$l = 4\sqrt{3}$

$B = 8(8) = 64$

$T.A. = \frac{1}{2}(32)(4\sqrt{3}) + 64$

$T.A. = 64\sqrt{3} + 64$

$V = \frac{1}{3}Bh$

$B = 8(8) = 64$

$h^2 = \sqrt{l^2 - 4^2}$ (by the Pythagorean Theorem)

$l = 4\sqrt{3}$

$h^2 = \sqrt{(4\sqrt{3})^2 - 4^2}$

$h^2 = \sqrt{48 - 16}$

$h^2 = \sqrt{32}$

$h^2 = \sqrt{16 \cdot 2} = \sqrt{16} \cdot \sqrt{2}$

$h = 4\sqrt{2}$

$V = \frac{1}{3}(64)(4\sqrt{2})$

$V = \frac{256\sqrt{2}}{3}$

12.
a. $\sin \angle A = \dfrac{\text{opposite}}{\text{hypotenuse}}$

$= \dfrac{4}{4\sqrt{5}}$

$= \dfrac{1}{\sqrt{5}}$

$= \dfrac{1}{\sqrt{5}} \cdot \dfrac{\sqrt{5}}{\sqrt{5}}$

$= \dfrac{\sqrt{5}}{\sqrt{25}}$

$= \dfrac{\sqrt{5}}{5}$

b. $\cos \angle A = \dfrac{\text{adjacent}}{\text{hypotenuse}}$

$= \dfrac{8}{4\sqrt{5}}$

$= \dfrac{2}{\sqrt{5}}$

$= \dfrac{2}{\sqrt{5}} \cdot \dfrac{\sqrt{5}}{\sqrt{5}}$

$= \dfrac{2\sqrt{5}}{\sqrt{25}}$

$= \dfrac{2\sqrt{5}}{5}$

c. $\tan \angle A = \dfrac{\text{opposite}}{\text{adjacent}}$

$= \dfrac{4}{8}$

$= \dfrac{1}{2}$

13.
$$d = \sqrt{(x_1 - x_2)^2 + (y_1 - y_2)^2}$$
$$d = \sqrt{(-3 - 2)^2 + (6 - 8)^2}$$
$$d = \sqrt{(-5)^2 + (-2)^2}$$
$$d = \sqrt{25 + 4}$$
$$d = \sqrt{29}$$

14.
$$m = \frac{y_2 - y_1}{x_2 - x_1}$$
$$m = \frac{4 - 2}{7 - 3}$$
$$m = \frac{2}{4}$$
$$m = \frac{1}{2}$$

15.
$$\text{midpoint} = \left(\frac{x_2 + x_1}{2}, \frac{y_2 + y_1}{2}\right)$$
$$\text{midpoint} = \left(\frac{2 + (-5)}{2}, \frac{-4 + 6}{2}\right)$$
$$\text{midpoint} = \left(\frac{2 - 5}{2}, \frac{-4 + 6}{2}\right)$$
$$\text{midpoint} = \left(\frac{-3}{2}, \frac{2}{2}\right)$$
$$\text{midpoint} = \left(\frac{-3}{2}, 1\right)$$

16. A point in the center of the triangle

17. Graph $x \geq -3$ and $x < 2$.

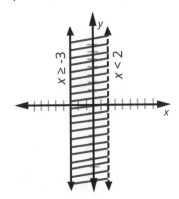

18.

1. **STATEMENT**
   $\triangle ABC$ and $\triangle DEF$ are rt. $\triangle$'s.
   $AC = DF$
   $\angle C = \angle F$
   REASON
   Given

2. **STATEMENT**
   $\angle B = \angle E$
   REASON
   All rt. $\angle$'s are =.

3. **STATEMENT**
   $\triangle ABC \cong \triangle DEF$
   REASON
   AAS

MATH 1010

ALTERNATE LIFEPAC TEST

NAME _____

DATE _____

SCORE _____

75 / 94

Match the following items (each answer, 2 points).

1. _____ segment *RS*

2. _____ line *RS*

3. _____ point *S*

4. _____ ray *RS*

5. _____ plane *R*

a.  R   S

b. •S

c. R   S

d. (parallelogram with R)

e. R   S

f. •R

Write the converse, inverse, and contrapositive of this theorem (each answer, 4 points).

6. If two sides of a quadrilateral are equal and parallel, then the quadrilateral is a parallelogram.

a. Converse: _____

_____

b. Inverse: _____

_____

c. Contrapositive: _____

_____

Complete the following truth table (each answer, 2 points).

7.

p	*q*	*p → q*
T	T	a. _____
T	F	b. _____
F	T	c. _____
F	F	d. _____

Refer to the figure to name the following items (each answer, 2 points).

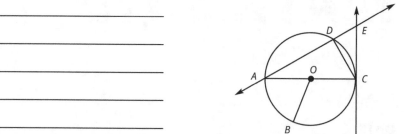

8. a. a radius _____

    b. a tangent _____

    c. a secant _____

    d. an inscribed angle _____

    e. a right triangle _____

Given the following diagrams, find the required measures (each answer, 3 points).

9. Given: $j \parallel k$
    $m \angle 1 = 120°$

    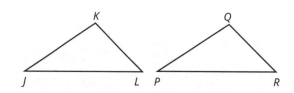

    a. $m \angle 2 =$ _____

    b. $m \angle 3 =$ _____

10. Given: $\triangle JKL \cong \triangle PQR$
    $m \angle J = 30°$
    $m \angle Q = 70°$
    $KL = 5$

    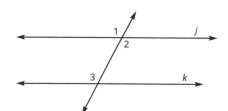

    a. $m \angle P =$ _____

    b. $m \angle K =$ _____

    c. $QR =$ _____

11.

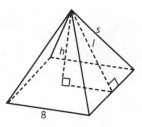

    T.A. = _____

    V = _____

12. State the required ratio for the labeled angle. Leave your answer in reduced fraction form.

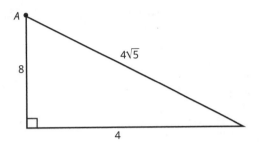

a. sin ∠A = _____

b. cos ∠A = _____

c. tan ∠A = _____

Solve the following problems (each answer, 3 points).

13. Find the distance between point U (-3, 6) and V (2, 8).

14. Find the slope of the line that passes through (3, 2) and (7, 4).

15. Find the midpoint of the segment whose end points are (- 5, 6) and (2, -4).

Sketch and describe the following locus (5 points).

16. What is the locus of points equidistant from all three sides of an equilateral triangle?

Sketch the following graph (4 points).

17. $\{(x, y): -3 \le x < 2\}$

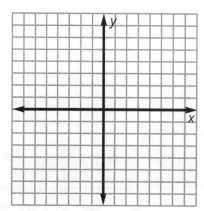

Complete the following proof (6 points).

18. Given: $\triangle ABC$ and $\triangle DEF$ are rt. $\triangle$'s

               $AC = DF$

               $\angle C = \angle F$

    To Prove: $\triangle ABC \cong \triangle DEF$

STATEMENT	REASON